C000022196

DIANE ARMSTRONG was born in Pola
with her parents on the SS *Derna* in 1948.

She received a Commonwealth schola
Sydney where she gained a Bachelor of Arts degree majoring in English and History.

Having decided to become a writer at the age of seven, Diane became a freelance journalist. She has won national and international awards for her articles, including the Pluma de Plata from the Mexican government and the George Munster Award for Independent Journalism in Australia. Over 3000 of her articles have been published in newspapers and magazines in Australia as well as in England, Hong Kong, Holland, Hungary, Poland, India and South Africa.

In 1997 she received an Emerging Writer's grant from the Literature Board of the Australia Council to write her first book *Mosaic: A Chronicle of Five Generations*, which was published in Australia in 1998. It was acclaimed by the late Joseph Heller and Nobel prizewinner Elie Wiesel, shortlisted for the Victorian Premier's Literary Award for Non-Fiction and for the National Biography Award. In 2001, *Mosaic* was published in the United States.

In 1999 Diane received a Developing Writer's grant from the Literature Board of the Australia Council to assist in writing this book.

Diane lives in Sydney with her husband, Michael. She has two children, Justine and Jonathan.

Also by Diane Armstrong

Mosaic:
A Chronicle of Five Generations

THE VOYAGE
OF THEIR LIFE

THE STORY OF THE SS DERNA
AND ITS PASSENGERS

DIANE ARMSTRONG

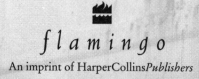

flamingo
An imprint of HarperCollins*Publishers*

The writing of this project has been assisted
by the Commonwealth Government through
the Australia Council, its arts funding and
advisory board.

Flamingo
An imprint of HarperCollins*Publishers*, Australia

First published in Australia in 2001
by HarperCollins*Publishers* Pty Limited
ABN 36 009 913 517
A member of the HarperCollins*Publishers* (Australia) Pty Limited Group
www.harpercollins.com.au

HarperCollins*Publishers*
25 Ryde Road, Pymble, Sydney, NSW 2073, Australia
31 View Road, Glenfield, Auckland 10, New Zealand
77–85 Fulham Palace Road, London, W6 8JB, United Kingdom
Hazelton Lanes, 55 Avenue Road, Suite 2900, Toronto, Ontario M5R 3L2
and 1995 Markham Road, Scarborough, Ontario M1B 5M8, Canada
10 East 53rd Street, New York NY 10022, USA

National Library of Australia Cataloguing-in-Publication data:

Armstrong, Diane, 1939– .
   The voyage of their life: the story of the SS Derna and its passengers.
   Bibliography.
   Includes index.
   ISBN 0 7322 6826 5.
   ISBN 0 7322 6868 0 (pbk.).
   1. Armstrong, Diane, 1939– — Journeys. 2. Derna (Ship).
   3. Immigrants — Australia — Biography. 4. Europeans —
   Australia — Biography. 5. Voyages and travels.
   6. Europe — Emigration and immigration. 7. Australia —
   Emigration and immigration. I. Title.
305.90691

Cover and internal design by Katie Mitchell, HarperCollins Design Studio
Cover photograph from *The Age*, 6 November 1948
Author photograph by Michelle Wilson
Typeset in 11/16pt Sabon by HarperCollins Design Studio
Printed and bound in Australia by Griffin Press on 80gsm Bulky Book Ivory

6 5 4 3 2 1   01 02 03 04

To the passengers of the *Derna*,
and all those who have crossed rough seas
to reach this place in the sun

ACKNOWLEDGEMENTS

My biggest thanks go to the passengers of the *Derna* who have been so enthusiastic about this project and so generous in sharing their life stories with me. When I began researching the voyage, fifty years had passed since our arrival in Australia and I didn't expect to find much memorabilia after all this time. I couldn't believe my good fortune when so many people gave me access to diaries, photographs, newspaper clippings and letters which they have kept all these years. I'm especially grateful to Helle Nittim Risti for her diary, Lea Ohtra Holm for her father's journal, Cyla Ferszt for her assistance and vignettes, and Dorothea Ritter for her tireless efforts which have produced letters and documents.

So many people have helped me with the research. I'd like to thank Harold Grant, former Chief Migration Officer who was seconded to the UNHCR, Ellen Hansen of the UNHCR in Canberra, and Trudy Huscomb Peterson at the UNHCR in Geneva who searched the IRO archives for information about Colonel Hershaw. The helpful researchers at the National Archives of Australia who found sheafs of documents about the *Derna* and its passengers were a pleasure to deal with, and Irene Sullivan in the Canberra office was outstanding.

Professor Konrad Kwiet, an authority on the Holocaust, was always willing to discuss issues and answer my questions. Despite his busy schedule, Mark Aarons, author of *War Criminals Welcome: Australia, A Sanctuary for Fugitive War Criminals since 1945,* was kind enough to read through the relevant chapter of the manuscript and offer helpful suggestions.

Father Michael Protopopoff of the Russian Orthodox church in Geelong, who has recently written a biography of Archbishop Rafalsky, shared his knowledge with me. Author David Latimer explained the mechanism of steamships. Mary Conomos, my first close friend in Australia, was indefatigable in trying to find Greek passengers. Vic Alhadeff, Nick Papas, Stelios Korkidis, George Spiliotis, Pauline Griffin, Dr Roger Motyka and Bev Rahman all put themselves out to help me.

I'm grateful to the editors of the Polish, Latvian, Estonian and Greek newspapers and the co-ordinators of the SBS ethnic radio programs who helped to publicise my search.

Throughout the years of research and writing, I've been nurtured by an army of wonderful friends who never seemed to tire of hearing me talk about this project. I'm very grateful to Jenny Cooke who volunteered to add the role of reader to her already huge workload as journalist, mother and student. Her chapter-by-chapter reading of the manuscript was incredibly thorough, her suggestions were invaluable and her humorous remarks in the margin were a delight. During our weekly cliff walk, Dasia Black pushed me to delve deeper and helped me to explore the significance of the story. I appreciate her intellect and empathy. My special thanks to my dear friends Raymonde Raiz and Wanda Matt who read parts of the manuscript and made perceptive comments.

I'm very lucky that my children, Justine and Jonathan, are so supportive and involved in my work. From the moment I began this project they were always willing to listen and offer helpful suggestions.

My deepest gratitude goes to my husband, Michael, whose pride in me borders on the embarrassing. It can't be easy living with an author who becomes so obsessed with a book that she can talk of little else, but he coped with his usual humour and grace. In between seeing patients, taking photographs and making cappuccinos, he found time to read the manuscript and make insightful comments. Michael, I'm glad that the *Derna* led me to you.

Words are inadequate to express my gratitude to Selwa Anthony, agent extraordinaire, who is indefatigable in her efforts and unremitting in her support. From the team at HarperCollins I've received the kind of enthusiasm and respect that writers dream about but rarely experience. I feel privileged to work with outstanding professionals like Shona Martyn, Linda Funnell and Kaye Wright.

Linda Funnell's sensitivity and relaxed manner make her a joy to work with. Nicola O'Shea has been a marvel of patience, good nature and efficiency. Proofreader Sue Grose-Hodge has gone through the manuscript with impressive thoroughness. I'm grateful to my warmhearted editor Mark MacLeod and appreciate his literary taste and meticulous scrutiny.

I'd like to thank the Literature Board of the Australia Council for their faith in me and for the grant which assisted me to write this book.

⌒

AUTHOR'S NOTE

Because of the large cast of characters, to avoid confusion the women who were unmarried during the voyage have been referred to by their maiden names throughout the book. Married names have been included in the index.

Although the endings of many Polish surnames change in the feminine form — e.g. Mr Kalowski but Mrs Kalowska — for the sake of simplicity I have used the masculine form of the names in the text and index. However, both forms appear in the transcript of the *Derna*'s passenger list.

There is a tide in the affairs of men
Which, taken at the flood, leads on to fortune;
Omitted, all the voyage of their life
Is bound in shallows and in miseries.

WILLIAM SHAKESPEARE,
Julius Caesar, Act IV, Scene iii

CONTENTS

PART I

THE VOYAGE ∼ 1

PART II

THEIR LIFE ∼ 239

Passenger List ∼ 477

Index of Names ∼ 481

Selected Bibliography ∼ 484

PART I
THE VOYAGE

PROLOGUE

THE POSTCARD FROM MARSEILLES

A postcard of Marseilles's Vieux Port, saturated with dark colours like an old painting, fell out of a letter that Aunty Slawa sent me from Poland several months ago. 'I thought this card would interest you,' she wrote.

As I turned it over, I caught my breath. I was looking at my mother's handwriting, which on its own is enough to evoke a rush of nostalgia and regret, but it was the date that made me stare with disbelief: 30 August 1948; the day we set sail for Australia.

In a hurried Polish scrawl she had written to her sister-in-law: 'We arrived in Marseilles today and sail this evening. The ship is big and comfortable. Danusia* and I are together but Henek is on his own, because they've separated the men and women. There is chaos everywhere and everyone is rushing to unpack but the calm ones like me are writing postcards.'

Across the front of the card, above the picture of the port, my father added, almost as though he had known that one day I'd want to know this: 'I'm posting the card from the ship.'

As I hold this card in my hands and read their words, I feel as though I am watching my parents at the very moment when we are about to leave Europe forever and begin our new life. They have

---

* My Polish name.

stepped through the magic mirror of time and stand before me with all their hopes and dreams for themselves and, above all, for me.

Ever since I began researching the voyage, I have felt the spirit of my parents comfortingly close. And now, like a brush of angels' wings, this card which documents the day of our departure materialises to encourage and empower me precisely at the moment I am writing about the voyage of our life.

Several times in the past, at significant crossroads of my life, something inexplicable has occurred to light up my path with meaning. The postcard from Marseilles is a sign that my parents who brought me to Australia are still watching over me, and that they have blessed my project.

I

In the oppressive August heat, the seeping drains and garlic-saturated kitchens around Marseilles's Vieux Port exuded an overripe stench that lingered over the waterfront. Down by the harbour, fish heads rotted on the cobblestones as fishermen in striped jerseys and navy berets threw their catch on the scales. The salty smell of fish and seaweed mingled with the reek of sump oil, and the water's surface gleamed with the iridescent colours of petrol spills.

Moored to the wharf, solidly white in the stupefying glare of a Provençal summer, the SS *Derna* looked handsome, proud and new. But Captain Stavros Papalas knew only too well that her appearance was deceptive. So did the stevedores who hadn't finished loading even though the ship was due to sail within the hour. They weren't fooled by the smell of fresh paint as they half-ran along the wharf, propelled by the cabin trunks strapped to their powerful backs. Stocky and broad-shouldered, with short tempers and foul tongues, they left behind them a trail of curses, gobs of spit, the biting smoke of Gauloises and the musky odour of male sweat that has hung over this port for centuries.

From the bridge, the captain could hear the carpenters and plumbers banging and hammering inside the ship, racing against time to complete a refit that needed at least another week's work. The communal washrooms that would soon be shared by over five hundred passengers were primitive, offered little privacy and were barely half-finished. The toilet doors were not attached and there were problems with the plumbing. Worse still, there were no laundry facilities of any kind. How the mothers of all those small children down on the wharf were going to manage in these conditions didn't bear thinking about. But any minute now the owner would turn up and tell him that everything was ready, and he would have to give the order to sail.

A stream of juicy curses rose to his lips when he thought about the owner of the *Derna*. If only he could convince him to delay the departure. The knowledge that he was responsible for the safety of over five hundred souls on a ship that wasn't seaworthy weighed him down. He lifted the cap off his balding head to wipe his brow and shifted his plump shoulders in his ill-fitting white jacket.

Squinting into the sunlight he gazed at the frenzied activity in the busiest port of the Mediterranean. Founded by Greek mariners at the time Homer had immortalised the epic voyage of his mythical hero Ulysses, Marseilles has seen ships and mariners come and go for twenty-six centuries. Two thousand years ago, proud Athenian triremes and stately Phoenician quinqueremes with pagan goddesses on their wooden prows sailed into this port, laden with grain, salt, silks, spices and purple dyes that they traded for metal from Provence. Later the Romans conquered it, erected docks and built the drains that stank as though they hadn't been flushed out for two thousand years. After the Roman Empire ended, while artisans were carving their religious faith into the stone portals of the great cathedral of Notre Dame, the ship builders of Marseilles were carving wooden saints on their galleys, and manning the vessels with Saracen or Senegalese slaves captured in battles far away.

Now, in 1948, it was the turn of migrant ships, clapped-out coal-powered hulks, to carry the dispossessed on new odysseys to far-off lands. Like this one, tarted up and converted at break-neck speed to carry passengers under the Panamanian flag of convenience. Blisters of rust and the scars of a thousand cargo voyages to Africa, the Seychelles and the Caribbean, showed through the fresh paint that, like a thick layer of make-up, attempted to conceal the ravages of old age.

The captain looked down at the porters shouting and cursing in a flattened Provençal accent while they loaded up. They jostled past the crowd to dump yet another load of crates, suitcases, cabin trunks, valises, boxes and bundles into the net which the creaking crane hoisted up and lowered into the hold.

As the voices floated up from the wharf, he watched the passengers who spoke more languages than the occupants of the Tower of Babel. Where did they come from, these dispossessed, despairing people, with their bundles, shabby bags and silent children? Even from this height the cacophony was deafening. People were shouting to each other, calling their children, running after porters to make sure their bags weren't left behind, and saying a last goodbye with the sadness of those who knew that this parting would last forever. Above the assertive sounds of German, a descant of Yiddish voices hovered between a joke, a question and an argument. Over the musical inflections of Russian came the penetrating staccato of Hungarian voices, the precise polite sounds of Polish, the lilt of Estonian and the hubbub of the ship's crew shouting in Greek and Italian.

The captain looked pensive. This mixed crew was another contentious issue. Even before the war, many Greeks had resented the Italians who had colonised their islands, but after Mussolini's alliance with Hitler, most of the captain's Greek compatriots loathed the Fascists, and he suspected that it wouldn't take much to inflame them. He'd have his job cut out keeping order between these two hostile groups who would be living in close proximity for the next five weeks. His jowls drooped. He was fifty-four and suddenly felt his age.

To add to his problems, he could already tell that the passengers weren't going to be easy to handle either. Down on the wharf he spotted that pushy young fellow Sam Fiszman who had come to see him the previous day. Fiszman, who was about to sail on the *Derna* with his wife and baby, had wanted to interview him for some Polish or Russian newspaper that he'd never heard of. He'd sent him packing. Having the defects of his ship aired all over the world wouldn't make him popular with the owner. But recalling the way the young man's eyes had blazed when he'd refused the interview, he sensed that he hadn't heard the last of Mr Fiszman.

* * *

Sam Fiszman was about to step onto the gangplank, a khaki Soviet army jacket draped over his shoulders. A row of Russian medals on his chest glinted in the sun as he grappled with bags and baskets in one hand, and helped his wife Esther with the other. In her arms she cradled a baby but looked like a child herself, with her huge doe-like eyes and delicate face.

'Just look at this chaos,' Sam was grumbling. 'That crew is hopeless. They can't organise anything properly. Not that I'm surprised, after meeting that boorish old bastard of a captain.' As little Maria whimpered and Esther shifted from one foot to the other, he added, 'You shouldn't have to stand in this heat for so long.' Turning around, he caught sight of a couple with two fair-haired sons who looked back at him with impassive faces. 'Probably bloody Nazis,' he muttered.

As usual, Esther tried to calm him down. 'I'm sure it won't be long now,' she said in her silken way, and looked adoringly at her husband, so dashing in his army jacket.

The erect man standing nearby with his wife and two fair-haired sons clearly did not share her admiration. Verner Puurand's eyes hardened as he looked at the hated Russian uniform. He had fled from Estonia to get away from the infernal Communists who had ruined his country and would probably kill him if he returned. They and their accomplices were responsible for all the catastrophes that had befallen Estonia. Why did Australia allow this brazen Communist to migrate?

Captain Papalas knew that many of the passengers had gone through experiences he could never imagine. With his cargo of Latvians, Estonians, Russians, Germans, French, Poles, Hungarians, Czechoslovakians, Greeks, Romanians and God knew what other nationalities, he was in charge of a floating United Nations. They came from concentration camps in Czechoslovakia, death camps in Poland, gulags in Siberia, forced labour camps in Latvia and displaced persons camps in Germany and Austria.

A haze of apprehension hung all around them. It rose from the worried voices of the mothers as they pulled their exhausted children up the gangplank, and seeped from the fathers whose heavy woollen coats with padded shoulders and thick lining were sometimes the most valuable item they possessed. All of them had the tightly clenched faces of those who were leaving their familiar world behind to embark on a new life in an unknown land. Some stood forlornly waiting to board, guarding all they had left in the world: a battered suitcase fastened with a fraying strap or a box tied and retied with string.

A boisterous group of high-spirited youngsters, all talking at once, milled around a tall greying man with a neatly clipped moustache and dark eyes that seemed to pierce the young woman he was talking to. This was the doctor accompanying the sixty-one Jewish orphans. Their passage had been paid for by the American Jewish Distribution Committee, JOINT, which together with the International Refugee Organisation (IRO), had chartered this ship. The captain knew that the shipping company was under strict instructions from the Australian government that no more than twenty-five percent of the passengers were to be Jewish, but looking around, he doubted whether this quota had been observed.

As the boys and girls stepped onto the gangplank, the doctor ticked them off his list one by one, as if on a school outing. Dr Henryk Frant and his wife Zofia were already wondering whether they had taken on too much in accepting the job of chaperoning this large, unwieldy group whose ages ranged from nine to twenty. In the short time they had spent together in Paris, there had been romances, broken hearts, arguments and intrigues amongst the youngsters. On the train from Paris, even the kindly Mrs Frant had become exasperated when that little livewire Alice Zalcberg lost her ticket, and she'd had to argue with the inspector to let the girl stay on the train. Most of the girls seemed amenable and well-behaved, but everyone knew that shipboard life loosened moral standards and they'd have to watch carefully to make sure their charges behaved themselves.

Dr Frant's penetrating gaze softened as it rested on a young woman who had gathered the younger girls around her. Too old to qualify for a free passage as an orphan, twenty-one-year-old Topka Barasz had been included in the group along with her three younger sisters in return for helping the Frants look after the younger children.

'Keep close to me, don't wander away,' she instructed them in her brisk way, hardly stopping for breath. 'Hold onto your bags, don't get lost, follow me down to the cabin.'

As they trundled along the gangway, Topka looked at her sisters with her usual mixture of indulgence and concern. Although the sisters had been separated in Poland during the war, she had found them all and managed to support them amid the chaos and privations of post-war Europe. If it had been possible, she would have wrapped them in cotton wool so that the sun would not burn their delicate faces or the wind make them shiver. There was sixteen-year-old Miriam, eleven-year-old Ruth and nine-year-old Bella, as pretty as dolls in the lovely outfits she had bought them before leaving. Topka looked around like a proud mother. She had to get them safely to Australia. She could still see her mother looking into her eyes before the war as she said, 'Topka, if anything happens to me, promise me you'll always look after the children.' She blinked away the tears. No matter what happened, she would keep that promise.

The captain looked at his watch and shook his head. They were due to sail very soon, but the loading was still in progress. He craned forward. Three knitting machines were being hoisted from the dock and winched into the hold. Beside them stood a good-looking young man with curly hair and an expensive Leica camera hanging around his neck. Eyes narrowed with concentration, he was watching every move of the stevedores as the machines swayed in the air and were lowered into the hold. With his well-cut suit and air of confidence, he stood out from the rest. Unlike most of the other passengers, who had no idea how they were going to make a living in Australia, Abie Goldberg had his future mapped out. His family came from Lodz, the textile centre of Poland, and he was bringing these knitting machines to Australia so that he could continue the family business in a country which, he had been told, offered great opportunities for textile manufacturers.

Standing close to Abie, a little girl in a white rabbit fur coat and matching bonnet had a face blotched from crying. As she looked up at the huge ship, tears rolled down Ginette Wajs's cheeks. Her aunt in Paris had told her that she was going to America to live with relatives, but she wanted to stay in France with the foster-father she adored. Her aunt's last words, hissed at her as the train for Marseilles pulled out of the Gare du Sud, reverberated in her ears like a curse: 'Tell your aunty in America what a bad girl you were and how much trouble you caused me.'

When the machines had been loaded, Abie turned to the little girl he'd befriended in the train earlier that day. Huddled against the worn plush seat, the child had sobbed from the moment the train chugged out of the station. Touched by her loneliness and distress, he had comforted her. 'Don't cry. I'm going on the *Derna* too, I'll stay with you until we board,' he promised.

Almost all the passengers were aboard when suddenly there was a screech of brakes, a shriek of laughter and all heads, including the captain's, swivelled around to see the cause of the commotion. A jeep pulled up on the wharf and two American sailors, snappy in their navy and white uniforms, jumped out and helped a young woman scramble out with her bags. Dorothea Ritter, whose thick brown hair curled around her laughing face, was saying goodbye to her escorts. 'I'll write soon, I promise!' she called out gaily and turned to wave one last time from the top of the gangplank.

In the eight days she had spent in Marseilles, she had been besieged by eager American servicemen in uniform. She hadn't been able to have a cup of coffee without those Yanks, with their funny crew-cut hair and unlimited cash, offering to take her on a boat trip to the Château d'If, a drive to the church on the hilltop, or for dinner to sample the famous bouillabaisse which she decided was distinctly overrated.

A fun-loving girl with a bubbly personality and a generously proportioned figure, Dorothea knew that if a man appealed to her, she could always get him interested. Stopping for breath, she glanced up at the ship. *What an ugly big tub*, she thought. But no matter how it looked, it would take her a long way from Germany. Although she wasn't Jewish, she couldn't stand living among those hypocrites any more.

Those Nazis who had so scrupulously adhered to the Nuremburg Laws, but now pretended that they had hated Hitler and helped the

Jews. She could still remember how her heart had pounded on Kristallnacht when glass had shattered all over the street where she lived, synagogues had gone up in flames and terrified old people were dragged out into the street, tormented and beaten.

Dorothea's mother was Catholic, her Jewish father had converted to Catholicism, and she herself had been brought up as a Catholic, but that had not prevented her from being stigmatised as a *mischling* or half-caste and rejected by the society to which she had always believed she belonged. In a nation where mass hysteria ruled, and young Aryans were seduced by camaraderie, camp fires and racist songs into worshipping a demonic leader, there was no room for the racially 'impure'. Dorothea could not forget her shock when the headmistress had told her that she had to leave school, just before she was due to matriculate. She still winced whenever she recalled the disdainful look on the handsome face of the officer she was dating when he found out that she had Jewish blood. 'Then I am sorry, but I cannot see you again,' he had said in the stiff voice that used to heil Hitler.

But dwelling on the past was not in her nature, and she looked eagerly around her, changing hands to lighten the load she was carrying. In one hand she held her red leather handbag and the precious Triumph Durabel typewriter in its black case. The typewriter was twenty years old and had belonged to an older cousin, but was still in perfect working order and might prove useful in Australia if she became a secretary. In the other hand she gripped her bulky hold-all, which she put down every few minutes to wipe away the perspiration streaming down her face. Her mother had insisted on having the brown pin-striped worsted suit made for her in Berlin, and she felt very elegant in it, with its fashionably long New Look skirt, but it certainly wasn't suitable for summer on the Mediterranean. As soon as they allocated her a cabin, she planned to go into the hold and pull her summer dresses out of the suitcase.

Her reverie ended as she stepped inside the ship and her eyes began to water from the overpowering smell of fresh paint. To the rousing beat of Liszt's *Hungarian Rhapsody* which blared over the loud-speaker, officers in white uniforms directed passengers to their cabins.

Straining to hear instructions spoken in unfamiliar accents above the commotion, most passengers were reassured by the *Derna*'s welcoming atmosphere. In the foyer, a bouquet of flowers brightened the table, and the maroon leather armchairs smelled invitingly new.

But excitement soon turned to dismay as couples discovered that they were to spend the voyage in cabins which were segregated dormitories. 'Surely there must be some mistake?' some of the newly married couples protested to officers who shrugged and turned away. 'Why should I spend weeks sharing a cabin with total strangers? Whoever heard of such a thing?' women repeated to anyone willing to listen. Mothers wondered how they were going to have any rest sharing a bunk with infants or toddlers, while childless women wondered how they were going to have any sleep with all those children in the cabin. Wandering around the ship in search of their cabins, they pushed and shoved, choking the companionways and crowding the stairs, eyeing each other with the barely disguised resentment of captives forced to make room in their cramped cell for new arrivals.

Watching the passengers board, the captain was alarmed that some of the women were noticeably pregnant. A moment later, the music stopped and a strongly accented voice was heard throughout the ship: 'Would all the pregnant women come to the purser's office straightaway?'

Coming out of the cabin with her six-year-old son Stefan, Halina Kalowski looked perturbed. She and her husband were thrilled to board the *Derna*, and not even the overcrowded cabins or the fact that they had to be separated had dampened their enthusiasm. After six anxious months in Paris, they were on their way to Australia at last.

'Why are they calling the pregnant women? What can they possibly want?' she wondered.

'They probably want to give you a better cabin and special food,' her husband Mietek speculated as they tried to find their way to the purser's office.

When Halina joined the other pregnant women, she was horrified to hear the captain say, 'You must leave the ship at once because we don't have any facilities for confinement.' She was in despair. They had waited so long in Paris for a passage that their money had almost run out. And if it hadn't been for the kind intervention of Abbé Glasberg, the Jewish-born priest who had speeded up their application, they'd still be waiting. To leave the ship now and have the baby in France was unthinkable.

'I want my baby to be born in Australia,' Halina said in a quiet but determined voice.

Some of the women who were in advanced stages of pregnancy had already begun to disembark but Halina started calculating. 'We're due to arrive in Melbourne on the 12th of October. That's only five weeks from now. Why shouldn't I stay on board? I'll only be six months pregnant when we arrive.' Then she grimaced in dismay, remembering that she had come forward with the other pregnant women. 'But I can't stay now that they've seen me and know I'm pregnant.'

Mietek looked around to make sure they hadn't been overheard. 'Don't worry,' he whispered. 'Run down to the cabin, change your dress and put your hair up. They won't recognise you. Just keep out of the way for a day or so and they'll forget all about you.'

She took little Stefan's hand and ran down to their cabin, feeling buoyant once more. Mietek was so smart. She felt almost guilty to think how lucky she was to have this second chance at happiness.

As the crew prepared to weigh anchor, Captain Papalas and some of his officers were on deck, straining to catch the words of a stocky man with a swarthy complexion, heavy-lidded eyes and tufts of cotton wool stuck in both ears, who was striding up and down the wharf, shouting and gesticulating. From his rumpled suit and unpolished manner, he could have been mistaken for an ordinary seaman if not for the white, well-shaped hands that he waved around to emphasise a point. It was Stavros Livanos, the millionaire owner of the *Derna*, shouting last-minute instructions. Even at this late stage, he was still trying to convince the captain that the ship was fit to sail.

Like the captain and most of the Greek crew, Stavros Livanos had been born on the lush island of Chios which for centuries has supplied Greece with sailors, ship-builders and shipping dynasties. Chios was the birthplace of Homer, and it was there that he had written *The Odyssey*. Livanos was ten years old when his father bought a steamship; from then on the boy had dreamed of nothing but ships. With the single-minded dedication that was to become his trademark, he surpassed his own dreams. After becoming the youngest chief engineer in the Greek merchant navy, four years later, at the age of twenty-one, he became the youngest ship's captain in Greece.

By 1948, when he was fifty-eight, Stavros Livanos had become a shipping tycoon and was still obsessed with ships: what they cost, where they sailed, why they were for sale and how he could raise the cash to buy them. Wealth gravitates to wealth, and as a result of the recent marriage of his daughters — Tina to Aristotle Onassis, and Eugenia to Stavros Niarchos — Livanos was part of the most powerful shipping triumvirate in the world.

Those who knew him said that Livanos achieved prominence by being determined, shrewd and miserly. From his father he had learned always to pay cash and never waste a cent. In shipping circles they used to say that Stavros would cross the Sahara on foot to save the camel-fare, and the term 'running a tight ship' might have been invented to describe the way he conducted his business. He bought old ships at cheap prices and it was said that he paid his crews the most miserable wages in Greece.

That's how he had come to buy this clapped-out vessel of 5751 tonnes which had been built in 1917 and should have been broken up for scrap metal long ago. The *Derna*'s history reflected the changing political realities of Europe in the first half of the twentieth century. In its first incarnation, as the *Kagera*, it had been built for the German East Africa Line as a cargo ship and accommodated only nine passengers. After World War I, it was seized by the Allies and ceded to France as part of the spoils of war. Several years later, in 1922, the French Line bought it, renamed it *Indiana* and employed it to ply between French ports and the Gulf of Mexico. After the fall of France in 1940, it was taken over by the United States War Shipping Administration as a transport vessel, but when the war ended, it was returned to the French Line.

Aware of the world-wide shortage of ships to transport migrants from Europe to Australia and America after World War II, Livanos seized his opportunity. In 1948 the Dos Oceanos Cia de Navigaçion, a Livanos enterprise registered in Panama, bought the SS *Indiana* and proceeded to recondition her as quickly and cheaply as possible. In a remarkably short time, two decks of the cargo ship were converted to cabins into which over five hundred passengers could be crammed.

With the change of character came a change of name and the SS *Derna* was born, although why its new owner chose to name his ship after a port in Tunisia is not known. Sailors believe that changing a ship's name is a bad omen, a superstition that Livanos should have heeded. He registered the vessel in Panama whose red and white flag ensured not only tax exemptions and cheap registration fees, but also freedom from the usual regulation of ship standards, crew wages and shipboard safety.

And now that he had decided the *Derna* was ready to sail on its maiden voyage, his captain was urging him to delay departure. Stavros Livanos was an attentive listener, almost as sparing with words as he was with money, but when he spoke, it was with steely determination. After spending so much on the refit, taking the risk of engaging a mixed crew of Greeks and Italians and filling the cabins with 545 passengers, there would be no delay. Succinct and forceful, he countered all the captain's objections. The ship must sail and the passengers would manage. But from the captain's worried face and sagging shoulders, it was obvious that he saw trouble ahead.

The *Derna* was pulling away from the wharf and excitement on the ship reached fever pitch as the passengers rushed to find a space against the taff-rail for their last view of Europe. How do you say goodbye to the land that has been your home and the home of your ancestors for centuries, where your sweat made the wheat grow and your hands made the roses bloom? How do you say goodbye to your ancestral spirits and the memory of loved ones you are leaving behind forever? How do you reconcile nostalgia with pain, longing with hope?

Some chattered nervously to their neighbours, while others stood in silence, their throats so tightly knotted with emotion that their necks ached. On the salty Mediterranean breeze they smelled the juniper forests of Estonia, heard the murmur of Polish wheatfields in the breeze and saw the swaying birch trees of Russia. Some thought of romantic rendezvous in Prague cafés or stolen kisses in the Vienna Woods that would never come again. Others wept for loved ones who lay in unmarked graves in blood-soaked forests. Parents held their children up on a rung of the rail and tried to instil some sense of the significance of this final parting.

Having written their postcard to my father's sister in Poland, whom they would never see again, my parents joined the other passengers on deck. I wonder how they felt at that poignant moment when, like Janus, the twin-headed god of the Romans, they looked simultaneously to the past and to the future. Like so many passengers, they had chosen Australia because it was as far as they could travel from the tragic past without falling off the edge of the world. With the courage of all migrants who abandon terra firma to be tossed upon unknown seas, they had cast themselves into an uncertain future with light suitcases and hearts full of hopes and dreams.

And what about me, a quiet nine year old with brown plaits and a serious face? Did I also stand against the rail as we sailed away? Did my father urge me to take one last look at the continent that neither he nor my mother was ever to see again? Perhaps I was impatient to unpack the skeins of wool I'd brought in my favourite colours of rose, blue, lemon and apple-green, and longed to unravel the yarn and knit fanciful designs of my own invention.

The hollow clank of the anchor and the long, lonely hoot of the funnel echoed over the ship and sent a sudden chill through our souls. In the dusk of the summer night, the city lights twinkled as the *Derna* edged further from the wharf. The elongated triangle of water separating us from the wharf grew larger. The ship ploughed a furrow in the sea, carving up the world into two fields: past and future.

2

When Dorothea had fought her way past the passengers blocking the companionways with their baggage and finally reached her cabin, she took one look inside and recoiled. Twenty-four bunks were crammed in from floor to ceiling like shelves in a cheap cupboard. They were arranged in tiers of three, with the bottom one almost touching the floor and the top one so close to the ceiling that if you sat up too fast you would bump your head. She had been allocated the middle bunk, which was so tightly sandwiched by the others that she was sure she'd suffocate.

She looked around in dismay. There was only one porthole and, wouldn't you know it, her friend Gilda Brouen with whom she had flown out of Berlin was already lying on the bunk next to it. 'Lucky pig,' Dorothea muttered. There was nowhere to put her things, no room to move in this stifling cabin. And where was the bathroom? To her horror, she discovered that the occupants of her cabin, as well as of several others, would have to share the primitive communal washroom at the end of the passageway. There was one bath, several showers rigged up over wooden planks, and a row of toilets with doors hanging unevenly off the hinges. She wrinkled her nose in distaste. How horrible.

Throwing her hold-all, typewriter and red leather bag onto the bunk, Dorothea mopped her forehead. She was going to die of heat in this worsted suit. Looking around, she noticed two young women smiling down at her. Ilse and Elfriede Hof were sisters who'd also come from Germany, so at least they'd be able to communicate. Elfriede, the more ebullient one, was already organised on the top bunk, recording first impressions in her morocco-bound diary. Dorothea intended to keep a journal of the voyage too, but first she had to find her luggage so that she could get out of this impossible suit.

While Dorothea sat disconsolately on her bunk, in a nearby cabin Elmars Kuplis and his wife Auguste were delighted to discover that they had been allocated the same cabin. The Latvian couple didn't realise that because of Auguste's unusual name, the purser had mistaken her for a man.

The error wasn't discovered until the other men in the cabin complained that it wasn't fair, as their wives had not been accommodated with them. Someone rushed to report the irregularity to the captain who summoned Mrs Kuplis to see him. 'How come you claimed to have a man's name?' he demanded in Greek while one of the officers translated his words into German so that she could understand.

'But Auguste is my name,' she protested, bewildered by the accusation.

Her explanation didn't satisfy him. 'Show me your documents!' he barked. She passed across her papers with trembling hands and the captain held them up against the light and scrutinised the photograph on both sides to make sure she hadn't pasted her own photograph onto a man's ID. Although he couldn't see any sign of falsification, he still wasn't convinced and spoke rapidly to his officer, glancing mistrustfully at the woman shaking in front of him. Finally, without a word of apology, he said, 'All right, but you have to move out of that cabin. We'll put you somewhere else.' Auguste left the office in tears, upset by his gruff manner, and it took a long time for her husband to calm her down.

The dinner gong provided a welcome respite from the general turmoil. Among hundreds of hungry, exhausted passengers, Elmars and Auguste, together with his mother and their five-year-old son, were directed to their places at the long refectory-style tables in the dining room. The meal was served surprisingly fast by sallow waiters in tired white jackets who scurried around with plates held high above the tables. Dinner began with a dish of olives which most of us eyed suspiciously, having no idea what they were or how to eat them. My mother and I bit into the peculiar texture, felt sickened by the taste and resolved never to eat them again. Braised beef and potatoes were served next, with bread as white and tasteless as cotton wool, but the chocolate pudding that ended the meal cheered up all the children, even finicky eaters like me.

The night hours passed slowly in the uncomfortably intimate proximity of strangers whose snoring, sighing and sweating made it difficult to relax. Dorothea tossed in her narrow bunk, irritated by all the bodies, and by the fitful crying and whimpering of the children.

As soon as the sun shone through the porthole, she jumped out of her bunk, ready to start searching for her suitcase. Down in the hold, she climbed over crates, cases, trunks, chests and boxes, starting at one end and working her way section by section through the mountains of belongings, without success. Perspiring profusely, she continued to search. It must be in here somewhere, she kept telling herself as she tried to suppress a growing sense of panic. She knew she'd brought the two cases from Germany because she remembered sitting on them in the cargo plane with the bucket seats which had airlifted her, Gilda and that nice fellow Fred out of Berlin.

But after crawling around the grimy hold, lifting up cases and pushing boxes aside for several back-breaking hours, her spirits sank. Perhaps her suitcases weren't on the ship at all. Either someone had stolen them or they'd been left behind in Marseilles. She sat down on one of the chests, blinking away the tears as she tried to figure out what to do. Apart from her clothes, the cases contained some carefully chosen pieces of Meissen porcelain her mother had given her for her cousin in Sydney, some family silver and the only photographs of her parents that she possessed.

Towards the end of the war, she had packed that photograph of her father before going down to the cellar with her mother, because the Russians were about to enter Berlin. Her father had been arrested and thrown into prison the previous year for criticising the Nazi regime and she had given up hope of ever seeing him again. Suddenly there was a knock on the door. Expecting bad news, she had opened it cautiously but when she saw who it was, her heart stopped beating and then she was screaming, laughing and crying all at once. There he stood, a blanket around his thin shoulders and a chunk of bread in his hand. That had been the most fantastic moment of her life. And now she was travelling to the end of the earth without even a photograph. But right now the biggest loss was her clothes. How was she going to get through the voyage in that loathsome cabin and this heat without summer clothes? Thank God she'd had the foresight to put one cotton print dress into her hold-all, but she couldn't live in that for five weeks.

She reported the missing suitcase to the purser, the stout Egyptian Turk who stared at her, blinking his heavy-lidded eyes. He obviously couldn't have cared less.

'Go and see the man responsible for the passengers travelling with the International Refugee Organisation. Maybe he will help,' he told her in his brusque way, probably relieved to pass yet another problem onto someone else. Dorothea found out much later that she hadn't travelled under the auspices of the IRO at all, because her cousin in Australia had paid her fare.

Clutching her typewriter, which she was determined not to let out of her sight, she ran along narrow companionways, took wrong turns, and climbed up and down stairs until she reached the upper deck and looked around. What a contrast! It was like entering the cool oasis of a luxurious hotel after staying in a derelict boarding house.

The man she had come to see had a swagger in his voice and the confidence of a man skilled at making the best of the opportunities that life threw his way, but despite his air of smugness, there was something likeable about him. Perhaps it was his courteous manner, or the bemused smile playing on his sensual lips when he looked at her. He had receding hair and a neatly trimmed moustache which he smoothed from time to time, but although she thought he was old enough to be her father, the way he looked at her was certainly not fatherly.

The Honourable Lt-Colonel Ogden Hershaw eyed this buxom young woman with the animated face as she told him about her lost suitcase in excellent English, so charmingly arranged in German syntax. Everything about her was effervescent: even her curly hair bounced around her face as she spoke.

'Your cases must have been left behind on the wharf. I'll ask the radio operator to wire Marseilles and make sure they send them out on the next ship,' he told her, and from the twinkling eyes and the irrepressible half-smile playing around his mouth, it was obvious that he was trying not to laugh. In spite of her distress at the prospect of having to make do for five weeks without a change of clothes, Dorothea soon found herself laughing with him.

He wasn't surprised to hear that her suitcase hadn't been loaded on the ship because he already knew of other luggage that had been left behind. He had already noted the inefficient way the crew had processed the passengers for boarding, and the air of lethargy that pervaded the ship from bow to stern. The crew were clearly a bunch of inexperienced riff-raff who stood around bickering when there was so much to be done. Of course the fact that the ship was owned by a Greek explained everything. Everyone knew that Greek ships lacked hygiene, discipline and efficiency, and no self-respecting English or Canadian sailor would ever work on one if he could help it.

The Honourable Lt-Colonel Ogden Hershaw, who was born in Norway forty-three years earlier, had become a Canadian citizen. During the war he served as a transport officer with the Royal Canadian Army and later became an administrative officer with the Royal Norwegian Air Force. His grandiose title did not originate from any act of military distinction but had been bestowed on him shortly before the voyage. After the war he had worked in public relations and advertising, and while assistant director for the Ontario Department of Travel and Publicity, he had done a favour for a politician who had given him the title in gratitude. In July 1948, seeking a change of occupation and environment, Ogden Hershaw, who was married at the time, had applied to the International Refugee Organisation in Geneva. They appointed him to escort 219 displaced persons travelling under the auspices of the IRO to Australia, at the handsome salary of US$ 2700.

Ogden Hershaw had no patience with anyone who questioned his actions, so when he boarded the *Derna* and met his charges, he was pleased to find that most of them were Estonians and Latvians: calm, quietly spoken people who appreciated whatever he did for them. The Balts were a jolly good bunch, not demanding like some of the highly-strung Semitic types he'd already noticed on board, who were always questioning everything and making a nuisance of themselves.

As he surveyed the comely young woman in front of him, his eyes fell on the Triumph typewriter in her hand. 'I brought it in case I end up working as a secretary in Sydney,' Dorothea explained. 'I had the pound key put in before I left so I can use it in Australia.'

He paused, obviously considering something. Although he had declared in his application that his German was adequate for the job, he knew that in fact he had overstated his proficiency. 'I'll need someone to type up reports, distribute soap and cigarettes, and make announcements in German, that sort of thing,' he said. 'You can type and speak German, so you have all the qualifications. Come and be my secretary during the voyage.'

Dorothea beamed. What a marvellous opportunity! She couldn't believe her luck, to be asked to assist this important man. Her disappointment over her lost clothes momentarily forgotten, she ran down to tell Gilda about the new job. On her way to the cabin she passed several passengers staring pensively at the receding coastline as the waves slapped gently against the side of the ship. Although it was morning, the sun already blazed down on the decks which burned bare feet and offered no shade. Most of the passengers had escaped the cramped, stuffy cabins and were searching for shade on the deck. She almost tripped over two young girls sitting on a bulkhead near the bow of the ship, obviously exchanging confidences, their fair hair falling forward and intermingling as they talked, engrossed in each other's secrets.

The younger, prettier one was Helle Nittim. She was wearing socks with flat-heeled shoes and the only cotton dress she owned, and looked up enviously at the chic long skirt and pretty shoes of the woman walking past. Pushing her long blonde hair back from her face, she wished she had high heels and dresses with long skirts, instead of the short skirts that made her feel like a hick from a country town. How she had sighed in front of the shop windows in Marseilles, longing for high-heeled shoes or new sandals, but she knew that her parents couldn't afford them. Looking down with distaste at her feet, she sighed. 'How am I going to get through five weeks on this boring ship, with nothing to do except think about Ilmar and write in my diary?' she complained to her friend Rita Lindemanis.

It was Rita's sympathetic smile that had first attracted Helle when they had met in the Bucholtz transit camp in Germany. She had also noticed Rita's brother Jack, tall and blond as a hero from Baltic legends, but not at all conceited. Helle looked away whenever he glanced at her so that she wouldn't give herself away. Although Rita and Jack were Latvian, not Estonian like her, all three were able to communicate in German. That was a relief, because many of the young people on this ship spoke languages she couldn't understand. Helle was flattered that this warm-hearted twenty-one-year-old woman was interested in her, and was soon confiding about her romance with Ilmar at the displaced persons camp, and how heartbroken she had been when they parted.

Forgetting everything and everyone around them, the two girls became so engrossed in exchanging confidences and sharing dreams, they didn't notice that the sun had burned their pale arms and faces. Tears mingled with laughter as they talked about their doomed romances. Like Helle, Rita had been separated from her sweetheart too, and wondered if she'd ever see him again. 'Eric and I were promised to each other from the day I was born,' she said in her dreamy way. 'His father had the neighbouring farm, and as soon as he saw me he said, "This girl will be my daughter-in-law."'

Helle was intrigued. 'But what if you hadn't liked each other?' she asked.

'But we did. We fell in love,' Rita said softly. 'Eric and I used to swim out to a big rock in the river near our homes, and we spent hours there, planning our future, and imagining how happy we would be when we got married.' She looked away and the radiant smile vanished, as though a light had been switched off. 'But that was before the war.'

In 1941 Rita's world had been smashed into pieces that never fitted together again. She was fourteen when the Communists trampled over Latvia and the men started to disappear. She couldn't understand why they had taken her father away when he hadn't committed any crime. He was a landowner with forests of oak and pine, fields of wheat, and cows that grazed on pastureland beside the River Memel which she often saw in her dreams. After her father was taken away, Rita became so depressed that she couldn't eat, sleep or concentrate on her books, and she missed a year of school.

Three years later, when the Germans were retreating and the dreaded Russians returned, they still didn't know whether her father was alive or dead. Terrified of the Russians, her mother said that they had to flee or they'd be arrested as well. Rita cried as she helped her unhasp the barns and stables and let all the cows, pigs and horses go free on the day they left their beautiful farm forever to become refugees in Germany.

Rita brushed away a strand of fine hair that the sea breeze had loosened, and pulled a face as she licked the salt on her lips. 'Can you tell that I used to limp?' she suddenly asked Helle, who shook her head in astonishment. 'It happened in Hamburg during an air raid. I ran into a building as soon as I heard the sirens, but the next thing I knew I was lying in a hospital bed and couldn't move my legs,' she said. 'They told me that the building had collapsed on top of me and that I'd never walk again. But you know what? I never really believed them!'

During the long year she spent in hospital, she gritted her teeth, dragged herself around in a grotesque, twitching parody of walking, strained until her tendons bulged and the sweat poured down her face, until she managed to hoist herself up. She clutched walls, chairs and tables, forcing herself to shuffle step by step until she finally proved them wrong. 'Look at me now!' she exclaimed. 'I'm going to the dance tonight. Are you?' Helle nodded. She was about to say something but stopped herself in time, too proud to ask whether Rita's brother would be coming. As if she'd read her friend's thoughts, Rita leaned over and whispered, 'Jack is in love with you!'

The dance was held at the back of the ship near the bar, where the prices were beyond the reach of most passengers. Young Alice, one of

Dr Frant's group, watched the handsome young French barman mixing cassis with soda water and coveted the fizzy pink drink. Dorothea, wishing that she could wear one of her pretty dresses instead of the boring print dress, arrived with Gilda, who had pinned her light brown hair into two soft wings on either side of her face.

Hoping to have an opportunity to sing, Gilda looked around for the band. Although her real name was Gisa, she had adopted the more romantic Gilda, which seemed better suited to her operatic persona. She had studied music at the Rome Conservatorium but after Mussolini's Fascists came to power, it became impossible for a woman who was part Jewish to continue her singing career either there or in Germany, so her dream of becoming an opera singer had been destroyed. Several years later, her chance of personal happiness was also shattered when her fiancé, a singer with the Berlin Opera, was killed in one of the last battles of the war.

In the soft Mediterranean night, the tensions of the day began to recede. The sky was studded with millions of stars, bigger and brighter than any they had ever seen, and so close that you could almost reach up and pluck them. Glasses clinked and bursts of self-conscious laughter swept over the deck. Occasionally bigger waves rocked the ship and pushed the girls off balance until they tottered and collided with the boys standing nearby, provoking giggles and instant introductions.

Young men stood around in awkward groups, looking speculatively at the girls who pretended not to notice them. The svelte, pretty ones like that blonde with the shoulder-length hair and tiny waist looked snooty, while the ones who returned their gaze were either too young or too dumpy. Emil Kopel noticed a striking girl with an enchanting smile and hair the colour of a cornfield in July braided on top of her head like a coronet. Beside her stood a girl with a similar hairstyle, probably her sister. In eager whispers, he and his friends conferred whether to take the risk and ask them to dance. They didn't look Jewish and he wondered whether he would be rebuffed.

From her side of the deck, Helle watched some of the Jewish boys. The good-looking one strumming a guitar gave her a mischievous grin, and she thought she'd like to get to know him. Then her heart started to thump because Rita and her brother were coming towards her. She told herself not to look too keen if he asked her to dance.

The *Derna* had a small selection of thick black records with red HMV labels depicting a white dog looking into the horn of a phonograph. One of the officers hand-cranked the gramophone to play the same few languorous tangoes and rhumbas over and over again: 'Besame Mucho', 'Amor, Amor', 'Jealousy' and 'La Cumpasita'. Some of the married couples started to dance, holding each other closer as they moved in time to the sexy beat, inflamed by the rhythm and the touch of their bodies, and knowing that after the dance was over they would have to return to their segregated cabins. Some of them, like Bronia and Heniek Glassman, hadn't been married very long, while Krysia and Heniek Lipschutz were experiencing an unexpectedly celibate honeymoon. Occasionally the men whispered in their wives' ears, the women blushed and shook their heads, laughed coquettishly, and shortly afterwards the couples went off arm in arm to look for a secluded section of the deck.

The officers were there too, snappy in their crisp uniforms and braided caps. The most popular ones were George Parthenopoulos, the purser, Kosmos Papalas, the third officer who was the captain's son, plump and good-natured, and George Alexiou, the radio officer. But all the women's eyes were on the first officer, John Papalas, who had the same surname as the captain. Tall, slim, charming and very handsome in the white jacket which set off his Mediterranean appearance, John sparked off fantasies in most of the single women, and in some of the married ones as well. Dorothea, who had been invited to join the officers' group, was thrilled when he asked her to dance, and closed her eyes as they swayed to the seductive rhythm of the music.

As soon as there was a lull in the dancing, Gilda stepped forward. As she began singing Mimi's plaintive aria from *La Bohème* in her clear soprano voice, everyone fell silent. Nostalgia descended upon the listeners, soft and palpable as the evening mist that rose from the dark sea. Nothing evokes past pain and pleasure as powerfully as music, and each note was a key to moments of ecstasy and loss. Puccini's wistful melody transported them to the best moments of their lives, the long-gone days of velvet theatre seats and gilded opera boxes, and for one bitter-sweet moment they tasted once again the pleasures of the culture and sophistication they had left behind.

When her song ended, there was a moment's silence before the spell was broken. Like the others, Dorothea clapped loudly, impressed by the beauty of her friend's voice and the mood she had created. She was still applauding when she looked up to see Colonel Ogden Hershaw standing by her side, smoothing his moustache. She thought he had come to give her instructions about her secretarial duties when he said in his suave voice, 'You know, I've been thinking. Here I am in a cabin with four bunks all to myself and there you are, squashed in with all that lot. Why don't you move in with me?'

For a moment her heart stopped beating and she was sure he could hear the tumult in her mind. Just thinking about her sardine can of a cabin was enough to make her jump at his offer, but how could she move in with a strange man? It wasn't that she suspected his motives, but it just wasn't done. What would people say? Reading her hesitation, he gave her a disarming smile. 'You don't need to worry. I'm hardly ever in the cabin, and I come in very late at night, so you'll have it virtually to yourself. No one will disturb you and you can come and go as you please.'

Dorothea flushed with excitement. Why not? There was no one on the ship whose opinion she needed to worry about and she knew she could look after herself. She had managed to get away from the Russian brutes who had tried to rape her in Berlin, so she would certainly be able to handle this elderly fellow if he ever tried anything. She smiled, already imagining the amazement on Gilda's face when she told her she was moving out of their cabin. This voyage was going to be a real adventure after all.

3

Three days had passed since we had left Marseilles and the ship still echoed with the sound of banging and hammering. Even over breakfast at the long refectory tables in the dining room, as we tapped the shells of eggs so small that they might have come from pigeons, and spread runny marmalade on white bread as tasteless as pulped cardboard, the noise didn't let up. 'They must be adding another deck in the hold so they can fit in more bunks,' someone joked, not realising that this wasn't far from the truth, because a hundred more passengers were due to board in Port Said.

It was now obvious to even the most optimistic passengers that the ship's freshly painted exterior, the Nulux mattresses which had been purchased in London for eleven pounds sterling, the white blankets and little privacy curtains in front of the bunks, were mere window dressing. The *Derna*'s façade resembled the passengers whose lively chatter and brave smiles concealed bitter memories and scarred minds.

Mothers travelling with babies and toddlers were in despair because there was nowhere to wash or dry their soiled clothes. Gitel Frid, whose three-month-old son Jack was so sickly that doctors didn't expect him to survive the voyage, would furtively wash his nappies in the shower, and smuggle them out sopping wet under her dress so the stewards wouldn't notice. Gitel was used to hardship: Morrie, her seven year old, had been born in a Siberian labour camp. Her cousin Leah Fein, who had a two year old on board, sometimes sneaked into the kitchen for a bowl of hot water to wash his clothes.

It was a struggle to keep the children clean but some of the mothers were not very fastidious to begin with, Clara Kraus thought. The woman who slept in the bunk below hers used to stuff her baby's dirty nappy under her mattress until morning. 'Please don't leave it in here all night. It's smelly and unhygienic,' Clara would plead, but to no avail. By the time she had finished speaking, the exhausted mother was already fast asleep and the stench flooded the cabin.

Not so long ago, Clara herself had been separated from her husband and forced to look after a baby among hostile strangers. Whenever she couldn't sleep, she would reflect on her life which had begun so pleasantly and predictably in her Jewish home in Budapest, but had taken so many unexpected turns. But it all had to happen that way, she thought serenely, because those paths in the end had led her to Jesus Christ who had helped her and her tiny sons to survive.

One sleepless night in the harsh labour camp near Viehoffen in Austria, when the temperature dropped to twenty-five degrees below zero and she was hungry, desperate and alone, with nothing for the new baby, not even a nappy, she made a covenant with God. She vowed to follow Christ to the end of her days if God guided her and helped her family to survive. She told no one about her decision to convert which left her feeling comforted and secure, but when the war ended, and she was reunited with her husband Jim, she kept her promise. Not just in gratitude, but because she had genuinely come to believe that Christ was her saviour.

She glanced lovingly at Peter and Paul, curled up asleep at the bottom of her bunk. Little Peter, skinny and serious, looking much older than his six years because of his round rimless glasses, had gripped her hand when they came into the cabin, and she knew that he was remembering the bunks in the barracks of the labour camp. The child had been so traumatised by what he had witnessed there that he stopped speaking for months, and it took a long time before she was able to bring a smile to his pale face. As her thoughts turned to the future, the words of the Hungarian poet Miklos Tompa floated into her mind. 'If you change your homeland you must also change your heart.' She wondered whether she would ever be able to change her heart and learn to love Australia as she had once loved Hungary.

The baby in the bunk below started screaming again, and despite her resolve to stay calm, Clara felt the anger rising all over again. What a wretched ship this was, carrying so many small children, yet providing no suitable food or washing facilities. She had always hated ships and had never intended to sail to Australia at all. That was why, when she and Jim had gone to the Jewish agency in Munich to organise their journey, they had paid over two thousand dollars for their flights — a fortune, more than most people earned in two years.

Her chest tightened as she replayed the scene in the Paris office when they had arrived to pick up their tickets. After leafing through papers and scrabbling in a drawer, the clerk had said, 'I'm sorry, Mrs Kraus, but there must be some mistake. We don't have any plane tickets reserved for your family, and there's absolutely no record of them in your file.'

Anger choked her. 'What do you mean?' she had demanded, her mouth so dry she could hardly get the words out. 'We paid two thousand dollars so that we could fly to Australia!'

He shook his head and looked away. 'Unfortunately there's nothing I can do about the plane tickets,' he said. 'But we do have berths on a ship that is due to sail soon from Marseilles.'

Clara exploded. 'This is outrageous! I paid for flights and that's what I want. I won't accept this!' But in the end she had to accept it because there was nothing to be done. Some cheat in the Munich office had pocketed their money and added their names to the list of passengers whose berths cost a fraction of what they had paid for the flights. 'If only I could get my hands on that swindler,' she muttered to herself as she turned carefully in her bunk, trying not to wake her sons.

Gradually the monotonous routine of shipboard life imposed itself on the passengers. To escape from the suffocating cabins, they spent most of the day on deck, chatting, playing cards, reading or just staring at the sky and the sea until it was time for lunch or dinner. Little boys chased each other around the deck while little girls played with their dolls. My father, a reserved man with greying hair, a moustache and a stiff leg that made him limp, was content because he had found bridge partners. But my mother, who had pinned her blonde hair on top of her head to keep cool, felt sea-sick, miserable and neglected.

Weighed down from infancy by secrets on which our lives depended when we were forced to live as Catholics in a Polish village during the Holocaust, I had become a shy, solitary child with a tendency to sadness, and felt more comfortable observing than talking. I had already begun unravelling the first skein of wool. Without a design to guide my handiwork, I started knitting in the hope that my imagination would transcend my limited skills and shape the yarn into something I could be proud of.

After the spartan conditions of the DP camps, the privations of post-war Germany, and the shortages and rations that prevailed over most of Europe, the prospect of being served three meals every day comforted most of the passengers, even though some of the food was unpalatable and strange. Helle's cabin-mate, seventeen-year-old Lea Ohtra, who was travelling with her parents and little sister Tiia, didn't know what to make of the three lone sardines that arrived on her plate. In Estonia they had eaten sprats on bread, never by themselves. And she had no idea how to eat those peculiar little black things which they served with every meal. 'Wait and see what the others do,' her mother had whispered. But at their table, no one seemed to know how to eat the olives, and invariably sent them back untouched, to the obvious disapproval of their elderly waiter who shook his grizzled head as he took the plates away.

By the third afternoon, time was dragging so badly that people kept checking their watches to make sure that they hadn't stopped. There wasn't much to see along the southern coast of Italy and the conversation was lagging when suddenly a siren pierced the air and the captain ordered all passengers on deck. A fire had broken out. All over the ship, passengers were shouting and pushing, clamouring to get out of the narrow passageways and onto the decks. 'Help! Fire!' some shouted, while others lamented, 'What shall we do? Where can we go?' At the same time, some people stayed put, convinced that this was merely a fire drill. As no such drill had yet been held, neither the passengers nor the crew knew where to assemble or where the life-belts were, and everyone ran back and forth in utter confusion.

Some said the fire had broken out in the galley, while others argued that it must have started in the overheated engine room. In fact, it had started with the banging and hammering heard earlier that day. The plumber had been welding a broken bedstead in one of the cabins with an oxyacetylene torch when a defective safety valve on one of the bottles caused an explosion. As he hadn't bothered to remove the bedding, the mattress had caught fire.

Soon flames were leaping out of the cabin and smoke poured onto the deck. After the alarm was raised, the inexperienced and poorly trained crew panicked. No one even knew where to find the key to unlock the fire extinguisher, and when one of the seamen finally found it, he tried to open it too quickly and it jammed.

In the meantime, there was pandemonium in the cabins, the companionways and on the decks, as terrified passengers tied their life-belts on with trembling fingers and looked for guidance that failed to appear. 'Look! We're turning in towards the shore!' someone exclaimed. This provoked new laments. If we made a detour to Italy, how long would we have to wait for another ship to Australia? In an attempt to restore calm, the captain relayed a message which Dorothea, who had already commenced her secretarial duties, proceeded to broadcast in German. 'You have nothing to worry about. The fire will soon be extinguished,' she translated. 'I will bring you safely to Australia.'

The officers also did their best to reassure the passengers. 'Since the fire didn't break out in the engine room, there is no problem,' they said. But neither the captain nor the crew inspired much confidence.

In the midst of the chaos, a woman raced along the deck screaming to her husband in Yiddish: '*Moishe! Moishe, happ der valiskes!*' Grab the suitcases! In spite of their anxiety, those who heard her burst out laughing. Where did she think she was going with those cases?

One of the sailors jeered, 'You'll be lucky to get into the lifeboat yourself, never mind about the suitcases!'

Sam Fiszman grabbed little Maria and rushed to the ship's hospital where Esther had been admitted because she hadn't been able to stop vomiting ever since we had set sail. Not that you could call this box-like cabin a hospital, with its three iron beds, an inexperienced orderly and a doctor who could rarely be found.

While mothers ran to save their children, one childless woman pushed them out of the way, scrabbled through her belongings and rushed out on deck clutching her prize possession, a fox fur stole. 'Look, she's rescuing her fur!' a cabin-mate scoffed.

Husbands, wives and children were gathering on deck. Honeymooners Heniek and Krysia Lipschutz clung to each other. Grabbing a plank of wood he found on the deck, Heniek told his petite bride, 'If we have to abandon ship, we'll both hang on to this.'

Watching the couples enviously, the widows felt abandoned. One of them was Sala Sznur, whose husband had been killed during the Holocaust. She was travelling with her six-year-old daughter Anna, whose dimpled cheeks and glossy black sausage curls won the admiration of all the mothers and the envy of all the little girls, including me. Wherever Sala looked, she saw men making sure that their wives and children were safe, but no one was looking out for them. *Did we survive the war just to become food for sharks? If the two of us perish in the fire or fall into the ocean, no one will know or care*, she thought bitterly, drawing her little daughter closer.

Meanwhile, Dr and Mrs Frant and Topka were running around assembling their charges, counting and recounting to make sure all were on deck. Most of the youngsters dismissed the fire as a mere diversion. Sixteen-year-old Kitty Lebovics, who was appealing in a feline way and much admired by the boys, watched the panic with detachment. After what she'd been through in Auschwitz, nothing worried her. At the age of twelve she had seen her mother taken away, lost everyone she loved, witnessed atrocities that she tried not to think about, and endured such hunger that death would have been a release. Now at least she wasn't alone. Dr Frant was in charge, and the whole group was together. Whatever happened would happen to them all.

Meanwhile, the fire raged unchecked and orange flames leaped from the cabin. When the crew finally unscrewed the valves of the fire hydrants, they opened them too fast and sprayed in the wrong places. In a scene that could have come from a Charlie Chaplin slapstick comedy, the seamen started running around looking for hoses to attach to the hydrants, but when they found them attached them at the wrong end.

To add to the confusion, they had trouble convincing the engine room that water had to be supplied on deck. That's when they discovered that some of the fire hoses had holes. Exasperated, Helle turned to her father. 'This is a madhouse,' she said. 'How will we ever make it to Australia with such a hopeless crew?'

Standing out on deck with the others, Vala Seitz clutched her little daughter's hand but seven-year-old Pauline wasn't frightened. The febrile patterns of the flames in the air fascinated her. She watched them glowing against the darkening sky when a kitchen hand rushed out on deck, slapping himself on the side of the head like a clown. His hair was on fire and he smelled like a chicken with singed feathers. He kept hitting himself until one of the passengers threw a towel over him and then he started gasping and flailing his arms because underneath the towel he was inhaling smoke and couldn't breathe.

Above the din, Liszt's *Hungarian Rhapsody* was blaring full blast, in the hope of distracting the passengers as the crew proceeded to souse the deck with water, turning it into a lake where delighted children sloshed around. Someone yelled that the lower deck was flooded. 'The ship's going to sink and we'll all drown!' Apparently one of the passengers had rushed out of the washroom when the alarm went off and left the water running. The crisis ended when the carpenter broke down the door to the communal bathroom and turned off the taps.

With the panic over, the passengers drifted back to their usual places on deck, no longer bored. There was a lively hum of conversation now that they had a drama to discuss and blame to apportion. When Vala and Pauline returned to their regular spot, they found the archbishop already stretched out in his canvas chair, unruffled by the day's events as he gazed serenely at the sunset sky. Like many other passengers, he was watching the shafts of light pour through the clouds with such intensity that even those who professed not to believe in God felt their lack of faith shaken.

But Theodore Porfirievich Rafalsky had no doubt about the divine origin of the celestial phenomenon. The archbishop was on his way to establish the first Russian Orthodox diocese in Australia and New Zealand. An outstanding secular and spiritual scholar, he had gained degrees in physics and mathematics before embarking on a prominent career in the priesthood, which had culminated in the present appointment. With his long wiry beard, black robe and the heavy silver *panagia* resting over his heart, he had an aura of spiritual nobility reminiscent of an El Greco painting.

What struck people most forcefully was his penetrating, compassionate gaze which seemed to cut through the physical appearance and see the soul beneath. With the humility characteristic of deep thinkers, he was interested in all ideas and treated everyone with respect. Vala was astonished that this saintly man showed as much interest in little Pauline's prattling as he did in the opinions of the adults.

Little Pauline, who thought that the fire had been very exciting, became the centre of attention as she chattered about the kitchen hand's hair and mimicked his jerky movements. An outgoing, confident child who wasn't afraid of anyone, she clambered onto the archbishop's lap and, to her mother's embarrassment, pulled the holy man's grey beard. 'I just wanted to see if it comes off!' the child retorted, and shot her mother a triumphant look when the cleric laughed.

He turned to their companion, Princess Metschersky, who was outraged at the crew's incompetence during the fire. Vala couldn't take her eyes off this elderly woman who looked every inch the aristocrat. Nadezhda Alexandrovna Metschersky belonged to the Russian royal family who had been murdered by the godless Bolsheviks. Tall, slim and elegant, the princess always wore simple black dresses with dazzling white collars which by some miracle she managed to keep immaculate despite the gritty soot that coated everything on board. Pauline was fascinated by the way the sunlight shone through the amber necklace that the princess always wore, making the large beads look like liquid honey. But although she longed to touch them, she never dared to ask.

Vala loved to listen to the princess's stories about the enchanted life she had led in the glorious days when the Romanovs ruled Russia. Nadezhda Alexandrovna's melancholy face lit up whenever she described the glittering balls she had attended in St Petersburg during the carefree days of her youth. In these detailed descriptions, Vala could feel the sensuous swish of silk dresses embroidered with seed pearls, see the crystal chandeliers reflected on the gilded wallpaper and hear the orchestra strike up the polonaise and the waltz.

She could imagine the princess, young and graceful, twirling across the dance floor in her silk slippers, waltzing with gloved archdukes, consuls and ambassadors who bowed so gallantly and kissed the tips of her tapered white fingers. She saw her swathed in furs as she sped in troikas through snowy forests of birch and spruce, with bells tinkling in the frosty air. More fortunate than many of her doomed relatives, the princess had managed to escape from the Bolsheviks, but was destined to eat the bitter bread of exile, first in Germany and now in Australia. She was travelling to Sydney to join her daughter who had married a French diplomat and had two children, so at least she would be with her family.

Like the princess, Vala was also travelling to Australia for family reasons. A lively woman who never ran out of conversation, she entertained her companions with stories and anecdotes. Beneath the merry exterior, however, she felt anxious. She was about to join a husband she hadn't seen for seven years. Ever since the war had separated her from Viktor in 1941, she'd had to fend for herself and was no longer the dependent girl he used to know. Their daughter Pauline, who was only ten days old when he was arrested, didn't know him at all, and Vala wondered how this headstrong child would react to having a father for the first time in her life.

As the sun dropped towards the horizon, the sky met the sea in startling slashes of fuchsia, crimson and purple. Lulled by the waves slapping against the hull of the ship, Vala thought about the strange coincidences that had brought her and Viktor together and then torn them apart so unexpectedly. Sitting forward, she began telling her companions her story which sounded like a romantic novel whose ending was a mystery. She and Viktor had met and fallen in love in Teheran in the late 1930s, never dreaming that within a few years they would be forced to live apart, at opposite ends of the earth.

'My father was a doctor in the Imperial Russian Army. He escaped from the Bolsheviks in 1917 and fled to Teheran where he met my mother. That's where I was born,' she began. Vala grew up in an international community of expat engineers and oil executives, and was educated in a French convent. 'Were those nuns strict!' She rolled her eyes. 'They used to wear those wimples that reminded me of aeroplane wings, and kept a big bunch of keys that rattled on their waists. No one dared to say a word when they were around. When Mother Superior died, they told us that her spirit was still in every room, watching us, and every now and then I'd sneak a glance at the ceiling, half expecting to see her up there!'

Vala leaped to her feet, and acted out the striding gait of the nuns, the tip-toeing of the girls and their guilty glances towards the ceiling. Her mimicry provoked so much laughter that people sitting nearby stopped talking and looked in their direction with the envy of those who have missed out on a good story.

Her husband's family had migrated to Russia from Germany at the turn of the century. Like Vala's parents, they too had fled from the Bolsheviks in 1917 and settled in Teheran. Viktor was twenty-nine when they met, a sophisticated, witty engineer who was smitten by the ravishing eighteen year old just out of convent school. They married shortly afterwards, on the eve of World War II. 'Life was wonderful in Teheran at first, but when the Russians and British occupied Persia in 1941, you wouldn't believe it: they interned Viktor just because he was an ethnic German. They deported him to Australia as an enemy alien,' she said, her voice trembling with indignation.

'Can you imagine how I felt?' Vala continued. 'There I was with a newborn baby and a husband deported to a country far away. I had no idea how I was going to manage on my own, what would become of him or when we would see each other again. But it got worse. They told me I would be sent to Germany with the other wives. They said we were being "repatriated". I was beside myself. I only had a German passport because of Viktor. Germany wasn't my homeland. I'd never set foot in the place and couldn't speak the language, but they didn't want to know.'

She paused as a gaggle of children ran past them, chasing each other and shrieking, following Anna Szput, a tall young woman who, like a Pied Piper, gathered the little ones around her and told them stories. Bored with the adults' conversation, Pauline wriggled off the archbishop's lap and ran to catch up with the others.

There were many children on the *Derna*. The older ones, like me, had the watchful eyes and serious faces of children who have grown up in a suffocating silence where secrets are known but never spoken. Some had suffered unimaginable abuse and witnessed things no child should ever see. The smaller ones, born in the post-war fever to create new families, were burdened by the responsibility of filling the empty spaces left by dead relatives and lost kinfolk.

Anna Szput's three year old, Ruth, never knew her baby sister who had died of malnutrition in Siberia seven years before. Like many of the Polish Jews on the *Derna*, Anna and her husband were deported because they refused to accept Russian citizenship when the Communists occupied Eastern Poland. After a six-week journey in a cramped cattle car, they stumbled out to find themselves in Archangelsk, a remote region of dense forests in the Arctic tundra. Twenty years old, modest and newly married, Anna loathed having to sleep in a hut with seventy-five other Polish prisoners. None of them had ever held an axe or saw, but if they wanted a bowl of herring soup at the end of a day's labour, they had to chop trees and saw logs.

This became increasingly difficult as Anna's pregnancy progressed. Several months later, she gave birth in the communal barracks with one piece of sheet around the bed and another covering her, her pain and fear compounded by embarrassment. Anna was skin and bone by then, and didn't have enough milk for her tiny daughter who died several weeks later. She was the first to be buried in the camp cemetery which soon filled up as prisoners died of typhus and malnutrition.

Not long after the baby died, Anna was summoned to the commandant's office. 'People are saying that you deliberately starved your baby because you didn't want to have it,' he said. Maddened by grief, she screamed at him. He was the murderer, it was his fault that she was starved and had no milk, how dare he accuse her of letting her poor child die? Infuriated by her wild outburst, the commandant picked up his revolver and pointed it at her face. Without stopping to consider the consequences, she knocked it out of his hand. When he dragged her outside, she knew that her life could end that moment. Pushing her into a freezing underground bunker, he lit a fire that smoked and smouldered, almost suffocating her, and locked the door. Three days later he let her out.

When Hitler broke the non-aggression pact he had signed with Russia before the war and invaded the Soviet Union, Stalin found himself fighting on the Allied side, so he released all the Polish prisoners from Siberian labour camps. But being released was the beginning of a new set of tribulations. In their wanderings across the Soviet Union in search of a safe haven, Anna and her husband joined hundreds of thousands of other destitute prisoners who had no means of supporting themselves and dropped dead of cholera, typhus and malnutrition. Central Asian towns like Bukhara, Tashkent and Samarkand that had once evoked exotic images, now became synonymous with desperation, crime and death. Anna and her husband ended up in Kirghistan where she managed to find work in the hospital.

When the war ended three years later, she was pregnant again. Although she had hoped to have her baby in Poland, the goods train they were travelling on meandered all over the countryside and little Ruth was born on straw in one of the box cars. By the time they reached Poland, she was six weeks old. On the *Derna*, she was a lively three year old who listened with rapt attention to the stories her mother told.

When the noise of the children had died away, Nadezhda Alexandrovna turned to Vala. 'Did they really send you to Germany?' she asked.

Vala nodded. 'They certainly did. The other women and I were put on a convoy of buses headed for Turkey. Just before we got to the border, the buses stopped. I'll never forget what happened next as long as I live. We were in the hands of Russian guards, rough women with harsh voices, who stripped us naked and took all our jewellery. I had to leave my poor Pauline lying on the scorching desert sand outside the tent, and of course she screamed the whole time. They even searched her nappy!

'Being a Russian émigré, I was in terrible danger,' she continued, 'because if they had found out that I was a White Russian, they would have arrested and deported me to Siberia. So I pretended to know only a few words. But when I pleaded with one of the guards to let me keep my wedding band she became suspicious. "So you speak Russian?" she snarled. I shook my head but she gave me a threatening look and told me that my ring had to go. She took my engagement ring too, a big square cameo exquisitely carved with Grecian figures. It left a white square on my finger for a long time.' Without realising it, Vala was stroking her finger as she spoke.

Pauline had run back to her mother because she was hungry, and was relieved to hear the dinner gong. As they walked down to the dining room, Vala remembered another story. 'You'll never guess what happened in Ankara,' she said. 'Von Ribbentrop turned up to welcome the brave German mothers who were returning to the Reich with their children, and asked to see the youngest child in our transport. It happened to be Pauline. He must have thought that I was a Hitler-loving hausfrau, because he bent forward and kissed her hand!' Pauline, who couldn't understand why they were laughing, was still examining her hand when they sat down at the table.

Late that night, while the *Derna* was skirting the coast of Sicily, a few people were still loitering around the deck. The second officer leaned over the rail, moodily puffing his cigarette, waiting for his watch to end. Unable to sleep or afraid to dream, some passengers walked around the ship, hoping that the exercise and fresh air would ensure a deep sleep. A few couples found a shadowy corner to embrace, and gazed at Ursa Major which shone brightly in the sky as if for them. Those who were gazing towards the shore suddenly stared in disbelief and rushed down to wake their friends and families. 'Come quickly! You'll never see anything like this again,' my father said as I stumbled out of my bunk half-asleep and followed him outside.

I saw a river of scarlet streaming down the side of a stark black mountain, carving a wide gash into its slope. With each convulsion the mountain spewed plumes of fire that lit up the dark sky. It seemed as though, deep in its bowels, the earth had been stabbed and bright arterial blood was spurting through its gaping mouth. It was 2 September and Etna, Europe's highest volcano, was erupting.

Crowded against the rails, we watched in silence. It was impossible to witness this display of elemental power without attaching some symbolic significance to it. For some, the volcano was a crucible in which the forces of evil were being exorcised; for others, it was a portent, but whether it presaged destruction or redemption no one could tell.

4

The vast ocean with its unhurried waves that had no beginning and no ending imposed its rhythm on the passengers. Time was suspended between the old world and the new. The past was unbearable, the future unfathomable. There was only the present moment stretching into eternity and they floated on it, lulled by the gentle rocking of the sea.

There was little sign of the teeming life that flitted and flickered beneath the surface, but occasionally someone cried out and pointed as the sea opened to reveal dolphins flipping in and out of the waves. Everyone craned over the rails to watch these playful creatures which, like good spirits, seemed to be guiding us. Seeing the dolphins reminded us of our connectedness with the natural world, and put a smile on everyone's face. Long after they had vanished into the depths, we continued to gaze at the water, hoping to see them again.

Lars Meder, a wiry twelve year old with reddish hair and freckles, hung over the rails, as did Helle's shy fifteen-year-old brother Rein who was happy to have found something to relieve the monotony at last. Only three days had passed but to him it felt like three months. During the day Rein played endless games of patience while at night he surveyed the sky to identify the constellations. Arnold Ohtra also studied the night sky, noting in his journal that Orion was higher here

than in the northern sky, while Ursa Major, his guiding star, was so
close to the horizon that at three o'clock in the morning its beams lit
up the waves.

The *Derna* was slowing down. Even the smallest ships that started off
as specks in the distance soon caught up, overtook us and disappeared
over the horizon. Sitting on deck watching the sea, Arnold Ohtra
painstakingly recorded our slow progress through the Mediterranean in
his journal, each entry consisting of terse comments and statistics about
the distance travelled and our slackening speed. 'Every tub overtakes us,'
he wrote. A tradesman, he kept apart from his fellow Estonians. Most of
them were professionals and he thought they regarded him as inferior.

Within the first few days of the voyage, the passengers had organised
themselves into groups according to nationality, religion and gender,
congregated on their usual spot on deck and watched each other with
indifference, condescension or mistrust. And within each group, sub-
groups formed, depending on age, marital status and gender. Within
the sub-groups, hierarchies soon divided people according to their
place of origin, profession and level of education. Czechs, for instance,
came from the Slovakian, Moravian, Carpathian and Hungarian
regions of the country, but those from Prague considered themselves to
be the only genuine Czechs. Polish city-dwellers from Warsaw, Krakow
and Lwow considered themselves superior to those who came from
small towns, especially those from the *stetls* who spoke Yiddish better
than Polish. Professional people like doctors, lawyers and academics
tended to group together, maintaining a superior distance from those
they regarded as uneducated, common or lacking in refinement.

When cabins were being allocated, the purser had tried to
accommodate people of the same nationality together, but nationality
did not guarantee harmony. One of the occupants of Topka's cabin was
a Polish woman who found close proximity to Jews so distasteful she
complained to the captain that she wasn't prepared to spend the entire
voyage living among people she detested. 'I don't want my little girl to
pick up their germs,' she said indignantly.

After hearing her out, Captain Papalas said, 'You're quite right. You
should not stay in that cabin. I will show you a place you can have to

yourself. Come with me.' She followed him expectantly until he stopped and made a sweeping movement of his arm towards the ocean. 'There's plenty of room out there, madame,' he said. Before she could gather her thoughts, he walked away. That night over dinner, the captain reported the conversation to Dr Frant with obvious relish.

The passengers' attitudes towards the captain varied according to perspective and experience. To Colonel Hershaw he was incompetent, to Sam Fiszman and the Kuplis couple he seemed an ignorant boor, while Halina Kalowski found him lacking in compassion. Dr Frant, Topka and Dorothea, on the other hand, found him fair and kind-hearted. Because he kept his distance from the passengers and was rarely seen, it was rumoured, without any evidence, that he drank.

There was little to do on the voyage but talk about the past, present and future. Women gossiped about the husbands who didn't understand them, the children who refused to eat or never did as they were told, or uncouth fellow passengers who left dripping underwear all over the washroom and the rails on the companionways.

Sometimes they exchanged recipes for tortes which required half a kilo of butter, half a litre of cream and a dozen eggs. After all, everyone knew that, unlike Europe, Australia was the land of plenty.

What the passengers knew about their destination could have fitted on a scrap of paper. Circumstances rather than preferences had dictated their choice of country at a time when few nations accepted European refugees, and fewer still admitted families and Jews. The majority assessed Australia's advantages in negative rather than positive terms: absence of Communism, absence of persecution and distance from Europe were the main attributes that had attracted them to this far-off corner of the globe represented on the map as a pink blob, about as far south as it was possible to go. Everyone had heard about kangaroos, which many expected to see hopping along the streets of Melbourne and Sydney, while others had heard about Australians' love of cricket and horse racing. Basing their expectations on films about the outback starring Chips Rafferty, some people visualised a cowboy country where they would ride horses and travel by horse-drawn carts in the cities.

Within several days, most of the passengers had found a congenial group, and in the territorial way that human animals have, they'd staked out their claims on deck and felt aggrieved if outsiders usurped their place. The most desirable spots were the few that afforded some shade which was in very short supply.

On Sunday mornings, the Christians attended religious services. Pastor Stockholm, who conducted Lutheran services, gathered the Estonians and Latvians for prayers at the stern. As they raised their voices in hymns and patriotic folk songs, the home they had been forced to abandon seemed a little closer. After centuries of foreign domination and suppression, the Estonians' pride in their identity continued to be nurtured through language and music. When Estonia and the other Baltic countries finally won independence in 1918, it was the first time in 700 years that Estonians were masters of their own fate, free in their own land. Only twenty years later, however, the nationalist euphoria was shattered when the Russians invaded again, occupying Estonian naval bases at Narva, Baltisik, Haapsalu and Parnu. By July 1940, Russia had annexed all the Baltic states and mass deportations of the perceived enemies of Communism had begun.

In the ship's small library, the sonorous bass baritone voice of Deacon Peter Gruchajew made the hairs stand up on the necks of the Russian Orthodox worshippers. In front of the elongated Byzantine face of Christ on the icons he had brought, Archbishop Rafalsky conducted the service. Fidgeting beside her mother, little Pauline pointed at the censer which he swung back and forth until it emitted a sweetly smoky fragrance. 'Why is his handbag on fire?' she piped in her clear voice. Vala tugged her daughter's arm. The things that child came out with. Standing beside them, Nadezhda Alexandrovna was praying, dignified as ever in her severe black dress relieved only by the white collar.

Among the worshippers was the large Matussevich family, all ten of them, standing quietly with their stern father. One glance from him was enough to hush any whispering, inattention or fidgeting. Unusually, this family had a cabin to themselves and spent most of their time in Cabin 14 rather than mixing with the other passengers. In the long dining room, where other children's voices reverberated with questions, arguments and demands, the Matussevich children stood out because of their exemplary behaviour.

They never started eating before their parents, never left the table while the meal was in progress and, what was even more astonishing, rarely talked during meals. If one of the boys grew restless or one of the younger girls started chattering, a nudge under the table from their eldest sister, or a severe look from their mother, was enough to silence them. Although some of the passengers shook their heads and muttered about military-style regimentation, everyone admired the children's respectful demeanour towards their parents, which they all agreed was too rare nowadays.

Olga Matussevich, a striking woman with dark hair parted in the centre above straight dark brows and intense black eyes, had a pensive expression reminiscent of the heroines of Russian plays. She brought up her children in the old-world manner that she had learnt in St Petersburg when her father was a diplomat in the days of the tsar. Brought up in a luxurious mansion, she had worn fur-trimmed cloaks with matching hats, ridden an Arab pony she had received from the Shah of Persia, owned aristocratic-looking borzoi hounds and was cared for by governesses in long dark coats. When the Russian Revolution broke out, Olga's father had fled to London with his daughter, educated her at boarding school and later had her social skills polished at a Swiss finishing school.

It was while visiting Prague during a Girl Guide jamboree in the 1920s that Olga met the taciturn, forceful Vasily Matussevich. Just as her father had done, Vasily had also fled from Russia. Having joined the White army as a cadet, his life was in danger when the Bolsheviks seized power. He escaped to Prague where he fell in love with the fetching, aristocratic Olga and married her, changing the course of her life in ways that she could never have imagined.

By the time war broke out in 1939, they had six children. In 1942 the family moved to Germany, where Vasily had apparently gone voluntarily as a worker. Two more children were born in Berlin where they all clung to each other while their building shook and bombs exploded all around them. When it was obvious that the Russians would soon enter the city, Vasily headed to Prague to avoid being arrested by the Bolsheviks because he had fought in the White army.

Left behind among the ruins of Berlin to fend for herself and their eight children, Olga had set off on foot with them and their few belongings across Germany in the hope of joining her husband in Prague, not knowing where he was or even whether he was still alive. They joined the mass exodus of refugees fleeing from the Russians. Pushing the two little ones in the pram and their belongings on a makeshift trolley, they trudged across the devastated countryside. They inched across bridges that barely hung together and wobbled beneath their tentative steps, and hastened past concentration camps where the nauseating stench of thousands of corpses piled up inside barbed wire fences made them press scarves against their noses and mouths. They pushed on past the rubble of Dresden. Not much longer now, we'll soon be there, Olga had promised, coaxing the exhausted, hungry children with occasional crusts of bread and a few raisins.

Eventually they reached Prague, where they managed to find Vasily. As Czechoslovakia was in the grip of the Russians, he was still in danger of being deported to Siberia so they made their way to Austria and lived in a DP camp in Linz. There, in 1946, Olga gave birth to her ninth baby, Peter Paul. He was only a few days old when her eldest daughter picked up the sleeping baby to bring him to her mother to feed. She looked at her brother's motionless little body and froze. He was not asleep. He was dead. Olga's screams resounded throughout the camp.

Although her last few years had been an unremitting struggle, and her impoverished circumstances contrasted bitterly with the life she had once led, Olga Matussevich insisted on maintaining the standards she had been taught. Even though she sewed the girls' clothes and could provide only them with the basic necessities, their manners and behaviour were impeccable. Olga herself never emerged from her bedroom until she was dressed and her lustrous black hair was pinned back from her high cheekbones, and her home, whether it was a cellar in Berlin, a room in an Austrian DP camp or an overcrowded cabin on the *Derna*, was always dusted and polished.

Whenever strangers looked at this family group they were usually drawn to the lively girl with a coronet of flaxen braids on her head. At sixteen, Nina, the second eldest daughter, had a rippling laugh and a quicksilver personality.

High-spirited and impulsive, she always found something to laugh about, and attracted admirers wherever she went. She was daring too, because it required defiance and resourcefulness to slip away from her parents who kept to themselves and forbade their daughters to mix with boys on the ship. Olga and Vasily had the suspicious nature of those whose history has taught them not to trust strangers. The only people you could rely on were your family, and you had to keep together and support each other, as Vasily was always telling them.

But the spirited Nina had already noticed that every evening many of the young Jews congregated at the stern where there was music, dancing and fun. Some of the boys strummed songs on their guitars, laughed and danced to romantic tunes on the gramophone. She wished that her parents would let her wear her hair loose instead of insisting on this old-fashioned hairstyle, but Emil Kopel, who was smitten with her, thought that her Russian braids looked charming. He would watch out for her as she strolled around the deck holding her younger sister's hand. Nina had discovered that her sister provided a good excuse for staying out of the cabin.

Emil was one of the sixty-one Jewish orphans who were travelling under Dr Frant's care. Although several of the youngsters had lost only one parent, the majority had lost both and most of their relatives as well. Many were left without family, home, possessions or even a photograph of their parents. Like Emil, most of them had suffered such inhuman treatment in the camps that when they were finally liberated at the end of the war, they were one sigh away from death.

They all had their own theories to explain why they had survived. Emil believed he owed it to the strict treatment he had received at school in the Carpathian region of Slovakia. When his father died in 1938, his mother had found it so difficult to cope with her nine children that she had sent him to a Jewish orphanage where the slightest misdemeanour, inattention or poor scholastic results were severely punished. During the war, when Emil became a slave labourer in the IG Farben factory at Auschwitz, all around him young men were dying from starvation and exhaustion, but he found the strength to keep going because his school had toughened him so much that he could haul railway sleepers on his thin shoulders and last for three days without eating.

When the war ended he returned to Czechoslovakia, ill and dying, but by 1948 he had recovered and was beginning to feel settled. He was learning the upholstery trade in his brother's shop in Teplice and had started going out with girls. In those heady days of regained health and freedom, few young people anticipated the dangers of Communism. Euphoric at the defeat of the Nazis, they were ready to believe the propaganda of their Russian rescuers about the new socialist society: a workers' paradise where everyone would be equal, without class distinction or discrimination. For those who had suffered from injustice, discrimination and persecution for much of their lives, this society appeared to offer hope for the future.

Emil might never have left Czechoslovakia if not for the softly spoken woman with the round face and wavy brown hair whom he met one night while visiting cousins in Prague. 'What are you doing with yourself?' Anita Freiberger asked him. 'Are you happy here?' He was taken aback but before he had time to reply, she went on to say, 'The Communists will soon get a tighter grip on Czechoslovakia. Wouldn't you like to get out while there is still time?'

Although Emil had never thought of leaving, he knew that the atmosphere was becoming tense. There were whispers about shadowy figures in trenchcoats who hung around the streets listening in to conversations, about censorship of the press, increased government control and paranoid accusations of conspiracies. In spite of the rosy glow with which the Communists painted their world, some people foresaw the imminent rise of a new totalitarianism, while others predicted the outbreak of another world war as tension grew between Russia and the West.

In the uneasy coalition between Communist and non-Communist parties in Czechoslovakia's post-war government, several ministers from democratic parties resigned en masse in protest at the growing manipulation by the Communists. Seizing their chance in February 1948, the Communists staged a coup and took over the government. The only non-Communist who remained in power was Jan Masaryk, the Foreign Minister. In the expropriations that followed, many merchants and tradesmen, including Emil's brother, had their businesses confiscated. Purges, plots, persecutions, witch hunts, torture and executions became more frequent.

When Masaryk fell mysteriously to his death through an open window a month after the coup, people whispered that he had been murdered. It seemed as though the trap could snap shut at any moment.

Although until then Emil had not considered leaving, the methods of the Communists worried him. He was already forced to spend every second weekend working for the party in a so-called voluntary capacity, cleaning streets or weeding gardens. After they took over his brother's business, it became obvious that they were determined to control everything. So when Anita Freiberger mentioned the idea of migrating to Australia, Canada or New Zealand, Emil sparked up. 'But how?' he asked.

'Leave it to me,' she replied. 'Come and see me in my office and I'll arrange it.'

Like Emil, most of the orphans on this voyage owed their chance to have a new life to Mrs Freiberger. She had been appointed by Œuvres de Secours aux Enfants (OSE), a Jewish organisation devoted to rescuing, helping and resettling Jewish children during and after the war. From her spartan office on Jozefovska Ulica in Prague, with its plain wooden table, big black telephone and old typewriter, this indefatigable woman processed applications from all over the country, organised the documentation and even accommodated some of the orphans in her little flat while they waited for their passage.

A Holocaust survivor herself who had been deported to the ghetto at Theriesienstadt before having time to complete her medical studies, she'd made it her mission to help these young people who had lost everything.

When she began organising their departure, she discovered that there were major obstacles. For one thing, they had no documents, and for another, some of the boys were over eighteen. This meant that they were eligible for military service and would not be permitted to leave the country, so their age and nationality would have to be concealed. This was a period when every transaction was carried out under the counter, in secret, in whispers, between the lines or on the black market. Anita used her personal connections to organise the documents, some of which contained incorrect dates and places of birth.

Before the war, her father had been a prominent scientist. His closest friend had been Mr Drtina, now the Justice Minister, and it was thanks to Drtina's co-operation and the efforts of his secretary, Miss Brohastskova, that the orphans were able to leave.

Money for their passage had been provided by JOINT, which also arranged their transfer by train to Marseilles. They travelled to Paris on the glamorous Orient Express, a train famous for intrigues, deceit and espionage. Mindful of Mrs Freiberger's warnings, the older boys did not utter a word of Czech during the journey, for fear that the guards would arrest them and bring them back.

On the train to Marseilles, Emil met David Weiss, who had not thought of leaving Prague until his older brother suggested it. Life was just becoming enjoyable again after the nightmare years. While imprisoned together with his father at Kufering, a Dachau satellite labour camp, David was forced to build barracks in such horrifying conditions that for the rest of his life he was unable to talk about it. Six hours after being liberated by General Marcus Clarke, he watched helplessly as his father died of typhus and malnutrition.

Three years later, however, in 1948, David was studying engineering and life was sweet again. In spring, lilac bloomed in parks where lovers cuddled on wooden benches or strolled arm in arm along the embankment of the Vltava. Prague's baroque spires and palaces were floodlit at night, and plays were performed in the courtyards and gardens of villas and museums. On the terrace of Manes, the artists' café, intellectuals discussed the meaning of life. At Flek's beer garden, at tables under chestnut trees, students downed steins of Pilsner and ate smoked sausage on black bread. When his oldest brother urged him to migrate because of the deteriorating political situation, David was eager to go to Palestine but as the ships bound for that country were being turned away by the British, he decided to join another brother in Sydney.

David's sociable nature and ready smile made friends wherever he went. A born peacemaker, he disliked confrontations and always managed to find an amicable solution. On the train to Marseilles he had met Harry Braun and André Wayne who became his cabin-mates on the *Derna* and often asked him to resolve their arguments.

Harry lost no time introducing himself. 'My name is Harry Braun and I like your smile and your teeth,' he told David. Harry was a dental mechanic, a tall boy with a shy, retiring nature who felt he owed his survival in Auschwitz to the fact that he had managed to make himself invisible.

André, the third member of what was to become a lifelong triumvirate, had been captivated by the mystique of Australia for a long time, and the prospect of a new beginning at the other end of the world, in a country with no anti-Semitism and no wars, fired his imagination. He was alone in the world, with no responsibilities, and although he was enjoying life in Prague, his pragmatic nature told him it was time to leave. The future beckoned. He scoffed when the others complained about the *Derna* and accused them of lacking a spirit of adventure.

Another of their cabin-mates, Bill Marr, had found life very lonely in Prague where he worked as a motor mechanic after the war. The days were long, food was rationed, and the atmosphere of political instability unsettled him. Rumours circulated that the Russians were going to stay on, that they'd soon start deporting people to Siberia and there was talk of another world war. It was about that time that he experienced the reality behind the Communist myth. He was standing at the main railway station talking to a friend when a locomotive carrying German prisoners bound for Siberia pulled into the station. Without any warning, one of the Russian guards grabbed Bill's companion and hauled him into the train. Horrified, Bill yelled that they had the wrong person, that his friend wasn't a Nazi, but it was like shouting at the sky. As expressionless as a cardboard box, the Russian refused to release his victim, and from his menacing manner Bill sensed that it wouldn't take much for him to be abducted as well. One of the German prisoners had escaped from the train, and since the guard was responsible for the whole group, he was making up the numbers. The identity of the captives was irrelevant as long as the numbers tallied. Bill didn't need anyone to convince him that it was time to leave.

When he asked at the Hebrew Immigrant Aid Society where Australia was, the officer chuckled. 'You go to the end of the world and turn right!' The most reassuring fact Bill heard was that Australia was an island.

'No borders means no wars,' he said. 'Australia will do fine!' The following day he went to see Mrs Freiberger.

He knew only too well what havoc borders could play with the lives of ordinary people. No one who saw the handsome dark-haired fellow with the angular jaw and affable manner would have imagined that only four years earlier he had not expected to survive. Like many of the orphans on the ship, he came from the Carpathian region, a disputed border province inhabited by Hungarians, Ukrainians, Slovaks and Jews. The war against the Jews began in earnest there after Adolf Eichmann marched into Hungary in 1944 and recruited the brutal local Nazis, the Arrow Cross, to round up the Jews into ghettoes and deport them to concentration camps.

Bill could still hear the drum resounding through his home town of Sevlus the day the town crier, in his dark blue police uniform, had stopped on every street corner to announce the latest news. As radios were forbidden, newspapers were expensive and few residents owned a telephone, this was the way of broadcasting official information. His message was short and shocking. All Jews had to leave their homes and move to a designated part of town.

Bill's parents were sitting around the table, stunned by the order, when three locals came inside, sat down and without any preamble demanded all their jewellery, silver, money and valuables. 'You have an hour to get out because a truck is coming to take you all to the ghetto,' they said. With trembling hands his parents packed the bed linen, a few clothes and crammed whatever food they had into a bag. As Bill glanced out of the window, he saw neighbours craning their necks to see inside, impatient for them to leave so that they could go through the house and take whatever was left. He was shaken to see people with whom they had lived side by side all their lives so indifferent to their fate, and ready to take advantage of their misfortune.

Inside the ghetto, over 10,000 Jews were squeezed into a tiny area with four or five people squashed into each room. As Bill and his family had no beds, they spread their bedding on the floor. *How could such injustice go on?* he wondered. *Why does God just watch and do nothing?*

Food in the ghetto was so scarce that in desperation the sixteen year old risked his life and ran home to bring back their goat, which had recently had a kid. The goat's milk was a blessing, especially for the mothers who had no milk for their babies. Several days later, Bill saw one of their neighbours riding past the ghetto in a big wooden cart pulled by long-horned oxen. His heart lurched when the man scrambled up onto the seat, peered into their yard and saw the goat. The following day another local entered the ghetto and demanded the goat. For the first time since their deportation, Bill broke down and wept. Swallowing his pride, he begged them not to take the goat, explaining that so many babies depended on its milk, but they ignored his pleas and dragged it away. Any lingering hope Bill had entertained that the locals would come to their aid vanished with the goat.

In spring, when tender pale green buds began to appear on the birches and poplars, Bill with his family and other inmates of the ghetto were loaded into trucks and taken to the railway station. They took what little food they had: a few boiled eggs, scraps of leftover potato. At the very last moment, on impulse, Bill grabbed a bucket. Each member of his family, his parents, five-year-old sister and seven- and nine-year-old brothers, all carried as much as they could manage. At the station, SS officers were waiting for them. 'Let me go to the pump to fill up the bucket with water,' Bill asked one of them.

'Only if you give me some gold or silver,' the guard replied.

Bill shook his head. 'They've already taken everything, there's nothing left,' he said. Perhaps this guard hadn't yet become completely dehumanised, because he looked away while Bill was filling the bucket.

He returned with the water to see his father lifting his grandmother up into the train which was about a metre above the platform, and clambered up himself. Shortly afterwards, the door was slammed shut with a clang and locked from the outside. Bill counted 104 people squashed into a box-car with barbed wire strung across the tiny window. That bucket of water saved their lives, because the journey lasted for six days and nights. During that time they were given no food or water, and were not allowed out of that suffocating, fetid waggon which had no provision for disposing of human waste.

They had no idea where they were going and wondered whether anyone would still be alive by the time they got there. In the past few years they had heard that almost the entire Jewish population of Poland had been murdered. They had heard about mass killings and mass graves. But Poland was a long way away, the stories were too far-fetched to be believable, so perhaps the rumours were false.

When the train finally ground to a halt, Bill discovered that the reality was more incredible than anything they had ever heard. As the doors were unlocked, inhuman voices yelled at them to get out of the waggon, whips and batons flailed their bodies and wolf-like dogs snapped and bared their fangs. What was this place? What was going on? As they lined up in front of the elegantly disdainful Dr Mengele, he pointed at people with his stick. Prisoners in striped uniforms shuffled around whispering instructions that made no sense. 'Stand up straight!' 'Say you're older!' Or, even more incomprehensibly, 'Give the child away!'

It appeared that they were being divided into two groups. Bill's mother and the younger boys were ordered to go to the left while Bill, his father and twelve-year-old brother were told to go to the right with those who had been selected to work. Not understanding the significance of the two groups, his father assumed that the women and children would not have to work like the men, so he urged his twelve-year-old son to catch up with them. Bill watched his brother crawling underneath the railway waggon, hurrying to join the women and children who were about to be stripped, shaved and pushed into the gas chamber.

On the ship the orphans never talked about their experiences. They had shoved them into a drawer marked never to be opened, locked it and kept away. As they strummed guitars, sang songs and glanced at the pretty girls walking past in their skimpy shorts, nothing existed except the present, and nothing mattered but the future that awaited them at the end of the voyage.

5

A light northerly breeze cooled the morning air on 7 September as the *Derna* passed the statue of Ferdinand de Lesseps at the northern entrance to the Suez Canal. While the ship sailed between the two breakwaters towards its mooring in Port Said Harbour, the crew knocked on all the cabin doors, urging passengers to keep their portholes tightly locked. 'If you're not careful, the coolies will slip inside and steal whatever they can find,' they warned.

Colonel Hershaw was ready for trouble. With his usual military approach, he had organised what he called a security corps from among the Baltic migrants and placed young Uno Mardus in charge. It was a popular choice. At twenty-five, Uno was good-natured and patient, the kind of person who could give instructions without sounding bossy or arousing resentment. Like so many of his fellow Estonians who had served in the Wehrmacht's auxiliary forces, he had fled to Germany in 1944 when the Russians were advancing. His father had been deported to Siberia where he had perished, and Uno knew that deportation awaited him too if he returned to his native land. While living in a DP camp in Germany, he had decided to migrate to Australia where his uncle had settled before the war. When Estonia was free again, he would return.

Uno stood at the rail, watching the *Derna* manoeuvre into position.

The breeze had stopped and the air swaddled them like a blanket. The passengers had been advised not to go ashore because Egypt was currently at war, and the Jews particularly had been warned to stay out of sight or they would be in danger when the authorities boarded the ship. From the day the fledgling state of Israel had been proclaimed by the United Nations four months earlier, it had been attacked by all its Arab neighbours. As a state of war still existed, the Egyptians regarded all Jews who sailed in their waters as enemies.

Jews who had survived the war and wanted to migrate now faced discrimination in the form of quotas imposed by the countries which had helped to vanquish Hitler. It was ironic that three years after the war had ended, Jews like my parents and me who had survived the Holocaust by keeping our Jewish identity secret, were obliged to conceal it once again in order to gain a passage to our new land.

Eight months before we boarded the *Derna* in Marseilles, Arthur Calwell, Australia's first Minister for Immigration and the architect of the post-war immigration policy, had set a quota for Jewish migrants. No more than twenty-five percent of the passengers of any migrant vessel were to be Jewish.

After the Japanese bombed Darwin in 1942, exposing the country's vulnerability to attack, Calwell became convinced that Australia must either populate or perish, because the national birthrate was too low to ensure security or sustain growth. The country numbered around seven million at the time and needed migrants to counter its fear of the 'yellow peril', the millions of Asians perceived as crouching on its doorstep, poised to invade. To maintain the homogeneous nature of the population, ninety-seven percent of whom were Anglo-Celtic in origin, British migrants were considered the most desirable, but to make up the numbers, other nationalities as well as Jews were to be admitted.

When the government's decision to encourage immigration became public, there was widespread opposition, especially to the Jews. Scurrilous cartoons in the *Bulletin* and *Smith's Weekly* depicted Jews laden with gold and diamonds walking off the ships, while racist articles described them as capitalists and exploiters. According to an opinion poll held in 1948, only about seventeen percent of the population favoured Jewish migration. Anxious to pacify public opinion, the government decided to limit the number of Jews but import more blond, blue-eyed Baltic migrants, whose appearance and ethnicity led them to expect smoother, faster assimilation. In spite of the quota, however, Australia in 1948 accepted more Jewish refugees per capita than any other nation apart from Israel.

While the Hebrew Immigrant Association (HIAS), together with the American Jewish Joint Distribution Committee (JOINT), subsidised the Jewish passengers, the International Refugee Organisation (IRO) sponsored displaced people living in DP camps, and these organisations had together chartered the *Derna*. The Australian government, which contributed six million pounds to the IRO, directed its immigration officers in Europe not to include Jews among their sponsored migrants. Their motive was largely economic: if Jewish organisations could be induced to pay for all the Jews, Australia's costs would be reduced.

Caught between the twenty-five percent immigration quota and the discriminatory policy of the IRO, some of whose officers were disturbed by the racist nature of the selection procedure, Jews found it increasingly difficult to obtain a berth. That was why my parents and I were among 1200 Jews who spent months in Paris waiting for a passage to Australia. Faced with an indefinite wait, some Jews, including my parents, decided to be included on the non-Jewish list.

Although we were described as migrants, we were really refugees, fleeing from Communism and persistent anti-Semitism. Even after the war ended, and ninety percent of the Jews in Poland had been murdered, violent attacks on Jews continued. Apprehensive about my safety, my parents sent me to a convent school in Krakow. Fifteen hundred Jews were ambushed and killed by right-wing nationalist groups and racist thugs in Poland in the years immediately after the war. But it was the pogrom in Kielce, in which a band of townspeople armed with pitchforks, clubs and axes, invoking medieval superstitions, savagely massacred forty-six Jewish survivors, that finally convinced many Jews they had no future in their native land. My father chose Australia because it promised tolerance, and was far from the ethnic and religious hatreds of Europe.

Most of the Jews saw Australia as a permanent sanctuary. This was particularly true of those from Poland, who felt disillusioned and betrayed. They had no wish to return to a land where they seemed doomed to remain hated outsiders. The country had become a graveyard, where fields and forests were nourished by the bodies of their mothers, fathers, sisters and brothers whose bones gleamed whitely in the furrows of new-ploughed paddocks.

Most of the Christian migrants, however, regarded Australia as a temporary haven where they could shelter until they could return to their homeland. The Baltic passengers who left the land of their birth with aching hearts and the songs of their native land running through their veins, believed that their exile would last only until the Communists were overthrown. That was Uno Mardus's plan, and he thought nostalgically about the forests and meadows of his native Estonia as he waited for the Egyptian police to board the *Derna*.

Not wasting any time, policemen in red fezes ran down the stairs and along the companionways looking for stowaways and, it was rumoured, for Jews. Their attention was drawn to a Ukrainian passenger standing at his porthole, camera pointed towards the harbour. They demanded to know what he was photographing and refused to believe that he was taking pictures of the hawkers. They confiscated his camera, ordered him to accompany them and took him off the ship as his distraught wife looked on. Her cabin-mates, the German sisters Elfriede and Ilse Hof, and a pregnant young Romanian woman called Elsie Pataky, tried to reassure her, although they were feeling far from confident themselves.

At the police station, after interrogating the prisoner, the officers sealed his camera and promised to return it the following day. Why they didn't simply remove the film, he couldn't understand. Before releasing him they demanded three pounds and four shillings. When he protested that he didn't have the money, they escorted him back on board where Colonel Hershaw came to the rescue. He never saw his camera again.

Meanwhile, the police continued searching the ship from top to bottom. Worried in case they stole anything, Uno Mardus accompanied two of them down to the hold but later he told his friends with a boyish smile, 'It's just as well they didn't take anything, because I don't know what I would have done if they had!'

Unsuccessful in their search, the policemen contented themselves with standing around on deck. Soon the ship was surrounded with small bobbing boats where white-robed men held up hands of bananas, leather sandals, woven straw baskets and intricately worked cushions. 'Here, sir!' they shouted. 'Look, madam! Nice bag! Cheap!' Passengers leaned over the rails for a closer look at the merchandise. In the heated bargaining that followed, small baskets were being hauled up and down on ropes looped around the rail along the starboard side.

Those who had no cash traded possessions. Non-smokers traded their issue of cigarettes, forty of which Dorothea distributed to the IRO passengers each week. Helle, who watched the proceedings with interest, was thrilled when her father bought her a soft leather bag by trading some costume jewellery he'd bought in Germany. One of the Czech orphans traded his soft brown alpaca hat for a hand of bananas he later shared with his delighted friends. It seemed inconceivable that for a few coins or an old hat you could buy almost a whole tree of this ambrosial fruit. A shout of laughter made people turn around to see Addy Bunzl, another of the orphans, struggling to try on his new suede shoes. By the time he realised they didn't match, the hawker was nowhere to be seen. A little girl's wail suddenly rose above the commotion: Haneczka Poczebucka, who turned eight that day, had just dropped her new wine-red fez into the water.

When his mother wasn't looking, twelve-year-old Lars Meder decided to play a trick on the hawkers with some of his friends. The boys peeled a few labels off some cans planning to pass them off as banknotes. They waved them at the vendors, signalling for them to send up some food. After pulling up the basket, they took out the merchandise and sent their labels down as payment, craning forward to see what would happen.

When the hawker saw that he'd been cheated, he shook his fist and shouted until the boys hastily sent the tins back. Luckily the hawker saw the joke, wagged his finger at them in mock anger and they all ended up laughing together.

Several transactions concluded on a darker note. The middle-aged Greek who ran the bar at the stern of the ship and charged outrageous prices for his cocktails and spirits was negotiating for a bottle of whisky. As soon as they agreed on the price, he rolled up his money and placed it in the basket, but when he tasted the contents of the bottle he'd bought, he spat it out. With a curse he flung the bottle into the sea, narrowly missing the hawker who ducked just in time.

Standing nearby, one of the crewmen was haggling over two tins of American bully beef. After much gesticulating and shouting, he sent the money down in the basket but when he pulled it up, it contained only one tin. Without a moment's hesitation the seaman picked up the tin, which weighed about a kilo, and hurled it at the hawker. It struck him on the temple and he fell into the water like a stone. In the ensuing fracas, the hawkers shook their fists and screamed for the police. Worried about possible repercussions, the officers warned the passengers to say nothing or the ship would be detained, so when the police arrived no one seemed to know anything.

Helle, delighted with her new bag, was even happier with the turn of events that evening. Rita's handsome brother, who to her dismay seemed to have taken a fancy to her cabin-mate Lea, now turned his attention back to her and they sat side by side in the warm Mediterranean night, watching the film projected on the upper deck. Under a starlit sky, the breeze ruffled her long hair while the crackly loudspeaker relayed the passionate tenor voice of Beniamino Gigli. Portly and middle-aged, he was the unlikely hero of a heavy-handed German romantic comedy with French dialogue and an unbelievable plot which few passengers understood, but the film's defects did not diminish Helle's enjoyment of the evening.

Early next morning, the loading began at a cracking pace. Amid much yelling the coolies, who were so thin that their bodies could have been used for an anatomy lesson, tossed boxes from one to the other until they reached the hold.

Passengers watched fascinated as 400 tonnes of Syrian onions were loaded up, bound for Colombo, and marvelled as dozens of lamb carcasses were dropped into the hold through one hatch, and crates of beer for the bar through another.

That afternoon, a Russian merchant ship docked alongside the *Derna*. The Baltic passengers froze when they looked into the faces of the Russian sailors. For several minutes they stared at each other with mutual dislike, until someone shouted an order and the sailors disappeared below. 'Our ship is the safest one afloat because we've got three captains,' quipped Bruno Tohver, a young Estonian. 'There's Captain Papalas, the first officer, and our Estonian submarine captain, Mr Puurand.'

'And what about Mrs Meder?' someone added. 'Her husband is a sea captain too, even though he isn't on the *Derna*!'

Elisabeth Meder was travelling with her son Lars to join her husband in New Zealand. They came from the island of Saaremaa on the west coast of Estonia, a fertile farming region where Lars remembered windmills whirring in fields of wheat, and picnics in juniper forests on warm summer days. His father, a sea captain, was away most of the summer, sailing schooners to catch pike, flathead and herrings in northern European waters. At the outbreak of the war, he had been sailing between Portugal and England when his ship was blown up by a mine. Almost everyone on board was killed but although he had survived, his wife was clever enough to pretend that he'd gone down with his ship, so the Russians wouldn't come looking for him. After spending the rest of the war years in Canada, Captain Meder had migrated to New Zealand. Lars couldn't wait to see him so they could cast their lines out together again, just as they'd done in Saaremaa when he was little.

After the usual breakfast of white bread, marmalade and tiny boiled eggs, some of the passengers nudged each other when a couple stepped off the ship and went ashore together. It was Dorothea and Colonel Hershaw, whose sleeping arrangements had already aroused knowing glances and whispers. Among the married couples who were forced to sleep apart in segregated dormitories, the level of sexual frustration was high, while among the single young men and women, whose hormones were racing, fantasies bubbled to boiling point.

This jolly, outgoing young woman didn't conform to anyone's image of a femme fatale, while the middle-aged, pompous escort officer was hardly a dashing Romeo. But just the same, eyebrows were raised and women whispered behind their hands whenever they saw Dorothea sunning herself outside their cabin. 'Scandalous,' the women sniffed. 'That fellow has got it made,' the men sighed.

Dorothea couldn't wait to go ashore. Ever since Marseilles, she had been wearing the same dress she had brought in her hold-all, and was delighted when Ogden offered to buy her some clothes in Port Said. Feeling the passengers' eyes on her as she stepped into the tender, because they had been forbidden to go ashore, made this excursion doubly enjoyable.

Distracted by so many strange sights in the town, she didn't know where to look. Crowds jostled along the pavements while on the roads English officers swerved in jeeps to avoid ricketty bicycles, trolleys heaped with sacks and bananas, and ox-carts piled with straw. There were few women about, but men in fezes and long loose shirts talked volubly as they weaved along the footpaths. In a small dark shop an insistent shopkeeper dragged them inside and proceeded to pull out his merchandise. Dorothea selected a blue polka dot skirt which flared out as she walked, a white blouse and cool sandals. Ogden Hershaw bought himself a fez which he placed on his balding head at such a rakish angle that she burst out laughing.

They sat down at a small round table in a coffee shop on a street of colonial buildings with wooden shutters and large verandahs. From a nearby table, Egyptian men surveyed Dorothea through half-closed eyes as they puffed thick clouds of aromatic smoke from the long bubbling *shisha* pipe they shared. After leaning forward to light her cigarette, Colonel Hershaw placed a cigarette in his long holder, sprawled back in his chair and inhaled. A street photographer squinted into his viewfinder and took their photo as they sat there, contentedly smoking, talking and watching the passers-by. When the photo was developed, the colonel presented it to her. On the back he wrote with a flourish, '*To my ship-mate and indispensable aide. Always, Me.*'

Before returning to the *Derna*, Colonel Hershaw had some business to attend to. He steered Dorothea by the elbow along steamy pavements until they entered a shipping agent's office where whirring ceiling fans stirred the soupy air. A handsome young man with smoothly combed brown hair and the urbanity Dorothea had always associated with English gentlemen introduced himself as John Brown. From the conversation he was having with Ogden Hershaw, she speculated that he was the ship's agent in Port Said. While typing some letters for him, she noticed his admiring glances. Before they left, he handed her a large plump fruit with a smooth golden skin and strong perfume. 'This is a mango. They're juicy and luscious,' he said looking into her eyes. 'I'll board the ship to find out whether you enjoyed it!' She laughed, flattered at the attention. What an attractive man John Brown was. She was sorry that she would never see him again, but as she had already discovered, life was a series of chance meetings, delightful in themselves and leading nowhere, but holding out the promise of another thrilling encounter when you least expected it.

6

By the time Dorothea and Colonel Hershaw had returned to the ship, a new crowd had gathered on the wharf ready to board, to the dismay of those who had already become territorial about their favourite place on deck. They surveyed the interlopers with distaste. What a noisy, uncouth lot they were. Mostly Greeks and Italians and, judging by their appearance, mostly peasants. 'It will be too crowded now and there won't be any quiet corners left,' Helle complained to Rita as they watched these men, women and children who swamped the ship like a tidal wave.

Luckily for our peace of mind, we did not know that the captain had agreed to take on an additional fifty Yugoslav migrants from the El Shatt camp in Egypt. When they arrived in Port Said ready to board, the Australian consular official accompanying them discovered that there weren't any berths. He was shocked to learn that despite the already overcrowded conditions on board the *Derna*, Captain Papalas had intended to accommodate them on stretchers to be pushed into every spare corner. The official referred the matter to a Lloyds surveyor who refused to allow the Yugoslavs to board on the grounds that the influx would dangerously overcrowd the ship.

But even without the Yugoslavs, the *Derna* was pushed far beyond the limits of comfort and safety by the newcomers. There were women with sun-dried faces and dark shawls over their heads, children in their best clothes, faded and worn, and men in shorts or crumpled shirts. Among these shabby people, one couple stood out. Arm in arm, Ina and Rudolf Musto strolled onto the ship, the woman's slim hips swaying in a slinky silk dress with a fox fur carelessly draped over one shoulder and a hat perched at a sultry angle on her smooth hair, the man in a wide-lapelled suit of finest wool, impeccably cut. They might have been Marlene Dietrich and Douglas Fairbanks Jr boarding the *Queen Mary* as they swaggered onto the deck, heads held high, seemingly oblivious to its dilapidated state and the impoverished condition of its passengers.

Slipping past the line of tired adults still waiting to be directed to their cabins, a little girl rushed on board with her older brother, followed by their two older sisters Mary and Betty. Impatient to explore their new surroundings, Vassiliki Fatseas and her brother Petro couldn't stand still. They had never been on a ship before and they jumped around, pointed at everything, nudged each other and concocted plans in high-pitched whispers and giggles, while their two older companions attempted to quieten them down.

The children had been in a state of constant excitement for the past few weeks, ever since the day when the whole Fatseas family had gathered at their parents' white-washed home on the Greek island of Kythera, and all the adults had lamented and sobbed. Although Vassiliki and Petro didn't know it at the time, the relatives had come to say goodbye to them. No one had been as broken-hearted as their ninety-one-year-old grandfather, who knew that he would never see them again.

Vassiliki had no idea why they were all crying, but since this was obviously expected, she too had buried her face in her hands and made loud wailing noises. Assuming that she was distressed because of the imminent parting, the adults did not notice that every few minutes she looked up, eyes dancing with mischief, and then hid her face and resumed her wailing. Twelve-year-old Petro, however, did not have to pretend. He was genuinely sad at having to leave his parents, especially his adored grandfather. 'You're going to Australia,' their grandmother

had said and sighed, wiping her eyes. Vassiliki nodded, stealing a quick
look at her brother, who had no more idea of where Australia was than
she did. Distance was defined by the neighbouring villages and the time
it took to reach them on foot. It took a whole day to lead the donkey
laden with wheat to the flour mill in the next village, and their concept
of distance didn't extend beyond that. For all they knew, Australia was
two villages away and they'd soon be back.

Kythera floats in the Ionian sea between the Peloponnese and Crete,
like an afterthought. Purko, where the Fatseas family lived, is one of
the forty villages that lie scattered across this rugged landscape of misty
moors and stony fields. Geography is destiny, and from time
immemorial, Kythera's strategic location between the Greek mainland
and Crete attracted a succession of invaders.

It had been a Minoan colony, Mycenean outpost, Phoenician trading
post, Egyptian harbour, Roman and Byzantine port, a pirate
stronghold, Venetian colony and a British outpost. Ruins of the
colonisers' graves, monasteries, schools and bridges still remain, but
the rocks and sands of the island have long buried their footprints and
covered them over with defiantly Ionian soil.

If Vassiliki had known that it would be many years before she would
return, she would have cried along with the others, because she loved
the simple rhythm of her village life. Every day she and Petro would
walk for two hours along rough goat tracks until they reached their
school in Hora, the island's capital, high above the aquamarine water
of Kapsali Bay. On hot summer days, they would run down the steep
path to the beach and swim in the warm water near the jagged outcrop
that was said to have been the birthplace of Aphrodite. In winter, Petro
loved hunting in the hills and shooting down sparrows with his
catapult.

Outside the *kafenion*, under the big-leafed almond tree, men
hunched over small wooden tables sipped thick sweet coffee or their
fiery *tsipoura*, the island's rough potent moonshine, while they played
backgammon and gossiped about their neighbours. The air was
perfumed with thyme and oregano, and carpeted with wild flowers.
After school, the children helped their mother pick tomatoes bursting

out of their vermilion skins, luscious sun-warmed figs and sweet melons, while the juice ran down their chins.

They rose at daybreak, drew water from the well and went to bed at sundown because for them, as for their ancestors, oil lamps were the only source of light, and oil was too precious to waste. They ate what they grew themselves and everything was done by hand. Their parents rose early to plough the fields and pick olives from gnarled silvery trees that had bent with the wind and watched generations come and go.

Petro loved squashing the grapes that were taken to the still to make the _tsipoura_. No money changed hands. The still-owner kept some _tsipoura_ and the miller kept some flour. The only way they earned money was by selling olive oil, if they had any left over. Their mother baked bread in her igloo-shaped oven once a month because wood was scarce. To make the bread last longer, they sliced and dried it into rusks they called _paximali_. Petro often had to scrape off the bluish mildew because the air in the village was so moist.

Small black goats scrambled over the stony ground, their tinkling bells breaking the silence of the Ionian hillside. Bees buzzed among the clover, wild thyme and rosemary producing the fragrant honey that Vassiliki loved to spread on her _paximali_. After a day spent working outdoors, her older sisters would take out their crochet hooks and looms and their nimble fingers would fly over blankets, lacy curtains, donkey saddle bags, floor rugs, pillow cases and tablecloths for their _prika_ or glory box, weaving their dreams into every stitch. Once a week, the women loaded their laundry onto the donkey's back and trundled down to the big tubs by the creeks or rivers. Vassiliki and Petro were sent to fetch firewood for the copper boiler while the women piled hand-made lace, linen and underwear into a large cane basket and soaked it in a bleaching solution with fine white ash sifted from the wood fire.

On Sundays bells pealed from the little white-washed Katafigali church above the olive groves summoning the villagers to pray in the dim candle-lit interior. Petro, who was the altar boy, would prepare the censer that he swung during the service, puffed up with pride at his important role as the aromatic smoke suffused the church. At Easter, the hairs on the back of his neck would stand up when the bells pealed and the priest announced to the congregation that Christ had risen. Then he would race outside with the other boys to let off home-made firecrackers, eat the eggs that had been dyed scarlet and inhale the miraculous aroma of the goat his mother always roasted for their annual feast.

But the island that enabled its children to grow up so close to nature offered less and less to the adults who struggled to eke out a living from the small plots of stony soil. It provided a bare subsistence but no income. For many years now, Greek men had been leaving Kythera for America and Australia, intending to return home as soon as they'd made enough money to provide for their families.

And now the Fatseas family was about to be split up once again. George, the eldest of the nine children, had already migrated to Australia with two of his brothers several years before, and had opened a restaurant in Mackay, the sugar cane region in Queensland's tropical north. Now the four youngest siblings were going to join him. With a heavy heart, Vassiliki's mother said goodbye to her children, wondering when she would see them again. Torn between her father and her children, she couldn't bring herself to leave the frail old man.

Vassiliki, Petro and their sisters Mary and Betty, who had never ventured further than to a neighbouring village, now set off to travel across the world. First by boat to Athens, then by train to Alexandria, where men wore long white robes and funny hard hats with tassels, women covered their faces with veils and spoke rapidly in a strange language they couldn't understand. On the next train, Vassiliki craned her head out of the carriage staring at miles of sand where men galloped on strange animals with humps and spindly legs. It was like stepping into a fairy tale and she didn't want to blink in case she missed anything.

The moment they boarded the *Derna*, this irrepressible little girl started looking around for games to play. Those long gangways and open spaces were going to be good for hiding and chasing. She soon spotted another Greek family with two girls. The younger one, Mattie Travasaros, who was her age, looked shy but friendly. While the two girls surveyed each other, the adults complained about the heat and the long voyage ahead.

Noticing that her daughter Mattie had wandered off with her new friend, Koula called her to come back at once. You needed eyes in the back of your head to watch those four children! Apart from her two daughters, Mattie and Katina, she was travelling with her teenage nephews, John and Stan, who considered themselves grown up and resented her efforts to control them. For a woman who had never left her island village before, travelling across the world with four children was a heroic enterprise, but anything was preferable to staying on in Kythera, neither maiden, wife nor widow.

The past ten years had been relentlessly tough for Koula Travasaros. Like many of the island men, her husband had left Kythera in 1938 to make his fortune in Australia, when Mattie had been six months old and Katina was two. The prospect of marrying off his two daughters had weighed heavily on him. Greek men traditionally toasted each other with the words, 'May you have male children and female goats', because girls were a liability from the moment they were born. Their virginity had to be closely guarded or no one would marry them, and when the time came for them to marry, they had to be equipped with a handsome dowry before they went off to live with their in-laws. Girls brought nothing but worry and expenses.

The life that Mattie was later to look back on as idyllic was in reality a struggle to survive, an unremitting contest with the rocky soil from which they had to wrest their food. Finding money to vary their diet with coffee or rice, or to buy a pair of shoes, involved complicated sums and months of saving. Mattie's deft fingers learned to spin the wool from their sheep and goats on her mother's spinning wheel. Sitting beside her on evenings when the fading light slanted through the wide-leafed fig trees, Mattie knitted sweaters and weaved blankets. There was no water or electricity in the flat-roofed whitewashed cottage her father had built with his own hands, so she fetched water from the well in the yard, and as soon as the sun went down they all went to bed.

Some nights, Mattie's sobs resounded through the house because her mother had hit her with a stick for some minor transgression. One of her biggest grievances was not being allowed to go swimming. 'If the boys can go, why can't I?' she used to complain on sweltering summer days when the air tasted of sun-baked grit. But she knew why. Girls weren't allowed to wear swimming costumes. Only harlots exposed their limbs to the lascivious gaze of men.

Their village, Travasarianka, was deep in the valley, and when Mattie looked up she could see the hillside village of Klaradika, where the man she later married in Australia lived with his family. They met at the monastery of Myrtidiotisa every year on 15 August, when the villagers made their annual pilgrimage to celebrate the Ascension of the Virgin.

The whole region buzzed with excitement as the women in their best dresses arrived on donkeys caparisoned in bright woven covers, bells and tassels for the occasion. At these gatherings, young men with blazing dark eyes stared at the marriageable girls who stole flirtatious glances back at them and giggled behind their hands.

Koula, who was only twenty-seven when her husband left, never suspected that circumstances would prolong their separation for ten years. Her spirits rose whenever his letters reassured her that he would soon return with enough money for them all to live in comfort. But two years later, when war broke out, everything changed. After Mussolini's ultimatum of October 1940 demanding Greek surrender, to which Prime Minister Metaxas replied with a proud and unequivocal 'Ohi' ('no'), Kythera was invaded by Italy. After the Italian soldiers retreated, the Germans occupied the island.

Food became scarce as the invaders commandeered the little that the villagers grew. Mattie's aunt did their washing and John and his brother would run to the soldiers' headquarters with the clean laundry in return for a little food. As no mail got through, Koula was completely cut off from her husband whose financial support she desperately needed. Through the long years of the war, she had no idea whether George was alive or dead. She felt like a wanderer lost in the desert without a compass or any hope of finding an oasis.

Added to the daily struggle to feed and provide for herself and her little daughters, especially in winter when their dried figs and sacks of flour dwindled, Koula had a distressing personal problem. *Taximeni*, as the wives of absentee husbands were called, had to be even more modest and vigilant than single women, to ensure that they gave no grounds for gossip. She had to dress in sombre colours, keep her hair covered and lead a monastic existence.

Talking to a man who wasn't a close relative would be enough to provoke accusations of loose morals. And that would mean ostracism for her and dishonour for her children, ruining their chances of making a good match. Perpetuating the vicious circle of oppression, those who had once been its victims became gleeful enforcers.

For a hot-blooded, strong-minded young woman, being subjected to the gossip of women whose suspicious minds did more embroidery than their fingers was like living in a glass cage. Koula accepted the morality and standards of behaviour that had been inculcated into her, but the relentless suspicion, the continued absence of her husband and the uncertainty of her existence weighed more heavily on her than the exhausting physical labour from sunrise to sunset. If George were to abandon them or die, this bitter existence would remain her fate forever, because she would never know what had happened to him.

Kythera was the first island on which the Allies set foot in Greece when English paratroopers landed at Kapsali in December 1944. For once there was something to celebrate. Bonfires blazed in every yard and fireworks lit up the sky. When the war finally ended in 1945, after the swastika had been pulled off the flagpole on the Acropolis, Koula received the first letter from her husband in six years.

Mattie, who only knew her father from the framed photograph that stood on the mantelpiece, and from her mother's oft-repeated stories, watched as her mother kissed the envelope over and over again. The following Sunday, her mother opened her cherished glory box, took out her best *vezeles* blanket, draped it around her shoulders and told the girls to hurry. Together they hastened along the sun-bleached stony path towards St Eirini's Church. When the little whitewashed church was about a hundred metres away, to Mattie and Katina's amazement their mother dropped to the ground and crawled the rest of the way on her knees. Oblivious to the pain and the blood that ran down her shins, she crawled along the church aisle until at last she came to the gilded icon of Christ.

Taking the blanket off her shoulders, she folded it and left her greatest treasure in front of the icon in thanksgiving. Mattie noticed that when the other worshippers turned and saw what her mother had done, they whispered to each other, raised their arms and slapped their thighs in the Kytherian gesture of amazement.

From his letter and the ones that followed, it was clear that George was still planning to return to Kythera as soon as he had earned enough money. Koula was horrified. That meant that she would have to continue living alone, tending the chickens and goats, digging the dried-out, depleted soil to plant the spindly tomatoes, marrows and eggplants, and being on her guard every day to ensure that she wasn't the subject of speculation and rumour.

As time went on, this modern-day Penelope grew impatient with spinning and weaving and waiting for her man to return while her youth ebbed away. Now that she knew he was alive, each year dragged more than the one before. It was true that he posted them parcels of clothes, tea, cocoa, chocolate, milk powder and sweets that sent the girls into raptures, but the message Koula was waiting for still didn't come. Other women from the village were leaving to join their husbands, but George kept insisting that he would return. Brought up to defer to her husband, Koula had to restrain herself from making the sharp replies that his letters provoked.

From those letters, it was obvious that he didn't realise that the country he had left ten years earlier had drastically changed. Although one war had ended, another conflict was raging throughout Greece. The Communist and right-wing resistance groups turned the country into a battlefield as they fought for supremacy. Travisianka was no longer a peaceful haven, but a battleground where Communist guerrillas hid in the mountains, kidnapping, killing and terrorising the villagers. All over Greece their self-appointed tribunals dispensed summary injustice, brutal torture and cruel deaths. They wrenched young children from their mothers and sent them to Communist training camps in Albania, Bulgaria and the Soviet bloc. Many teenagers, including girls, were forced to join them as guerrilla fighters. Although the guerrillas' campaign in Kythera was not as savage as on the mainland, some homes were set on fire and men fled into the hills to escape capture. 'This is not the right time to return to Kythera. It's far too dangerous here,' Koula wrote to her husband, exasperated with his stubborn attitude. Finally in 1948 she made a decision.

'I can't wait any longer,' she wrote. 'Please send the money for our passage because we're coming to join you in Australia.'

When he gave in, they began their journey. Apart from her daughters, Koula was taking her teenage nephews, John Comino and Stan Travasaros, to Australia. Athens awed them with its wide paved streets, motor cars, indoor toilets, tall buildings, and sales assistants who placed your purchases into paper bags. They pressed their noses against the shop windows and marvelled at the abundance they saw.

Every day they would pass a man pushing a square trolley yelling '*Kasata pagotaaa! Kasata pagotaaa!*' Curious to see what he was selling, Mattie and Katina peered shyly into the trolley. Quick to take advantage of their interest, the man urged their mother to buy a treat for the children. Too proud to reveal her ignorance, Koula bought two little packages and placed them in her handwoven village bag without asking what they were. 'You can have them after dinner,' she said. Before long, Koula felt something wet and sticky leaking out of the bag. The ice creams had melted. The *pagota* must have gone off, she said, her face flaming with embarrassment.

From Athens they had flown on to Alexandria, then by train to Port Said. On the banks of the Nile, Mattie watched astonished as women washed themselves in the river. Changing trains in Cairo had been nerve-wracking for Koula. Unable to ask anyone for directions, she was terrified that one of the youngsters would be left behind, especially her nephews who were always running ahead. The tumult at the station was confusing, so many people surging forward with frightening dark faces they had never seen before. Realising that she would never manage to push the four of them and their baggage past the people crowded around the door of the compartment, she grabbed her charges and, with superhuman strength, pushed them in through the window and climbed in after them. Although the compartment was so jammed that they had to stand in one spot for the entire seven-hour journey, at least they were on their way to Port Said.

Finally Mattie climbed the gangplank of the huge ship which would take them to Australia and to her father. As the officers in their white uniforms and stiff caps checked their papers and directed them to their cabins, she wondered whether her father looked like any of them, and whether he would like her when they met.

7

A middle-aged man in a navy beret, with a jacket thrown over his shoulders, stood leaning over the rail, talking quietly to a young woman who averted her sullen face as he spoke. Alina Potok was angry with her father because she had fallen in love in Germany and had longed to go to Israel with her boyfriend, but her father had forbidden it and forced her to go to Australia instead.

What right did he have to tell her what to do at eighteen, she fumed, when at the age of thirteen she had managed to escape from the Nazis and had fended for herself for three years during the war. She had never told him what she'd gone through in that terrible time in Poland, Germany and Austria, but looking back she could hardly believe it herself.

Even though what happened wasn't his fault, she was angry in a way she couldn't explain. They were strangers. Brought up by a nanny in the Polish city of Bedzin where they had lived an affluent life, she hardly knew her father before he was deported to Siberia at the beginning of the war. And he hadn't told her about his wartime experiences either. Perhaps he didn't want to distress her, although she no longer became distressed very easily. Salezy Potok believed in getting on with life, not dwelling on the past, and that suited her too.

When he had last seen her, she was a child of ten, and now she was a woman. But after all these years, just because they had found each other again, he couldn't expect to treat her as a child and run her life. And here he was asking her to be more ladylike and behave more discreetly, because some of his busybody companions were gossiping that she was spending too much time with one of the Greek officers.

In front of them, a pall of fine coal dust shimmered in the air as men with mahogany skin and thighs as thin as chicken bones tossed sacks of coal to each other on a makeshift rope ladder. The coal loading had been in progress for the entire day and the passengers were riveted by the ceaseless activity of these agile men whose eyes glowed in their dark faces.

Occasionally one of the passengers would hold out a slice of bread, and several labourers would pounce on it and place their blackened hands together in a gesture of thanks.

A young man walked over towards them. It was Salezy Potok's cabin-mate Morris Skorupa whose throat knotted as he looked at the men devouring the bread. This sight took Morris back to a time he wanted to forget, when he had been imprisoned at the Posen labour camp during the war. They had been so hungry that they sprinkled sand into the meagre portions of watery food, so that the newcomers would gag and leave their rations to the older inmates who were so starved that they waited like vultures for the extra food. It made Morris shake his head when he heard his companions at the dinner table complaining about the food on board. How quickly people forgot.

In the Nazi gulag, few people ever mentioned Posen, perhaps because so few survived it. Just reaching the end of the day there was a triumph. Although Morris tried not to think about it, scenes that were seared into his mind would often slide back. Again he would see that fourteen-year-old boy's skinny body swinging limply from the gallows, between the bodies of two older men hanged because they had stolen a rotting potato from a frozen field. If he allowed himself to remember, he could still feel the agony of his joints and bleeding hands as he levelled a hilly potato field with a spade that could hardly break the frozen ground. Standing nearby, the guards watched for him to stop or falter, their hands twitching on their cudgels, whips or pistols. Only two years earlier, he used to play in the local Maccabi soccer team against young men like these who would cross the border from Germany every Sunday for a keen but friendly game.

For months, along with the other prisoners, he laboured with picks and spades to construct a railway junction so that thirty locomotives would move on turntables to enable German units to travel to the Russian front. Thousands of prisoners died of exhaustion, starvation, beatings or gunshot wounds because every foreman had the power of life and death over them. Fewer than one in ten made it to Auschwitz, the next stop on this highway to hell.

Like these coolies loading coal, they had worked from dawn until dark, but sometimes when they staggered back to camp, one of the bastards would order them to unload bricks for another four hours. By the time they were dismissed, the disgusting slop made from rotting vegetables was all gone. Yet despite all the hardship, something in Morris's stubborn nature refused to give up.

He had a strong will, a talent for getting on with people and a shrewd wheeler-dealer mentality which helped him to find ways of improving his situation, even in the toughest conditions. Thinking back, he suspected that his ability to stay neat and clean had made guards and camp officials well-disposed towards him.

He turned and waved to a woman sauntering past with her little daughter whose fez had fallen into the harbour the previous day. With an appreciative eye for good-looking women, he had noticed the tall, willowy Tania Poczebucka with her radiant smile. Women liked Morris, and two had placed themselves in great danger to help him during the war. The gentle German wife of the brutal chef at Posen surreptitiously filled up a red enamel bucket with food that he shared with his starving friends. And Stefcia, the Polish girl who worked at the camp, risked her life to smuggle bread for him. Even when she was caught and interrogated by the Gestapo, she didn't give him away.

A breeze ruffled Morris's wavy brown hair and as he smoothed it down, he felt the cicatrice. He'd got the scar the day he and another prisoner had found a trench full of potatoes in a frozen field outside the camp. No bounty-hunter in search of buried treasure ever gazed at a chest full of gold with such joy. Their frozen fingers shook as they lit a fire to cook the potatoes, but before they could bite into the hot, floury flesh the farmer galloped towards them. They jumped to their feet and bolted, but Morris slipped and fell while running across the railway line. Above him, on the horse, the farmer lashed out with his whip, again and again, until his head was split open like a melon and blood poured down his face and back. Several days later, when two other prisoners were discovered cooking potatoes in the same field, they were dragged back to the camp and hanged. If the farmer had brought him back instead of whipping him, he would have been hanged too.

In the spring of 1943, when the camp in Posen was liquidated, Morris was one of the few left alive. The prize for survival was transportation to Auschwitz. The name meant nothing to him. But when they unhasped the waggons and he saw the SS in their jackboots, the snarling dogs, the guards cracking their whips, yelling 'Raus! Raus! Schnell! Schnell!' and looked up to see machine guns trained on them from the towers and the yellow searchlights sweeping over them, he knew he'd arrived in hell.

Morris turned away from the rail. He said nothing about these experiences to Salezy Potok or his daughter, and they, like him, never spoke about theirs. It was a time they all wanted to forget, hoping that silence would eventually bring oblivion. Noticing Alina's unhappy face as she stared into the distance, he tried to distract her with the prospect of seeing the Suez Canal, but she continued to gaze moodily out to sea.

The coal loading had brought back distressing memories for Alina too. The dry smell of the black dust reminded her of the day when, at the age of thirteen, she had crawled into the coal recess behind the cellar with her mother and other relatives in Bedzin to hide from the Germans, whom they could hear stomping on the other side of the wall. The sputtering retort of gunshots had made her jump in terror. The next sound she heard was harsh voices yelling at them to come out and stand against the wall with their arms up.

Her father had already been deported to Siberia, and now she and her mother were about to be deported to Auschwitz. When they were at the railway station with all the other Jews who had been rounded up that day, her mother slipped the gold chain from her neck and passed it to Alina, together with a photograph of a German in Wehrmacht uniform. 'Run away as soon as you can,' she whispered. 'It's your only chance.' Pointing to the photograph, she said, 'Tell them it's your father.' Alina knew that it was the German aristocrat her aunt had married, who lived in Berlin with their daughter. As soon as the guards looked the other way, Alina ran behind a building and kept going. She never saw her mother again.

The dangerous time of curfew was approaching. Panic-stricken, she rushed to her nanny's house but was told that she'd have to leave in the morning. The Germans searched houses close to the station and if they found a Jewish girl hiding there, they would shoot them both. The following day Alina tried her parents' former chauffeur, who advised her to travel to Berlin in search of her aunt and German uncle. Unclasping her mother's gold chain, she handed it to him in return for money that would buy a rail ticket.

Alone and without any identity papers or documents at a time when the might of the Third Reich was focused on killing every Jewish man, woman and child, Alina travelled on trains around the country until she crossed the border into Germany. Whenever inspectors demanded to see her papers, she pretended to be part of some peasant family in the compartment or showed them her uncle's photograph, insisting that she was travelling to join him. Through sheer force of will, she got through every passport control.

She arrived in Berlin not knowing where to go, but instinct led her to her cousin's apartment. Not long after she arrived, the air raids began and German women and children were evacuated from the capital. When her cousin and her family joined the exodus, they left Alina behind because, having no documents, she put them in danger. Alone in the apartment while phosphorus bombs fell on Berlin and flames leapt up towards the sky, Alina cowered in a corner and jumped with each explosion, expecting the building to collapse on top of her at any moment. Even now, five years later, just thinking about it made her tremble, and the sound of fireworks made her hysterical.

When her relatives returned to Berlin, they decided that they couldn't risk their lives by keeping Alina any longer. The girl set off on her wanderings again, back to Poland where she hoped to find someone who would take her in. In the dead of winter, she searched for a family friend, an ethnic German whom she found employed at the IG Farben factory at Auschwitz. Without realising where she was, or that her mother was interned there at the time, Alina spent the frosty night in a hut on its outskirts.

The man she had come to see arranged for her to become a farmhand in the Tatra Mountains, and told the farmer that she was the daughter of a Polish officer. For the next few months Alina tended the cows, although they frightened her. She helped in the fields, walked for miles to church on Sundays, and ate from the same bowl of baked potatoes and buttermilk as the peasants.

But when the money ran out, they told her to go. Once again she travelled all over the country until she reached Warsaw where some Polish people agreed to hide her in their cupboard so no one would find out she was there. She felt safe with them until a visitor to the house warned her that her benefactor planned to turn her in. 'You're tall, you could easily pass for fifteen. Why don't you volunteer to work in the Reich? You'd be safer there than in Poland,' he advised.

With the false documents he obtained for her, Alina travelled to Austria with a group of Polish volunteer workers, but had trouble finding work because she looked so weak and ill. The only person willing to employ her as a maid was the doctor in the labour camp whose crazy, sadistic mother beat and starved her. In despair, Alina volunteered for factory work, but as she wasn't strong enough to produce the required quota, she was sent to the Hungarian border to dig trenches. Exhausted and ill, she was eventually sent to another factory where a Viennese workmate called Greta took pity on her. Greta did most of her work, brought her food, and treated her as a daughter. When the war ended, Greta took her home and together they hid from the Russians who rewarded themselves for liberating Europe by raping every woman they could find.

At the recollection of the wonderful woman who had loved her like a mother, tears welled in Alina's eyes. She had never told Greta that she was Jewish but when the war was over, Greta had said, 'You can stay with me as long as you like. I'll look after you and educate you, but first go back to Poland to see if some of your relatives have survived.'

The sound of a Polish couple speaking Yiddish on the deck chairs behind her reminded her of the emotional moment she experienced the day she returned to her home town, Bedzin. By the time the war ended, Alina was convinced that she was the only Jew left alive, but on the tram in Bedzin she overheard two women cheerfully speaking Yiddish. Her mind turned somersaults. Yiddish! So she wasn't the only one after all! That's when she knew that the war was really over.

Shortly afterwards, Alina discovered that her father had returned from Siberia and was looking for her. The past five years and all her sufferings had created a chasm between them that felt unbridgeable. And now, miserable at having had to part with her sweetheart in Germany and travel to the other side of the world, she felt more distant from her father than ever.

Evening in Port Said dropped suddenly out of the sky, without the gentle intervention of a European twilight. The muezzin's guttural chant floated above the palm trees, and after spreading their prayer mats on the deck, the Egyptians policing the ship dropped to their knees and prostrated themselves in prayer. Alina's father, whom the Polish women described as a real gentleman, was talking to his cabin-mate Emanuel Darin who pointed to a group of Egyptian officials standing around on the wharf. The *Derna* was due to sail that night, but from their raised voices and the way they repeatedly turned to look at the ship, it looked as though there was a problem.

Over dinner, there was more noisy gossip than usual, and above the clattering of knives and forks, the passengers speculated and complained about the newcomers who had recently boarded. That glamorous couple — were they were film stars travelling incognito, high-ranking diplomats or charmers with a shady past? Everyone had seen Colonel Hershaw and the German girl go ashore together. 'What has that guy got that we haven't got?' one of the young men sighed, to which another retorted, 'A big cabin!' There was a rumour that one of the officers had been discharged for having an affair with a passenger, but others scoffed, saying that if they started putting officers off the *Derna* for sexual peccadillos, there'd be no one left to sail the ship.

At the captain's table, the conversation was less lively that night. Captain Papalas was preoccupied, the Egyptian purser addressed himself mainly to his wife, and the ship's doctor stared into his wine glass as usual and said very little. The captain's fat, slow-moving son Kosmos kept up an amiable flow of small talk, while Dorothea chatted to the first officer about her impressions of Port Said.

The captain was mulling over a problem that had arisen because the assistant purser had unexpectedly left the ship, creating a vacancy that would be difficult to fill. Someone was needed to act in a public relations capacity and help resolve the passengers' endless complaints. The mothers in particular needed help, as no suitable food had been provided for the babies and toddlers. With meals to prepare for 545 passengers and 137 crew members, the temperamental chef had his hands full as it was. The ideal person would need to know several languages and have an understanding disposition. Not like the chief purser, an Egyptian Turk whose attitude left a lot to be desired. Some of the passengers had already complained about his arrogant, abrasive manner.

But the issue that lay heaviest on the captain's mind had nothing to do with pursers or baby food. The *Derna*, which was scheduled to sail through the Suez Canal that night, had not received a clearance from the port authorities. He looked at the clock. Soon the ships would be marshalled in a convoy. He had argued with the officials and contacted the owner about the delay. He could do no more.

Late at night, the sound of Czech folk songs, the strumming of guitars and an occasional burst of ribald laughter at the risqué lyrics resounded in the bar area at the stern. People strolling around on deck noticed unusual activity on the wharf. A big car pulled up, and when the chauffeur opened the door, a lively young blonde swung her long slim legs out of the back seat and was met by port officials who addressed her in a deferential manner.

As the sound of their voices floated across the water, one of the officers standing on deck beside Emanuel Darin gave a knowing smile. 'Our ship left Marseilles without proper documents from Lloyds relating to our registration or cargo. The port authorities are saying that we're not seaworthy. They don't want to let us sail through the canal,' he explained. 'See that blonde down on the wharf? That's the owner's daughter. She's come to convince them that the *Derna* is seaworthy after all!' He chuckled, rubbing his thumb and forefinger together in a gesture implying that money was about to change hands. Tina Livanos Onassis, the nineteen-year-old daughter of Stavros Livanos, who had married the much older Onassis against her father's will, had arrived in Port Said to enable us to continue our voyage.

Several hours later, at four in the morning of 10 September 1948, the *Derna* was marshalled into sixth place in the convoy of nine ships ready to sail through the Suez Canal.

8

The hundred-mile-long Suez Canal that separated Europe from Africa was so narrow that the ships ahead of us seemed to be gliding on land. 'Leave your knitting for a minute and come and have a look,' my father called to me. 'This is one of the wonders of the world.' He explained that before its construction about 120 years earlier, ships had to sail all the way around the Cape of Good Hope. 'Imagine having to sail on the *Derna* for months instead of weeks,' he chuckled.

My mother, whose creamy complexion had acquired a greenish hue ever since we boarded, groaned at the thought. The ship which she had described as 'big and comfortable' in the postcard to her sister-in-law, had become a rocking prison cell. Usually cheerful and energetic, she felt bilious from the constant motion and dreaded spending the next five weeks in our hot, overcrowded cabin.

Sailing through the canal and watching everyday life along the banks, we seemed to have stepped back into Biblical times. My father pointed to the sad donkeys trotting patiently around the mill-wheels, the goats grazing outside mud huts, and the veiled women shrouded in black who drew water from the well, just as they'd done in the days when Rameses' daughter had found Moses among the bulrushes. My father loved facts and relished the power of knowledge, perhaps because it made him feel secure in a life that had been filled with uncertainty and trauma.

The fierce sun was blazing down on our heads when the *Derna* reached the point where the canal widened into the Great Bitter Lake and had to wait for the northbound convoy to pass. A small motor launch that had steadily been gaining on us caught up and drew alongside to allow someone to board, and a few moments later one of the officers came up to Dorothea. 'John Brown is looking for you,' he said. She could hardly believe her eyes. The exciting man she had met in Port Said was standing in front of her, smiling. This was like a scene from the movies; things like this just didn't happen in real life. As he held out a bottle of French cognac, he murmured, 'I had to find out if you liked the mango!' She burst out laughing at the absurdity of it. Quietly he said, 'I had to see you again.' Before clambering down to his launch, he turned back. 'I'll never forget you,' he said.

Staring at the wake of the departing motor boat, from which John Brown was still waving, Dorothea felt dazed. The idea that after such a brief encounter this gorgeous man had followed her along the Suez Canal to Aden seemed so improbable that she was tempted to think she had imagined it. A shadow fell across the deck and she looked up to see Colonel Hershaw. With a bemused smile, he said, 'That John Brown you took such a liking to. They're saying he's the owner's son.' Dorothea was intrigued by this exciting development, but as it later turned out the rumour was false. Stavros Livanos's only son was a fourteen-year-old schoolboy at the time, not a debonair shipping agent sweeping young women off their feet.

Dorothea didn't have much time to ponder the identity of the mysterious John Brown because it was time to join the other officers in the captain's cabin for a glass of champagne on the occasion of his name-day. As they raised their glasses to toast Stavros Papalas's health, Dorothea looked around and caught the first officer's appreciative glance. It added to her enjoyment of the occasion to see that she was the only woman who had been invited to the party.

As we sailed through the canal, parallel with the railway line and oil pipeline, we passed small administrative offices in between dun-coloured Arab villages with their incongruous Coca-Cola ads.

Occasionally we caught a glimpse of white villas behind tall palms. From regular checkpoints, British soldiers riding jeeps waved and tooted to salute the passing ships. Sometimes, however, the gestures were less friendly. Bruno Tohver's sense of propriety was offended to see some of the locals turning their backs to us, raising their robes and showing their bare buttocks.

The following morning, as we sailed through the Gulf of Suez, a slight breeze gave a little relief from the heat. As we rounded the Sinai Peninsula, the landscape became more mountainous. Everyone was out on deck, shading their eyes and craning their necks to catch sight of Mt Sinai in the distance. Elmars Kuplis, a devout Christian, felt tears spring to his eyes when he saw the land where Jesus had once trod. It had suddenly been transported out of the realm of stories and scriptures to become solid reality.

For many Jews it was a heartache to come so close to the Promised Land, yet be unable to reach it. A reflective silence fell over the usually ebullient orphans in Dr Frant's group. Some of them would have migrated to the new land of *Eretz Israel* if it hadn't been for the embargo placed on Jewish migration by the British before independence, and the war that had been waged there ever since. Now they felt like traitors for placing their security above solidarity with the pioneers who were building up the Jewish nation.

Sam and Esther Fiszman felt sad when they watched the Promised Land receding from view, perhaps forever. After the war ended, Sam had thrown himself into the struggle for a Jewish homeland. It was while he was recruiting and training young Jews in the Polish town of Sosnowiec to fight in Palestine that the most haunting face he'd ever seen appeared in front of him.

Esther was sixteen when they met, with clouds of auburn hair to her shoulders and dreamy eyes that shone like starlight. Unlike some of the brazen young women who threw themselves at him, she was modest and principled, but she was strong too and not afraid to say what she thought. He couldn't get her out of his mind.

At the age of twelve, Esther had been transported to Auschwitz where her parents had been killed. If it hadn't been for a caring older girl called Magda, who had taken the frail twelve year old under her wing and hidden her in the laundry when she became ill with typhus, Esther would not have survived. She and Magda were separated during those chaotic last months of the war when the Germans had evacuated the death camps and shunted starving, emaciated, disease-ridden prisoners across the frozen countryside on foot, to destroy all evidence of their crimes. Esther often thought about Magda with love and gratitude, and wondered what had happened to her.

It made Sam fume to think of Esther, after all she'd gone through, lying on a narrow bunk in the pathetic sick bay that was euphemistically called a hospital, with a doctor who had no interest in his patients and a captain who washed his hands of the whole ship. From the moment the *Derna* had set sail, Esther's stomach had rolled up into her throat. She couldn't keep any food down, and had become so thin that her eyes seemed bigger than her face. During the day she kept three-month-old Maria in the sick bay with her, but at night, when Sam strung up a hammock for the baby above his own bunk, her crying often disturbed the other occupants of his cabin who complained bitterly.

A welcome breeze sprang up off the water, and as Sam drew his Russian army jacket around his shoulders, he felt someone staring at him. He turned around and met the disapproving gaze of a group of men who were muttering to each other. Although Sam did not understand what they were saying, he knew that they came from the Baltic countries. He glared at them. Their countrymen had greeted the occupying Nazis with welcoming smiles and flowers and some had rushed to join the police units which helped the SS round up the Jews. From those ranks some had been recruited into the death squads that gunned down tens of thousands of men, women and children into pits dug in nameless clearings and secret woods.

Sam knew that wearing his army jacket provoked them, and revelled in the provocation. Nazi-lovers. They'd fought on the wrong side, and now that the Russians had invaded their countries, they had to run for fear of retaliation. It served them right. But the thought that some of them were now migrating to Australia, bringing with them their blood-stained hands, SS tattoos and religious prejudices, made him fume.

Although the war had ended three years earlier, Sam continued to fight his battles in his head. Those who passed him on deck saw a nuggetty fair-haired young man with one opaque eye and an intense, restless manner reminiscent of Kirk Douglas. Sam was a coiled spring ready to snap. At the age of twenty-three he had already lived through enough to write an action-packed autobiography. At thirteen, when together with his mother and sister he had been immured inside the Warsaw Ghetto, he smuggled arms for the Jewish underground. Crawling through the sewers that ran under the ghetto and drained into the Vistula, he pushed his way for hours through stinking filth, past slimy rats that brushed against his legs and squealed in the dark, while he hung onto the slippery rails. He had to memorise the entire route, especially the positions of the German posts above ground, so that he would know where to emerge into the blinding light when the clock struck the appointed hour.

He had to hope, while holding his breath for those heart-stopping minutes it took for the manhole cover to open, that the shoes he saw as soon as the lid was raised belonged to the courier and not a Gestapo officer or an extortionist, or he was lost. As soon as the cover was off, they exchanged parcels, and he returned clutching the precious explosives or guns for the ghetto leaders. Making this trip several times a week required a cool nerve, a defiant attitude and, above all, the conviction that he'd get back safely.

He had just returned to the ghetto after such a mission and was hoisting himself out of the sewer when a boy rushed up and warned him to hide because the Germans were looking for him. He just made it to the recess behind the wall of the room he shared with his family seconds before two soldiers burst in. When his mother said she didn't know where he was, they grabbed her and his younger sister and pushed them into the yard. Through the window, Sam stopped breathing as one of the soldiers aimed his rifle and fired. Someone pressed their hands over his mouth so that his scream couldn't be heard as his mother and sister slumped to the ground.

As Sam walked away from the rail to look in on Esther and the baby, he noticed that the Baltic group was still looking his way, and felt icy shards in their glances. Someone spat the word 'Communist' as he passed. If they had had their wish and the Nazis had won the war, he and Esther would both be dead by now. But they had survived, and now there was little Maria to take the place of all the parents, grandparents, aunts, uncles and cousins that they'd lost.

His anger melted for a moment when he thought about the baby and recalled how she had come by her Catholic name. When the nun at the Notre-Dame Hospital in Paris where she was born had asked him what they would call her, he replied 'Malka', after his mother. The nun frowned. 'What sort of name is that, monsieur?' When he explained that it was the Hebrew word for queen, she beamed and said, 'Ah, that means Maria!'

Hunching his shoulders as he strode past the hostile faces, Sam stopped when he came to Archbishop Rafalsky, sitting as usual near the forward deck, surrounded by his Russian entourage. While the *Derna* chugged towards the Great Bitter Lakes, Sam sat down beside the archbishop who was the most charismatic person he had ever met. It seemed to him that this saintly man could see his soul and knew that he was a good person even though he wasn't a believer.

Memories of the Warsaw Ghetto were still roiling in his mind. 'My biggest enemies are God and Hitler,' he blurted out. 'Because if God could allow my innocent sister to be killed, then he was no better than Hitler.'

To his surprise, the archbishop didn't look shocked. 'I understand how you feel, but in time perhaps you'll realise that it was not God who made these things happen,' he said in his soothing voice.

If Sam had not been so angry with the Creator, he may have concluded that God had intervened to save his life on the day he had been buried under a pile of rubble during a battle near the German border. After the disastrous Warsaw Uprising, he had joined the partisans to fight the Germans. His unit had been engaged in hand-to-hand combat when a shell exploded, knocking him unconscious just before a building collapsed on top of him. Some time later, a passing Russian soldier noticed a hand sticking out of the ruins and felt a faint pulse. Three months after being rescued, Sam woke up in a field hospital, shell-shocked and blind in one eye.

When the archbishop suggested that perhaps God had had a hand in his survival, Sam explained that he believed in the socialist principle of equality, not in religion. 'The philosophy sounds noble,' the archbishop agreed, 'but the reality does not live up to the ideal. That was a terrible thing that Stalin did, destroying the kulaks, persecuting the priests and trying to control people's minds by banning religion. But the church isn't blameless either,' he mused. 'Too often it has placed dogma above human life.' Sam felt privileged to know such a wise and tolerant man. For the first time in his life he understood why some religious leaders attract disciples who sit at their feet and follow them all their lives.

Inside the cabins at night, the heat was suffocating. Desperate for air, the passengers scrambled for a space on deck, dragging their blankets and pillows with them in their search for a hammock, a canvas deckchair or just a level space on the timber floor. The crew disapproved of their nocturnal camping. The blankets were getting filthy and the bodies lying on deck got in their way when they swept up the dirt each morning. The coal burned by the Derna's engines spewed from the funnel as black smoke and coated everything with soot. Young boys held their sides and laughed when they looked at each other in the morning, not realising that their own faces were also smeared with grime. Little Pauline, who slept on deck beside her mother, would giggle when she woke up and saw the white imprint her head had made in the centre of her blackened pillow.

An undeclared war broke out between the passengers and the seamen, who became increasingly callous. While sweeping, they would cover everyone with clouds of soot, and continued hosing the deck even if people were lying there. Protests were met with shrugs.

Within a few days of leaving Marseilles, it was obvious that the combination of Greeks and Italians in the crew was explosive. Hatred between them smouldered and occasionally erupted in violence. It was not unusual for the passengers to step into a passageway and see a Greek seaman chasing an Italian steward, or to come across two combatants with fists raised or flick-knives poised ready to strike.

There were complaints all round. The crew protested about the unruly behaviour of the passengers who complained to Colonel Hershaw about the heartless attitude of the crew. Not wanting to trouble himself unduly with these counter-accusations, Hershaw delegated his deputy, Uno Mardus, to deal with the passengers. 'Let them know that they can't spread themselves out as if they are at a lawn picnic. Rules have to be observed,' the escort officer said. Since the only alternative to sleeping on deck was suffocating below in the cabins, Uno tackled the unenviable task with his customary good humour. A few conciliatory passengers promised to keep their blankets inside, but most of them shrugged off this unrealistic expectation. Some of the young Jewish survivors of the Holocaust, however, interpreted Uno's request as an attempt to assert power. 'Didn't anyone tell you that the Nazi regime is over?' some of them would retort.

With Uno Mardus to liaise between the passengers and Dorothea to type his letters and memos, make announcements in German and distribute the weekly issue of soap and cigarettes, Ogden Hershaw had plenty of time to relax. He chatted up the smashing young girls on board and talked to the Baltic migrants whose company he found very congenial. He particularly liked talking to Verner Puurand. Puurand had been the commander of the Estonian submarine the *Kalev* before the war but had fled to Germany when the Russians were advancing on Estonia. They conversed like men of the world who understood the political realities behind the façade that fooled many others. A frequent topic was the threat of Communism which they believed would ensnare the whole world if the West didn't wake up in time.

It was a topic close to Verner Puurand's heart. The presence on board the *Derna* of so many Jews alerted him to trouble. From what Colonel Hershaw had told him, most of them described themselves as Czechs, Poles, Hungarians and so on, but what he wanted to know was how they came to have passports when Christian patriots like himself, and others in the IRO group, did not. He suspected that they were Bolshevik agents issued with passports by post-war Communist governments. He confided in Colonel Hershaw that the obnoxious young fellow who strutted around in his repellent Russian army jacket was undoubtedly a Communist agitator. He didn't trust some of those Jewish youngsters either, singing propaganda songs, playing Russian music on the gramophone and upsetting everyone.

Verner Puurand's authoritative manner and former naval status won the respect of his Estonian companions who were impressed to have a submarine commander in their midst. As a lieutenant just out of naval school, he had been sent for training to England where two submarines were being constructed for Estonia. On his return, he was placed in charge of the *Kalev*, which had been named after a legendary Baltic hero.

In 1939, when the Russians took over Estonian naval bases, those connected in any capacity with the previous government were deported and often shot, but Puurand retained his position. This was the period of mass deportations, when terrified Estonians kept their suitcases packed, close to the door, in case men in trenchcoats banged on the door at midnight, pushed them into cattle cars and deported them to Siberia. No one who had worked for the Estonian government was safe, but Puurand explained that he and his family had escaped persecution because he spoke Russian and the Russians needed his naval expertise.

In 1941, when Hitler broke his pact with Stalin and attacked his former ally, the Germans entered Estonia to be greeted by cheering crowds who believed that they would help Estonia gain its independence from Russia. The prevailing belief was that, while the Russians' agenda was permanent subjugation, the Germans' invasion was a temporary wartime strategy. Drawing on latent anti-Semitism, the Nazis recruited Lithuanians, Latvians and Estonians into the *Einsatzgruppen* death squads which turned the Baltic states into a slaughterhouse. Latvia's Jewish population of about 90,000 was almost completely wiped out by death squads such as the infamous Arajs Militia in Riga. In a triumphant dispatch to Berlin in October 1941, General von dem Bach Zelewski wrote: '*Today there are no more Jews in Estonia.*' That wasn't quite accurate: there were still about 400 left, but within a few months they too were rounded up and killed.

Despite all the help given to the Germans by their Baltic allies, after their devastating defeat in Stalingrad in 1943, the Russian army began to advance as inexorably as the winter frost, driven by their lust for revenge. When they were about to enter Estonia in 1944, those who had any reason to fear retribution fled for their lives. It was then that Verner Puurand and his family moved to Germany. After the war ended, they moved to the American zone where he became the Baltic Liaison Director and supplied the American occupying forces with guards from among his compatriots.

That was the account that Puurand gave to Colonel Hershaw and some of his Estonian ship-mates. What he omitted to tell them, however, would have made a far more interesting story, one that would have astonished his companions.

When he wasn't exchanging political ideas with Colonel Hershaw, Puurand spent some of his time on the *Derna* teaching himself to play the accordion that he had bought in Germany on his aunt's advice. Before leaving, he had converted the money he had earned from the Americans into jewellery, but when his aunt in Brisbane wrote to say that accordions were scarce in Australia, he bought one in order to sell it for a profit on his arrival. And in case the customs authorities asked him to prove that it was his own instrument, he taught himself to play. It was a welcome distraction from this appallingly run ship whose antiquated engine room and wheezing machinery gave him very little confidence that the voyage would be completed on time.

9

As we approached the Gulf of Aden, the temperature continued to rise until we seemed to be sitting inside a lighted oven. Helle, who had joined the Estonian choir and folk dancing group, was relieved that rehearsals had been scheduled for early morning, but even at dawn there was no relief from the humidity.

The constant rocking made Halina Kalowski dizzy. Placing a damp cloth on her aching forehead, she wondered how she was going to last the voyage in her condition. She noticed that she was not the only pregnant woman who had remained on board in defiance of the Captain's order. Another Polish woman, Irka Falek, was also expecting, as was the Romanian Elsie Pataky.

Only the pleasant company of her cabin-mate Matylda Czalczynski helped to distract her from the spinning sensation. Always quick to help others, Matylda sat beside her, brought glasses of water and soothed her with her cheerful conversation. From the sadness in her eyes, Halina could tell that something was distressing her but she was too tactful to ask. When Matylda was ready, she would tell her.

The ship moved so slowly through the canal that some of the passengers thought it must be a thousand, rather than a hundred miles long. As everyone's fascination with this engineering feat began to wane, they drifted back to their usual activities. My father picked up his English grammar book, my mother chatted with Zofia Frant, while I concentrated on my knitting again and tried not to drop too many stitches. Occasionally small children ran past shrieking, while inside the lounge, the older ones like the Frants' eleven-year-old daughter Christine sat on the floor and played rummy or patience with Topka's youngest sister Bella.

In the centre of the middle deck, some of the Jewish orphans clustered around Otto Halm, a Czech boy who improvised his own lyrics to popular songs as he strummed the guitar, while others sneaked off with their sweethearts, away from Dr Frant's gimlet gaze. The married couples whiled away the hours gossiping and sharing the little they knew about Australia.

In one such group, the strong voice of Heniek Glassman dominated the conversation. An entertaining raconteur with an anecdote for every occasion, he was the centre of attention as he waved his arms around to emphasise his point.

'You wouldn't believe it,' he was saying, 'but I was offered the chance of emigrating to Australia back in 1936. One day this tall guy from overseas turns up in my textile factory in Lodz. It turns out he's a Jew from Bialystok called Fink who migrated to Australia of all places. I'd just bought some new machines and he wanted to see how they worked. So he asks me to come and talk to him in his hotel. "Leave everything, pack up and come to Australia, you'll make a lot of money," he tells me. Well, we used to weave Australian wool but I'd just opened a business and didn't want to leave. And when I mentioned it to my father, he threw up his arms in horror. "You gone crazy? You know where is Australia? America I understand, but what for you need Australia?" '

His listeners, Cyla and Max Ferszt, the Faleks and the lovely Tania Poczebucka and her much older husband, laughed appreciatively, but Heniek hadn't finished. Leaning forward, he stabbed the air with his index finger. 'Listen, you want to hear something funny? This year, when we get our landing permit, guess who signed it? That same guy! Fink! He did it as a favour for my cousin in Melbourne. Didn't dream it was for the person he tried to talk into migrating twelve years ago!'

Listening to his lively stories, it was hard to realise that Heniek had lived through the horror of Birkenau, Flossenburg and the Death March and after returning home had discovered that his first wife had died in the Stutthof death camp. Bronia, as always, listened indulgently. The Glassmans were the kind of couple whose marriage made people wonder what this well-spoken, refined woman with a classical education had seen in this hot-headed opinionated man who spoke with a Yiddish accent. Bronia's mother, who was travelling with them to Australia, had regarded the marriage as such a misalliance that when Bronia told her she was going to marry Heniek only six weeks after they'd met, she had been appalled. 'Over my dead body!' she told her daughter. 'What do you know about him?'

Bronia had shrugged. 'I don't need to know anything about him. I want him.'

From the moment they met, she had been attracted to Heniek's forceful personality and masculine presence. She admired his good taste in clothes, the way his ties matched his well-cut suits, and the way he held her when they danced. 'You didn't marry me, you married my clothes!' he used to joke. And to tease him, she'd agree. In the unconscious way we choose our partners, she had instinctively known that his decisive, ebullient personality would balance her own introverted nature.

Looking at her friend Irka Falek's swelling abdomen, Bronia recalled scenes that had been seared into her mind and would never be erased. While she had worked in the hospital inside the Krakow Ghetto, German SS men would sometimes stride across the ward, tear a baby from the arms of its screaming mother and throw it out of the window with as much emotion as if they were tossing away a cigarette butt.

From the ghetto she had been sent to a labour camp run by the Luftwaffe and worked there for over two years. Although the conditions were tough, the commandant, Captain Fischer, was not a sadist and treated them relatively well. As Bronia spoke both German and Polish, she was put in charge of twenty-five women, but when four of them ran away, she was held responsible. Never would she forget her terror when the SS officers who ran the camp told her to get undressed and start digging. Her body shook so much that she could hardly hold the spade. This was the end. She would never see her parents again, never marry, never have children, never watch the sun rise again or see the Germans defeated. For twenty-four hours they kept her there, naked and terrified, poised on the edge of her life. Then Captain Fischer came out and said something her numbed mind could hardly grasp. 'Get dressed, *Fraulein*. They've decided not to execute you.'

While conversations swirled around her, Bronia sighed. The most distressing thing was the way that the camps had changed her. Before the war, she had been kind and caring: sharing her lunch with a poor school friend, and dropping a few zlotys into a beggar's bowl. But in the camps she became a stranger to herself. When her best friend was taken away, she wasn't upset. Just numb.

During the Death March, she had stumbled across the German countryside for miles every day, so frozen that her bones ached, and so exhausted that she was afraid to sit down for fear of never being able to get up again. She woke one morning and saw that the woman lying next to her had died in the snow where she lay, blue and stiff. Bronia had stepped over her and staggered on. And she hadn't felt a thing. Now, staring at the tankers and freighters moving along the canal without really seeing them, she thought, *That was the worst thing the Germans did. They desensitised and dehumanised us.* This was the price of survival, but how did one live with the knowledge of what lay just beneath the skin of humanity?

The sound of singing interrupted her reflection and cut across her friends' conversation. On the other side of the deck, the Balts were rehearsing, their clear strong voices harmonising in folk songs under the direction of their enthusiastic choir-master. Watching them, she began to speculate whether some of these tenors and baritones who were now singing so beautifully had helped their Nazi allies to persecute the Jews. Some of them probably had the SS tattoo in their left armpit, one of her companions said. Unless they'd had it removed, of course. 'The Australian government has imposed a quota on Jews. I wonder whether they have a quota on Nazi collaborators as well?' someone else commented.

In a quiet voice Bronia said, 'After the war, I was working in Czechoslovakia as an interpreter. Whenever they caught German women they suspected of being Nazis, they brought them to me for questioning. It wasn't hard to detect the evasions and lies. I'd ask, "What were you doing in 1942? Did you have enough to eat? Where did you get food?" Most people in Europe were still poor, sick and hungry but these German women looked so well-fed and well-dressed in the clothes, diamonds and furs they'd stolen from Jews. I was very bitter. The Nazis had killed my sister who was five years younger than me, and my father too. One brazen SS woman I was questioning gave me a vindictive look and hissed, "You're so young but so wicked!" I saw red. "Listen," I told her, "if our positions were reversed, you would want to get your hands on me, not just ask polite questions."'

Her companions were nodding. 'Did you ever catch anyone well-known?' one of them asked.

'Himmler's sister-in-law,' Bronia said. 'They had found her in the Sudetenland where many of them hid, hoping to flee to Switzerland. When I said, "You must have had a good position during the war," she said, "I certainly did, thanks to my brother-in-law." "And who was that?" I asked. "Himmler," she replied. She was proud of being related to one of Hitler's cronies.'

The oil tankers, cargo ships and merchant marine vessels in the Straits of Aden and the wheeling of gulls overhead added to the excitement of approaching Aden, our next port of call. Catching the elusive whiff of land evoked for Arnold Ohtra the well-loved smell of the fishing ports in Tallinn and Haapsalu. The British Protectorate of Aden stood on a barren peninsula in Yemen near the entrance to the Red Sea. Built in the crater of an extinct volcano, the town was surrounded by a jagged crown of precipitous cliffs. Radio-transmitting towers poked into the cloudless sky, linking this strategic trading port with the rest of the British Empire.

Shortly after we docked, the loading began, and tanks of drinking water from artesian wells on the mainland were hauled into the holds. Soon a barge loaded with coal moved alongside the *Derna*, a ladder

was swiftly attached to its side and an army of Arabs in white loin
cloths climbed up until two of them stood on each swaying coir rung.
With the well-rehearsed movements of acrobats who depend on each
other's timing for survival, two men picked up the hessian bags full of
coal and placed them on the back of a third man, who threw it to the
men on the first rung. They caught and tossed it to the next pair and so
it went all the way up the ladder, until it reached the deck and was
emptied down the hatch. Each toss was accompanied by yells and
chants and proceeded at an amazingly brisk pace. Not one movement
was wasted. How noisy and primitive this was, all done by manpower
without any machines. Watching them, Helle found it hard to believe
that this was the twentieth century.

Petro Fatseas was so fascinated by this spectacle that he craned over
the rail at such a precipitous angle that his exasperated older sisters
were sure he would fall into the coal barge. As the loaders tossed the
bags up the ladder, counting out the tally, two of the *Derna*'s Greek
seamen stood nearby. 'Let's start a fight to distract them, so they'll lose
count,' Petro overheard one of them saying. 'We'll get a few more bags
out of them that way. God knows we'll need it if we're going to get this
wreck to Australia.' To Petro's amazement, they started throwing mock
punches and yelling until the loaders' attention was diverted and they
stopped counting. After a few minutes, the two seamen went off
slapping each other's shoulders and laughing, while the rhythmic
loading and counting resumed.

The passengers could not have been more riveted if they'd been
watching a circus performance. Arnold Ohtra marvelled that people
could be reduced to virtual slavery in their own country, and recorded
in his journal that 'the coolies were as thin as Mahatma Gandhi after a
100-day fast.' When some of the passengers gave them food, the
officers soon came running and told them to stop.

'Look at them,' my father pointed, shaking his greying head in
distress. 'Their thighs are no bigger than your arm.'

While the loading was in progress, the crew dragged out a large
tarpaulin, tied its edges to the rail and filled it with water to form a
swimming pool. Within minutes it was almost solid with splashing

children and teenagers, revelling in the miraculous effect of cold water on overheated skin and ignoring the mildewed, gunky canvas.

After the new passengers had boarded, the first officer, John Papalas, came over to Dorothea to introduce an Italian girl of seventeen who was travelling on her own to Australia. 'Her relatives were worried about her so I told them I knew just the person to take care of her,' he said. The dashing John Brown went out of Dorothea's mind as she looked up into the handsome face of the first officer whose manners were as attractive as his appearance.

The young girl standing beside him had thick dark hair that waved down to her shoulders and a wide smile. The two young women hit it off from the first moment. A few days later, when Colonel Hershaw mentioned casually that he'd suggested to the Italian girl that she should come and share his cabin as well, Dorothea was enthusiastic. 'There's a spare bunk and you'll be much more comfortable in with us than in that horribly overcrowded cabin,' she told her protégée. 'We've even got a fan.' What she didn't say was that she would be glad to have another woman in there for company. It wasn't that she felt unsafe with Ogden, but there had been a few occasions when he had been fresh and tried to kiss her. Having another girl in there would ensure that there would be no further unwelcome advances.

While the *Derna* had been loading up with coal in Aden, the Australian information officer who had escorted the Yugoslav migrants to meet the ship in Port Said sent a memo to the Department of Immigration in Canberra. Concerned by the conditions on board, he took the unusual step of adding an unsolicited comment to his report. 'Although officially I should not butt in,' he wrote, 'I am afraid the *Derna* may prove a "headache ship" if the Australian press takes it up. She is definitely overcrowded, has been limping along at about nine knots because of boiler trouble, and has far above her twenty-five percent quota of Jews.'

Before long, the headache was to develop into a migraine.

10

The night we sailed from Aden was a restless one. It was impossible to sleep in the cabins, while out on the sooty deck angry voices rang out from the galley, dishes crashed and men chased each other along the companionway. A foul odour pervaded the ship and everyone looked around for its source. At sunset, Arnold Ohtra looked up and saw a disturbing sight. Large black birds with long hooked bills and forked tails were circling the ship. Arnold took them for vultures but they were probably frigate birds. Some landed on the mast and rigging and waited, like polite undertakers marking time until the cadaver appeared.

By morning, the stench was so overpowering that we all pressed handkerchiefs to our noses. The mystery was solved when the crew emerged from the hold, hauling up putrid carcasses of lamb with butchers hooks still attached. They flung the meat, which had a greenish tinge and a slimy opalescent sheen, onto a tarpaulin that they tipped up so that the meat slid into the Indian Ocean. For the next two hours, everyone stood on deck to witness this surreal spectacle. People who had been starved in labour camps and concentration camps, and hadn't seen meat for years, watched as three tonnes of reeking lamb were jettisoned into the foaming waves.

Those who had cameras, like Bruno Tohver and Abie Goldberg,

leaned over the rails, their shutters clicking. Outraged passengers threatened to inform the Australian newspapers about this disgusting incident. Everyone had a theory. Some thought that the lamb which had been loaded in Port Said or Aden must have been rotten, while others believed that the refrigeration had broken down. On such an antiquated ship, in such heat, when ice was the main source of refrigeration, it was a miracle that the meat hadn't rotted sooner and that an epidemic of food poisoning hadn't broken out.

Suddenly there was a commotion at the stern. Someone was calling out and pointing at the sea. A fast-moving black fin was slicing through the waves. Was it another dolphin? Everyone surged forward. Over there too! Two more fins emerged. Then a shout aroused excited shudders in the crowd. Sharks! Scenting the carrion, the predators had followed the trail of rotten meat through the waves.

The mood darkened and a sense of claustrophobia began to close in. We had not been allowed off the ship since boarding two and a half weeks earlier, and had not been able to send or receive mail. After the episode with the rotten meat, many passengers felt anxious. Would there be enough food to last until Colombo? What would happen if someone became seriously ill? Not only were the medical facilities non-existent but the ship's medico, Dr Themelis, kept very brief consulting times and refused to see anyone outside these hours. And even when he was prepared to see patients, his advice was laughable. Aspirin and mercurochrome were the full extent of his pharmacopoeia.

The chef's decision to serve curried beef that night almost caused a riot. The passengers, who were not familiar with curries, took one look at the yellowish sauce, remembered the putrid carcasses, pushed their plates away and stomped out of the dining room. Shortly afterwards, Colonel Hershaw had to face an angry delegation who accused the chef of poisoning them with rotting meat and demanded that he convey their protest to the captain. 'In their ignorance, they thought that the curry was rotten lamb,' the colonel sneered at the captain's table that evening.

As escort officer for the migrants sponsored by the IRO, his job was to liaise between the passengers and the captain, but he hadn't expected to be harangued by so many passengers or to find himself in such a difficult situation. The curry was just the latest in a never-ending litany of complaints he'd received. Obviously he couldn't do anything to improve the appalling congestion in the primitive washrooms where mothers had to do their children's washing in the small basins or in the shower recesses. The soap that the efficient Dorothea distributed every week was of that pungent carbolic type, better suited to treating sufferers of infectious diseases than to normal bathing. What was worse, there wasn't enough of it, so that he'd had to reduce the rations, just as in wartime.

Colonel Hershaw had found out that there were sixteen babies under a year old on board, but the ship had made no provision for feeding them. Surely they didn't expect babies to eat olives, pickled vegetables and lamb? Fortunately one of the mothers in his group was a young German doctor, Irene Abrahamsohn, who was travelling to New Zealand with her mother and baby daughter. He was relieved to hear that Dr Abrahamsohn had undertaken to supervise the cooking of semolina for the babies, and was on hand to advise mothers with feeding problems. And that striking Estonian blonde with the two children had started organising a duty roster for the mothers to help prepare the babies' food.

The Estonian woman, Silva Rae, was appointed assistant to the purser shortly after we left Aden. While the captain and the purser had been wondering how to find a replacement for the assistant purser who had left the ship in Port Said, the answer to their problem had come from an unexpected source. The officers had taken a fancy to four-year-old Tarno Rae, a blond cherub who loved parading around in their caps. When the little boy heard them say that they were looking for a woman who spoke several languages, he suddenly piped up. 'My mummy can speak five languages,' he said. They burst out laughing but when he insisted that it was true, they asked him where she was.

A few minutes later, Tarno was pulling his mother by the hand to meet the purser. Thirty-three-year-old George Pathenopoulas saw a young woman with soft fair hair down to her shoulders, a slim figure and shapely legs accentuated by high-heeled ankle-strap shoes. As soon as they started talking, he noted that she had the calm, patient manner needed to deal with the passengers, some of whom were rather excitable. And little Tarno had been right. She did speak five languages.

Silva Rae was travelling to Australia with Tarno, her ten-month-old daughter Anneke and her parents. Before leaving Germany she had divorced the man she had married before the war. Like most Estonians of military age, he had joined the German army as part of the auxiliary SS but when the war ended and he returned, he became violent towards her and Tarno. Her parents had supported her decision to leave him and decided to migrate to Australia with her. They took care of the children while she worked in the purser's office.

Several passengers recognised Silva from the time she had worked for the IRO in Germany, processing applications for displaced people who wanted to migrate. They were grateful because she had been compassionate when helping them fill out their applications. Occasionally distressed young men stood before her and admitted to having the tell-tale SS tattoo in their armpits, but insisted that they had been forced to enlist and had done nothing wrong. Feeling sorry for them, she had recommended their applications.

She had completed a library course after the war and had worked in the United Nations Relief and Rehabilitation Administration (UNRRA) library in Munich, so she was not worried about earning a living in Sydney. Her aunt in Waitara, who had sponsored them, had made inquiries at the Mitchell Library in Sydney and had been told that there would be a job waiting for her. Silva couldn't wait to start working in the grand colonnaded building her aunt had described so enthusiastically.

Meanwhile she enjoyed her new status on the *Derna* in what was basically a public relations job. Sitting at a desk outside the purser's office, she spent most of the time trying to help people sort out their problems. Whether they complained about conditions on the ship or their inconsiderate cabin-mates, she found that if she listened sympathetically and let them talk, they usually calmed down and provided their own solutions. And it was pleasant to work with the purser, who was attentive and appreciative.

The most common complaints that she referred to Colonel Hershaw were about leaking cabin roofs. Some passengers also protested about moisture seeping into the hold and damaging their luggage. But although he took this matter up with the captain, who promised to have the leaks repaired, the problem persisted. To add to the colonel's frustration, there was the vexing issue of the dirt that blew into the cabins. You couldn't expect people to live in rabbit warrens that were cramped, unventilated and constantly fouled by filth and rubbish.

Colonel Hershaw was disgusted to find that food scraps, wrappings, vegetable peelings, eggshells and other refuse from the galley were tossed overboard every day as though the ocean was a garbage dump. Ashes were also disposed of the same way and often blew into the cabins through the portholes.

After persistent agitation, he succeeded in getting the carpenter to nail together a wooden chute so that all the rubbish would be directed into the sea, but his victory was short-lived. They hadn't done the job properly. The chute was too short and the ashes and garbage continued to blow back into the cabins. By now most passengers had given up asking for fans. Preferring to take their chances with the belligerent chief purser, they slept out on deck.

Although Colonel Hershaw had managed to obtain one precious fan for the cabin he now shared with the Italian girl as well as Dorothea, it failed to make the temperature tolerable and every night the three of them would drag their mattresses out onto the bridge. One morning, the first officer, John Papalas, called Dorothea aside and from his unusually grave expression it was clear that he had something on his mind. 'I thought you should know that I saw Colonel Hershaw making love to your cabin-mate last night on the bridge,' he said. 'One of the other officers saw it too. She's very young, isn't she?'

Dorothea was so shocked that she could hardly speak. How could that have happened without her knowing? Thinking back to their sleeping arrangements on deck, she recalled that Ogden lay between her and the Italian girl so that if she had turned away and slept on her side, it was possible that she hadn't heard anything. She knew that he had approached other young women. One of them was Gilda. He had told her that he fancied her and wanted to sleep with her, but Dorothea had never suspected that he would stoop so low as to try and seduce such a vulnerable young girl. And to make it even worse, she had been asked to look after this girl to make sure she arrived safely in Australia.

With her usual directness, Dorothea wasted no time in confronting her young cabin-mate. 'What's going on?' she asked.

The girl blushed and looked down. 'The Colonel is so nice, a real gentleman,' she said.

'But he's old enough to be your father!' Dorothea exploded.

'I love him and he loves me,' the girl replied, her dark eyes shining.

Dorothea was indignant. 'Did you know that this gentleman of yours has tried to seduce almost every woman on the ship?'

Stunned, the girl stared disbelievingly at Dorothea, her romantic dreams evaporating around her. 'Is that true?' she whispered. Dorothea put her arm around her protégée's slumped shoulders. 'I did not know, I believed what he said,' the girl sobbed, humiliated at having been deceived and used. 'Why didn't you warn me about him?'

Stung by the reproach, Dorothea retorted, 'I had no idea that he would do anything like this.' But he certainly wasn't going to continue, she decided.

Indignant that he had taken advantage of his position on the ship to seduce this innocent girl, Dorothea mulled the situation over. Holding on to the rails because the sea had grown rougher and the waves slapped more forcefully against the ship, she wandered down to the lower deck where the Jewish youngsters usually spread themselves out. Surrounded by a group of admirers, David Kucharski was clowning around and blowing his bugle. Deep in conversation with Magda Reich, Fred Silberstein looked up and saw Dorothea who greeted him briefly but walked on.

From the moment they'd met on that American army transport plane that had taken them out of Berlin, Fred had liked Dorothea's bright, friendly personality. He was delighted to hear that they were both sailing on the *Derna*, although she was bound for Sydney and he for New Zealand. He was disappointed that she spent so much of her time with that arrogant colonel and so little with him and his friends.

Dr Frant was patrolling the deck, his eagle eye searching out his young charges to make sure that they weren't annoying the other passengers. Some of the boys were high-spirited and he'd already had complaints from Colonel Hershaw about them vandalising the settees in the mid-deck lounge. Why, out of over 500 passengers, his boys were blamed for the damage he could only guess, but he was determined not to give anyone cause for criticism. As for the girls in his charge, they were a bigger headache than the boys, disappearing at nights and getting up to God knew what trouble. He had a responsibility to protect these girls from predatory males who might take advantage of them, although he had to admit that some of them looked as though they would be quite happy to take part in amorous activities.

Dorothea, who happened to be walking past, stopped when she saw him. Dr Frant was just the person to discuss her problem with. He listened with a sombre expression as she related the story about Colonel Hershaw and the Italian girl.

'That's disgraceful! She can't stay in that cabin any longer and neither should you,' he barked. 'The sooner you both move out, the better.' This Colonel Hershaw was obviously an unsavoury character. Apart from the disgusting story about him and the Italian girl, he knew that the Colonel spent most of his time hobnobbing with the Baltic group and stirring them up. Some of the Jewish passengers had overheard him making anti-Semitic remarks.

Later that day, when Dorothea discussed the situation with the first officer, he also urged her to move out of the colonel's cabin as soon as possible.

'Why don't you use mine?' he suggested. 'I'm mostly on night shifts, so you'll have it to yourself.' Grateful to have found a solution, she stretched out on a deck chair and started recording the day's events in her journal. John Papalas reached over, took the book out of her hands and made a swift sketch. When he handed it back to her, she was amused to see that he'd drawn the *Derna* and written underneath, '*A big heart in a small ship*'.

11

The little girl with the big bow on top of her short fair hair ran up to the lifeboat and, with a flip of her small hands, lifted one corner of the tarpaulin stretched across it. Standing on tiptoes she peered inside. Lying there were a boy and a girl with their arms entwined and their lips pressed together as though glued to each other. Suddenly aware of the chink of sunlight, two pairs of startled eyes clicked open and stared back at her. Shock at being discovered and anger at being spied on gave way to relief when they saw that it was not their suspicious chaperone but a tiny girl gazing down at them with an expression of intense yearning.

Lifting up the lifeboat covers to look for lovers inside was one of Ginette Wajs's favourite pastimes. It was as though seeing signs of affection in others somehow compensated for the lack of it in her own life. It helped to distract her from the sense of abandonment that engulfed her whenever she thought of the horrible aunt who had dragged her away from foster-parents she adored, just like the wicked witch in a fairy tale.

But Ginette did find a fairy godmother on the *Derna*. Topka opened her big heart to the unhappy little orphan in her cabin. Every day she helped her dress and took her to the washroom, despite her protests. Ginette hated those ugly cubicles with doors hanging off or missing, where you stood on rough wooden planks that smelled musty and sour from the constant humidity and no ventilation. She closed her eyes so she wouldn't see all those naked women, their breasts flopping all over the place, lathering themselves with unpleasant-smelling soap and splashing the floor with suds and scummy water.

Ginette would watch the mothers soaping their children, administering an occasional sharp slap on wet bottoms, or enfolding them in a loving hug. She couldn't remember her mother who had placed her in a convent in Paris to keep her safe, and was taken away to a concentration camp soon afterwards. She remembered the crunchy gravel path leading to heavy wooden doors, and the nuns who wore strange bird-like wimples. Best of all she remembered her foster-parents, the Roddiers, who took her out of the convent to live in their château, gave her a pony to ride and treated her like a princess. She went to church with the family and believed that she was Catholic like them.

Her perfect life ended suddenly, as perfect things always do, on the day when a stranger's shadow fell across the Roddiers' sunny doorstep. While Topka washed her hair in the noisy washroom, Ginette blinked away the tears as she remembered being dragged away from the family she loved and taken to an apartment in Paris where a cold-eyed woman awaited her.

The woman, who was her aunt, spent most of her time in bed, mourning for her husband who had recently died. Ginette was to discover much later that as he lay dying, her uncle had told his wife that he wanted to claim his niece from the Roddiers before they adopted her. It must have been out of a sense of duty that her aunt had brought her to Paris because, as Ginette soon discovered, it was not out of compassion. Feeling as unwanted as Cinderella, one afternoon she crept into her aunt's room at the top of the stairs. Her aunt advanced towards her from the darkened room with a look that sent chills down Ginette's spine, grabbed her shoulder and pushed her out with such force that she tumbled down the stairs. As she lay sobbing at the foot of the stairs, she stared at a piece of tooth that had broken off in the fall.

Ginette believed that she was Catholic until the day her aunt caught her kneeling beside her bed and pulled her to her feet. 'Get up off your knees and stop that nonsense!' she snapped. 'You're Jewish!' The words vibrated through Ginette's body like an electric charge. It couldn't be true. How could she be Jewish? She had prayed to Jesus in the lovely rose-scented chapel at the convent with the nuns and the other girls, and had sat beside her foster-parents in church on Sundays. She'd heard about the Jews. They were the ones who had crucified Our Lord, the priest said. The children at school chanted ditties about Jews because they didn't like them. Her aunt had to be lying. But her kind cousin, whom she trusted, told her that it was true.

Unable to cope with her misery and confusion, Ginette had tantrums and screaming fits. Her aunt's scathing comments and strict punishments only made things worse, and an impasse developed in which the little girl waged war whichever way she could. Finally her aunt said that she was not prepared to put up with her bad behaviour any longer. As she was too naughty to stay in Paris, she was to go and live with another aunt in America. Australia was never mentioned.

Ginette became distraught as her departure approached. Although her aunt had forbidden her to contact or even mention her foster-parents, she never stopped hoping that one day they would be reunited. Sometimes she would slip down to the Metro and wait on the platform in an agony of anticipation, hoping that the doors would open and her beloved foster-father would emerge and whisk her off. But now she was being sent far away and would never see them again. Ginette's screams, pleas and promises fell on deaf ears. The beautiful outfits her foster-father had bought from the boutiques in the Rue de Rivoli were packed up. Her aunt dressed her in her white rabbit fur coat and matching bonnet and put her on the train to Marseilles, where she was to board a ship. She was nine years old.

And now the rabbit fur coat, along with all her other clothes, had gone. After the shower, when she had bent down to pull out her suitcase and put on a clean dress, it wasn't there. She and Topka looked in vain under all the bunks. Everyone said there were thieves on board, and while they had been in the washroom, someone must have sneaked into the cabin and stolen her suitcase. Now she had nothing to wear. Tears ran down her cheeks. Topka sat down beside her and hugged her thin shoulders. 'Don't cry,' she consoled the child. 'I'll find something of Bella's to fit you and then we'll go down for dinner. Maybe they'll have chocolate pudding again tonight.'

Ever since the rotten carcasses had been jettisoned, lunch and dinner on the *Derna* had consisted mostly of spaghetti served in tomato sauce. 'Today for a change we've got tomato sauce and spaghetti,' the wags used to joke. For central Europeans not used to pasta, this menu was unpalatable and indigestible. Helle's little sister Maret became so desperate for variety that once she sprinkled sugar on the tomato sauce.

My father, who was always philosophical, said that a vegetarian menu was healthier anyway, while my mother, who like most Europeans found the gamey smell of lamb unpleasant, didn't miss the meat, but she couldn't digest the pasta. To add to her problems, I was a terrible eater. The smell of melting paint that permeated the ship took away my appetite, the sour taste of pickled vegetables made me feel sick, parmesan cheese reminded me of vomit, and I had to be coaxed to eat anything.

Of course the absence of meat didn't bother the observant Jews who had avoided it because it wasn't kosher. One of them was Leon Wise, a French orphan like Ginette. Although the last time he had seen his parents was eight years before, when they'd put him on a train to the safety of a children's home in France's unoccupied Vichy zone, he steadfastly maintained the dietary customs that he had learned at home. At fourteen Leon was the youngest in his cabin, but also the most fastidious. He kept his blanket tucked in, his sheets smooth and his clothes neatly folded, and was irritated by the sloppy habits of his cabin-mates. 'You've trodden on my blanket again and left dirty marks on it,' he would complain to André Wayne, whose bunk was above his. 'Can't you use the ladder?'

'That kid's nagging again,' André would groan. Abie Goldberg, who had one of the upper bunks in their cabin, also irritated his cabin-mates by hanging his suits in front of the porthole — which blocked the limited flow of air, they kept telling him.

Leon was a quiet, resolute boy who tried to work things out for himself, but a worrying situation had arisen on board. Several times while he walked along the narrow companionways, his path had been blocked by a flabby Greek seaman with receding hair and a fat face who stood sickeningly close and tried to kiss him. Although Leon couldn't understand what he was saying, the ingratiating smile and insinuating tone made his stomach churn. Being thin and wiry, Leon always managed to duck and run away. Although he lived in dread of these encounters, it wasn't something he felt he could discuss with his companions, not even his older brother Henri.

The ship was rolling more than usual when Leon finished tidying his bunk and ran out of the cabin to join his friends. Suddenly his way was barred. The old seaman was advancing towards him and before Leon had time to turn and run, he pushed him against the wall. Hardly able to see past the burly fellow, Leon tried to escape but the man started fumbling with his belt, bent his flabby face towards his and reached out his large hand to fondle him. With a sudden surge of strength, Leon broke away and sped down the stairs, his heart hammering in his ears.

He made straight for the barber's salon. Vincent Buignez was a twenty-seven-year-old Marseillais, one of the few people on board with whom Leon could speak French. The tall young barber had the sympathetic nature and easy flow of conversation that went with his profession, and the boy felt at ease with him. A pretty young woman who was having her fair hair rolled in curlers smiled up at him, and he recognised her from the purser's office where she worked. The penetrating smell of peroxide hit his nostrils as he flung himself into a chair, panting.

'*Qu'est-ce qu'il y a, mon petit?*' asked the barber, putting down the curling tongs when he saw that the boy was white and gulping air.

Leon didn't need to say very much for the barber to grasp the situation. '*Vieux salaud!*' he spat in the imagined direction of the molester. 'He'll come after me again, I know it,' Leon said.

A hard look replaced the barber's usually affable expression. 'Don't worry, he won't bother you again. Leave it to me. Just tell me what he looks like.'

A few days later, Vincent sent a message for Leon to come down to the salon. He froze when he saw his stalker sitting in the barber's chair but Vincent turned to him with a surreptitious wink. 'Is this the man you told me about?' he asked in a loud voice dripping with menace. When Leon nodded, the barber began to sharpen his razor very slowly on the leather strop without saying a word. He was still sharpening it when he put his face very close to that of his client.

'See that boy?' he murmured. 'See this razor? If I ever hear you've touched him again, I'll cut your balls off!' While a bead of perspiration broke out on the man's domed forehead, Vincent turned to Leon and said loudly, 'If this bastard ever bothers you again, you just come and tell me, okay?' Leon left the salon feeling more light-hearted than he'd felt in weeks. He ran up the stairs two at a time until he reached the deck where his friends were singing folk songs.

I heard the sound of young people laughing and singing while I stood beside my father as he lit a cigarette, inhaled and pointed to the sea. 'This is the Indian Ocean,' he said, and I could tell from his tone that he found this quite exciting. To me it looked no different from any other water we had sailed on, but the concept of oceans intrigued me. How did they know where one sea ended and another began? Was there a sign in the water, a mark of some kind? And all the waves that flurried the surface of the ocean as far as I could see, where did they begin and where did they end? Was it over there, on that straight line dividing the sea from the sky? My father shook his head. 'It isn't really a line at all, it's an illusion,' he explained. 'You always see it in the distance but you can never reach it.'

I stared at the vast sea that had no beginning and no ending, and grappled with this perplexing idea. If each of those little waves was part of the ocean and each ocean was connected with every other ocean, and there was no dividing line between the sea and the sky, it was really all one thing. I looked down at the waves that slapped the side of the ship, one at a time. Did they know that they were part of a huge ocean, identical to every other wave, or did they think they were unique? My father smiled indulgently at my questions and hastened inside to play bridge with Dr Ament and Mr Potok while I went back to my knitting. By now I had used up all the skeins I'd brought with me. Since my resources were so limited, I had to begin unravelling what I had knitted and use the wool again. Perhaps this time I would drop fewer stitches or at least make the gaps less obvious.

As I sat next to my mother and Zofia Frant and rewound the wool, I caught a few words of their conversation, although from their lowered voices and the occasional glances they cast in my direction, they obviously didn't want me to overhear. Mrs Frant was a tall, stately woman with crinkled reddish hair and a slightly worried expression in her short-sighted eyes. People often came to her for advice because she was forceful, kind and down-to-earth. 'We found another couple skylarking in the lifeboats last night,' she was telling my mother, and they launched into a discussion of the problems of chaperoning young people eager to make up for lost time. Their youth had been taken away from them along with everything else they'd ever had — freedom, security, parents, grandparents, brothers and sisters, schooling, home. And now that life was momentarily carefree, and they had no parents watching them like the other teenagers on board, nature had reasserted itself. Mrs Frant didn't begrudge them their romances but she was keenly aware of the responsibility of being a chaperone to sixty-one lively youngsters.

Seeing little Ginette run past, she chuckled, recalling what the child had said at dinner the previous night. 'You know why the waiter is so nice to me? Because he thinks I'm your daughter!' She was touched because she knew that behind this spontaneous comment was the yearning to be part of a loving family. She and her husband had become very attached to the affectionate little girl who often cuddled up to them.

Zofia Frant and my mother had a great deal in common. Both had come from assimilated Jewish families in Poland, were married to professional men and had one daughter. They spent much of their time discussing their plans for Australia although neither of them knew much about it. Before leaving Paris the Frants had searched for any books they could find but had only found stories about convicts, houses built on stilts and Aborigines.

'It was my destiny to come to Australia,' Zofia said in her low, well-modulated voice. 'Back in 1935 my father had filled out the application form. He told my mother that the ground was starting to burn under their feet in Poland and that they should leave as soon as possible. Unfortunately my mother wouldn't listen.'

The Frants were heading for Sydney because foreign doctors only had to study for three years there instead of five in Melbourne. Unlike Zofia, my mother didn't know how my father would earn his living. At forty-seven he thought he was too old to study dentistry again, especially in a foreign language. Someone in Paris had told him that buttons were needed in Australia, so he had bought a second-hand button-making machine and planned to go into business. Discussing this with Zofia, my mother raised her straight eyebrows so high that her brow furrowed, and her grimace showed clearly what she thought of that idea. 'Henek is a wonderful dentist but he has no business sense whatsoever. He's too straightforward.'

Another subject that preoccupied them was their daughters. Like me, Christine had survived the Holocaust in Poland by posing as a Catholic, but while I had stayed with my parents the whole time, she had been separated from hers. When the children interned in the Warsaw Ghetto were about to be deported and killed, Christine was smuggled out. She spent the rest of the war with her devoted Polish nanny who risked her life by taking care of her and pretending she was her illegitimate daughter.

Not long after the Frants had arranged for Christine to be smuggled out, they were pushed into cattle waggons bound for the Treblinka extermination camp. Knowing the fate that awaited them, they had made a pact to commit suicide rather than be pushed into a gas chamber, and Dr Frant had hidden a phial of morphine and a syringe in his pocket. As the cattle truck rumbled towards its destination, he was about to inject his wife when one of their fellow passengers shouted that he had managed to file through an iron grille that barred the small opening. With feverish help from the other occupants, the grille was pulled out and one by one they jumped out of the speeding train; Zofia first, then her husband. Dazed and bleeding, they stumbled through the fields until they came to a village. The priest who opened the door to their timid knock refused to let them in or even to give them a glass of water. Afraid of being discovered by the villagers and turned over to the Germans, they hid in the forest for days until the partisans found them.

Zofia looked over at Christine, a smiling eleven year old with pink cheeks and thick dark plaits, playing rummy with Topka's youngest sister, and confided to my mother that she was worried about her daughter. After all the traumas and upheavals she had suffered, how would she adjust to life in a new country? My mother's reply was characteristically positive. 'I'm sure she'll be all right. Children adjust more quickly than you think.' Perhaps she was thinking about me as I cast on stitches quietly beside her, mistaking my docile demeanour for adjustment.

Every evening Dr Frant would make the rounds with his torch. Its beams swept into the shadowy nooks and crannies of the ship as he lifted up the lifeboat covers, usually accompanied by Topka. He only had to rest his piercing gaze on her for a moment and call 'Topka!' and she would drop whatever she was doing and come running. At first this peremptory manner and the penetrating gaze that seemed to bore into her skull had scared her, but it didn't take long to realise that underneath his gruffness he was very kind.

Dr Frant's hated torch became the subject of plots among the orphans, who resented this invasion of privacy. One night the torch disappeared mysteriously, never to be seen again. Despite intensive questioning, the culprit was never found.

The orphans were not the only ones who embraced in secluded corners of the ship. Married couples also searched for places where they could release the pent-up sexual frustration that resulted from the segregated sleeping arrangements. Some of the men smuggled wives into their cabins during the day, but privacy eluded them whenever the other occupants returned unexpectedly for a jacket or a book. Although some couples modestly curtained the bunk off with a sheet, the creaking and murmuring gave them away, much to the merriment of the teenage boys. 'Look, there they go again!' André Wayne would laugh, pointing in the direction of the swaying bunk. Desperate to find a private place, some couples chose the washroom in the vain hope that late at night it would be deserted. Elsie Pataky, who was pregnant, frequently used the bathroom at night and would walk in to find a couple in transports of lusty delight in the bath. Mothers wanting to use the bath late at night to rinse out dirty clothes were sometimes astonished to discover that it was otherwise occupied.

Elsie didn't need to spend much time washing clothes because all she had was the white blouse and navy pleated skirt she wore every day. Her sandals had already fallen apart and she'd had to toss them away and go barefoot. She had been even further advanced in pregnancy than Halina Kalowski when the voyage began, but because of the privations she had suffered while waiting for a passage, she only weighed forty-seven kilos, so no one suspected that she was six months pregnant. As the weeks passed, she accommodated her expanding belly by unpicking the pleats one by one.

On a ship full of people who had crossed many borders and led complex lives, Elsie's ethnic background was more unusual than most. Born in Poland to an English mother who had been brought up in India during the days of the Raj, Elsie had grown up in Romania where most of her mother's family lived. From her intensely patriotic and monarchist mother, she inherited her love of King and Empire. When faced with the need to leave Europe, she knew that the only countries she would consider migrating to were those coloured on the map in the comforting pink of the British Empire.

When the war ended, Elsie had found herself alone in Romania. By then her mother had died of typhoid, and most of her relatives, who had British passports, had been repatriated to India and England. Having been adopted by her Romanian stepfather, she had lost her British citizenship and was stranded. With the Communists in power, food scarce, and Russian soldiers prowling around in search of women, she didn't feel safe and didn't know what to do. In desperation she even thought of marrying someone in India by proxy so that she could emigrate, but when she fell in love with Ignac all her problems were over.

They moved to Vienna and married in April 1948: he in a heavy coat and white hose under knickerbockers, a flower in his button hole and a soft wide-brimmed hat pulled down over his narrow face; Elsie wearing a picture hat over her thick dark hair, a bouquet of spring flowers and a happy smile. The following day a landing permit arrived from her aunt and uncle in Brisbane.

Not long before leaving Vienna, they saw a movie called 'Bush Christmas' with Chips Rafferty, which formed their image of Australia. Wide open spaces, children riding horses ten miles to the nearest school, boiling the billy and making damper at bush picnics — that's what they expected to find. From her aunt's letters they already knew that Ignac would be earning eight pounds a week, and tried to figure out how long it would take them to save up for a horse and buggy.

Elsie's uncle, who had been the financial adviser to a maharaja, paid 500 pounds for their passage to Australia. When Elsie and Ignac were notified that they should leave at once, she had just done the washing. There was no alternative but to stuff all the wet clothes in a suitcase and travel to Innsbruck on the first leg of their journey. They were so destitute that when Ignac found a piece of mouldy bread on the street, he swooped on it and brought it home. They washed it carefully and shared it, relishing every mouthful. While waiting for the ship, they met Kurt Herzog and two other young men who were waiting too. When Kurt realised that Elsie and Ignac didn't have the money for a hotel room, he bullied the others into donating a few marks so that the newlyweds could have a room to themselves.

Next day Elsie went to the Jewish welfare office in town and pushed her belly out to emphasise her pregnancy. She returned to the hotel jubilant, loaded up with food for them all.

The Australian immigration officer warned them not to let their travel documents out of their sight on the way to Marseilles, no matter what happened. 'When you go through the checkposts, the Russians might ask for them, but don't let them take your papers or you won't get them back,' he stressed. On the train, a menacing Russian soldier with a pistol in his belt demanded their documents and they had to obey. As he strode away with them, Elsie became hysterical. 'We'll

never get to Australia now. They'll send us to Siberia,' she kept saying
while Ignac and Kurt tried to calm her down. After what seemed like
hours, the Russian guard finally returned and handed back their papers
without a word.

In the twenty-four-bunk cabin she shared with Elfriede and Ilse Hof,
Vala Seitz and her daughter Pauline and Gilda, Elsie slept in a bunk on
the bottom tier, just above the engine room. The intense heat rose
through the floor and caused her to break out in an itchy rash that
tormented her every night. As her bitten nails were too short to give
any relief, she kept a comb under her pillow for scratching. When she
wasn't getting up to go to the toilet in the washroom, she was scouring
her skin with the comb, and in the morning she was so sore and
exhausted that she could hardly move.

In that cramped cabin, the frequent arguments between Mrs Seitz
and her small daughter broke the tension. The temperamental mother
would shout at her daughter in rapid, voluble Russian, while little
Pauline would answer back in equally voluble German which made
them all laugh.

Elsie's stories about her encounters with love-making couples in the
washroom provided another source of merriment. But those who
continued their nocturnal trysts on deck risked becoming the object of
the chief purser's punitive attitude. Like the self-appointed abbot of a
monastic order, Adnan Molvan took it upon himself to enforce the
separation of the sexes. Couples in the throes of passion would
suddenly find their blanket pulled off and see a stocky little man
looking down at them. When Cyla Ferszt and her husband Max
escaped to the relative seclusion of the upper deck one night, a light
suddenly shone in their faces. Staring down at them, the chief purser
grabbed hold of their blanket and tried to yank it off, hissing, 'Not
allowed! Go back to your cabin! You're not allowed here!'

Cyla was a sensual woman who adored her handsome husband. She
had fallen in love with him at first sight when she was a schoolgirl and
he was a debonair, successful society photographer in Warsaw, but the
thought of being discovered by the insolent chief purser on his nightly
crusades made her anxious. Besides, the last thing she wanted was

another pregnancy. As it was, Slawa, their three year old, was a handful on the boat, fretful and miserable, and it took a long time to settle her down at night so that they could slip away.

Adnan Molvan was probably the most hated officer on board. And his wife, whom he had brought on the voyage ostensibly as a nurse, was equally unpopular. Passengers often complained to Colonel Hershaw that these two sneaked around the decks at night, spying on the passengers and waking them up to check whether they'd paid for their hammocks or deck chairs, because the chief purser augmented his income by charging passengers three pounds per deck chair. They reported that some nights Mrs Molvan's speech was slurred and raucous, her gait unsteady and her breath reeked of alcohol. Uncouth and arrogant, the pair behaved like prison guards, which only reinforced the impression many passengers had already formed, that they were interned on a floating prison run by disorderly and incompetent jailers.

Things came to a head when one of the pregnant women confronted Colonel Hershaw and insisted that something had to be done about this outrageous pair. She complained that the previous night they had woken her up in the early hours of the morning, pulled the mattress out from under her, and kicked until she let go of it.

Although the colonel didn't have much faith in the captain's ability to deal with the Molvans, he marched the chief purser and his wife up to the captain's cabin. He asked the captain to reprimand them severely and to order them to apologise to the pregnant woman. 'If I hear another complaint about their behaviour again, I want them locked up and put off the ship at the next port, so they can't upset any more passengers,' Colonel Hershaw stormed. Captain Papalas agreed with everything the escort officer said, and surprised him by giving them an unusually sharp rebuke. 'The old boy gave them a thorough overhauling,' the colonel rejoiced later. 'I only hope he does something about that hopeless doctor.'

Dr George Themelis was Colonel Hershaw's other *bête noire* on board. None of the passengers had any confidence in this medico who tried to remain invisible apart from occasional appearances on deck near the bar to worship the setting sun, as the colonel used to put it. Apart from the two hours a day that he consented to see patients, the sick bay was closed. On one occasion, when a passenger became seriously ill, Colonel Hershaw had to threaten him before he would unlock the sick bay and see the patient.

Rumours about him proliferated. Some of the crew members referred to him as 'Madame Kornelia,' implying that he was homosexual, while others whispered that he didn't have time to see patients because he was dallying with a Latvian passenger who did not allow her husband's presence on board to deter her from having a fling. This led others to speculate, somewhat maliciously, about what would happen if the chief purser found the doctor *in flagrante delicto* on deck during his nightly rounds.

Captain Papalas was well aware of the incompetence of the doctor who was in charge of the health and well-being of almost seven hundred people. God only knew what would happen if someone became seriously ill, or if an epidemic broke out. He was grateful that Dr Frant was always willing to lance a boil, check someone's pulse and look after sick children. Then there was that German woman doctor Abrahamsohn whom the mothers used to consult about feeding problems. Fortunately Ceylon was only a few days away, and he assured Colonel Hershaw that as soon as they reached Colombo, he would discharge Dr Themelis.

12

Life on board consisted of loneliness and despair patched with a thin veneer of bonhomie and the numbing repetition of daily routine. Between the traumas of the past and the uncertainties of the future, anxieties fed on themselves and multiplied. What work would the passengers find when their only school had been a village pasture or walled-in ghetto, and their university a concentration *lager* or DP camp? Where would they live when they arrived? How would they manage in a country where they would not understand what people said?

Three weeks had passed since we'd left Marseilles and the general morale matched the sullen colour of the sea and sky. As though she had absorbed the anxieties of the passengers, the *Derna* limped along more slowly than ever in the torpid air. In the cabins, the temperature at night soared to thirty degrees. Pools of sweat formed beneath the passengers as they sat on deck, fanning themselves with pieces of paper folded into pleats. When it rained, water leaked into the cabins, formed puddles on the floor and damaged their few belongings. Without meat, the food had become more starchy and monotonous than ever. My mother, along with other Polish passengers, had bought tins of sardines from the hawkers in Aden and supplemented our stodgy diet with sandwiches she made in the cabin, chopping up the onions she obtained from the kitchen.

Drinking water became a major problem. After Aden, it had a brackish taste. Some passengers wondered whether the Egyptians had sabotaged our water supply, but others reasoned that it was probably because it came from artesian wells. Although we were always thirsty, the water tasted so musty that it was an effort to get it down. But the quantity soon became a bigger problem than the quality. Whether it was because they had miscalculated the amount of water required or because of the unexpected length of the voyage, water became rationed, so that it became increasingly difficult to get any for washing. Desperate for water to wash the baby, Sam Fiszman resorted to breaking the padlock on the kitchen door one night to take a jugful. When a crew member caught him, the captain recorded the incident in the log book and warned him not to damage the ship again or he would be locked up.

Early each morning, before the heat made every movement an effort, some of the Estonians gathered on deck for folk dancing and choir practice. Helle, who knew all the dance steps, demonstrated the jooksupolka with Uno Mardus. She was supple and light on her feet, and her long fair hair swung in time to the music as her feet trod the intricate steps of their traditional dances. The much-loved tunes from their youth brought memories of their native land flooding back and, with them, the hope of returning home one day. Under the direction of Pastor Stockholm's son, their voices joined together and brought the spirit of Estonia comfortingly close.

The Jewish youngsters sang too. Sometimes they sang the stirring songs of the pioneers who cleared the swamps of Palestine to transform the Promised Land into reality. They would join hands and dance while they sang 'Hava Nagila' and 'Avenu Shalom Aleichem'. Sometimes they sang spirited Polish, Russian and Czech folk songs from their childhood, about village lovers, the vastness of the steppes or the whispering splendour of birch forests. Drawn to their singing, I would sometimes stand at the edge of their group and listen. Their songs reminded me of the deep, resonant voices of the Russian soldiers who sang around the camp fire and carried us children around on their shoulders after they liberated my Polish village from the Nazis. I knew that throughout the war our lives had hung by a thread because the villagers threatened to turn us over to the Gestapo. My mother told me that if the Russians hadn't arrived when they did, we probably wouldn't have survived.

Every night the teenagers met at the bar. The few who had money would occasionally buy a cassis and soda or a lemonade from the broad-shouldered young French barman Jean-Pierre, whose physique the young girls admired. In this area, which they nicknamed Pigalle, they played the same few records over and over again, held each other tightly and closed their eyes while they danced. On those magical nights, when the salty sea breeze ruffled the girls' hair and tickled the hairs on the boys' arms, they forgot the hideous blue numbers tattooed on their forearms. Life beckoned like a moonlit road and everything was possible.

Fred Silberstein danced with Magda Reich who seemed to have everything: intellect, personality and looks. As they moved slowly around the deck, he tried to blot out the fact that after the voyage they would probably never see each other again. Magda and her brother, who were in Dr Frant's group, were going to Melbourne while he was heading for New Zealand. She was determined to study, and from the long, earnest discussions they often had about philosophy, literature and history, he had no doubt that she would do well in any field she chose. Fred had a dream too: to become a chef, but how he would achieve that he had no idea.

The desire to become a chef had originated in the strangest of circumstances. In the summer of 1942 in Berlin, just as he was coming out of school one afternoon, a man in a long coat and hat had suddenly blocked his way. Without saying a word, he grabbed Fred's left shoulder and pushed him into a car that sped through the city until they reached Gross Am Wannsee, a lake he had often visited in summer with his parents. But this was no holiday treat. That afternoon his life changed forever. He was no longer a schoolboy with caring parents and a comfortable home, but a slave labourer among strangers.

Thrown out of his sheltered, loving home and into this brutal environment at the age of fourteen, Fred was shocked by the torrent of abuse screamed by the SS guards who called him a filthy stinking Jew or *Schweinhund*. He staggered under back-breaking blocks of stone he hauled in the grounds of the colonnaded villa that was the headquarters of the Nazi elite.

Occasionally a slim Nazi with a narrow face and prominent nose would stop in the grounds and crack jokes with the guards about how good it was to see the Jews working. From photographs he had seen in the newspapers, Fred recognised him as Adolf Eichmann and was amazed to hear him addressing the prisoners in Yiddish from time to time. Eichmann had been sent to Palestine in order to become better acquainted with the culture and character of the people whose genocide he was about to organise. What Fred didn't know was that five months earlier, in this very place, the architects of the Holocaust had drafted their blueprint for the Final Solution. Its implementation was to become Eichmann's achievement and ultimately his death warrant.

On New Year's Eve 1942, hundreds of high-ranking Nazis were invited to a party. After a day spent lugging rocks in the grounds, Fred was ordered to help in the kitchen. The chef was a terrifying drunken Nazi who made Fred's hands shake. Holding up a razor-sharp knife, he would stand so close that his alcoholic breath made the boy's eyes smart. 'If a Pole or a Jew ever answers me back, want to know what I do?' He made a swift slicing motion with his knife. 'I cut their tongue out. So watch it!' Washing the dishes that rattled in his hands, Fred hoped he wouldn't drop anything, while the chef ranted and threatened in his slurred voice as he lurched around the cavernous kitchen.

They were still preparing for the reception when two men strode into the kitchen, took the chef by the arms and dragged him outside. Then they turned to Fred, who had flattened himself against the cupboard to avoid being noticed. 'Come here!' one of them roared. 'You finish the cooking, quick!' Spurred on by terror, Fred summoned up whatever he could recall and, using his imagination and culinary instincts, proceeded to bake dozens of German doughnuts filled with cheese, knowing that his life was over if his memory failed him. It was only after he had finished, long past midnight, and was rewarded by a rare treat, a big enamel mug of black coffee and one of his doughnuts, that the irony of the situation struck him. They had relied on a Jewish boy to come to the rescue by cooking for the Nazi elite.

Despite living in constant fear, Fred made one personal statement of resistance at Wannsee. While planting iris bulbs in the garden beds under the nose of the brutal guard, he wondered what the Nazis would do next spring when they looked out of the window and saw that the flowers outside their headquarters formed the six-pointed Star of David.

But he never found out because in February 1943 he was deported to Auschwitz. With his fair hair, regular features and bright blue eyes, Fred fitted the image of the idealised Aryan far better than most of the SS officers who gathered there to discuss how to rid the world of the Jews. As he was being pushed into a truck destined for the death camp, one of the guards whispered, 'This is your last chance. Stop being Jewish. You could easily pass as an Aryan. Run away and join the Hitler Jugend and save yourself.'

Without hesitating even for an instant, Fred shook his head. He wasn't going to pretend he was one of them. A Buddhist sage once said that when faced with a difficult decision, one should always choose the harder path. But split-second decisions are not made by conscious thought processes and in the nightmarish years that followed, Fred sometimes wondered why his unconscious had opted for the difficult path instead of the easier one he'd been offered.

At the railway station they were packed into cattle trucks, jammed so tightly together that there was only room to stand. Doors clanged and were bolted behind them and the train moved off. Fred had no idea where they were being taken, but looking around at the others who were with their families, he ached with loneliness. When he heard some people talking about resettlement, he felt a surge of hope. Perhaps he would be reunited with his parents. For three days they travelled, locked in without food or water, tormented by hunger, exhaustion and thirst. But for Fred, who was painfully modest and fastidious, the most excruciating aspect of the journey was the degradation of having no toilet and no privacy.

It was early on a frosty winter's morning when the train finally stopped and shards of ice fell off the door as it was unhasped from the outside. They had arrived at Auschwitz. The glaring searchlights were diffused with yellowish fog. On the platform German guards were screaming, lashing people with whips and truncheons and yelling abuse, which Fred found more lacerating than the physical brutality. Straining at the leash, German shepherd dogs snarled as they bared their razor-sharp teeth. '*Los! Schnell!* Hurry up!' the guards yelled, whipping and beating them as they tried to get out of the waggons. In all the noise and confusion, he heard them shouting, 'Women, children and old people to the left; men to the right!' He watched families hugging and kissing as they were parted, the women carrying their children.

As he was shunted along with the other men, someone whispered in his ear, 'Tell them you're older.' Fred had no idea what he was talking about. He'd been brought up to believe that lying was abhorrent and dishonorable, but a moment later when a high-ranking Nazi officer impatiently asked his age, without thinking he blurted out, 'Fifteen and a half,' instead of fourteen.

'How many bricks can you carry?' the officer asked. Fred didn't know what made him say five, but it was obviously the right answer because after giving him a vicious kick, the officer ordered him to join the men on the right.

Along with hundreds of others, he was pushed into a hut and told to strip and shower. Everything in Fred recoiled. Never in his life had he been naked in front of strangers, but the stinging whips of the guards and the ferocious snapping of the dogs made refusal unthinkable. After an icy shower they were given no towels, but coarse striped uniforms with no underpants or shoes. Their hair was shaved by rough hands and questions were answered by beatings and curses. Hell had no room for the word 'why'.

Dazed by the surreal scenes and inexplicable behaviour all around him, Fred heard someone yelling at him to hold out his left arm. While guards stood around ready to quell any trouble, a man behind a table pricked tiny dots into his skin with what looked like a long Waterman pen. Numb with shock, Fred saw that it was a number: 106792.

'You're not a name any more,' the man jeered. 'From now on you're just a number.'

It didn't take Fred long to realise that he had arrived at an efficient death factory where he didn't count even as a number. Half an hour's walk away was the industrial site called Buna where he became a slave in IG Farben's synthetic rubber factory. Every day the guards, who had the power of life or death over their prisoners, played their favourite game. They would snatch a prisoner's cap and toss it away. When the unfortunate man ran to retrieve the cap, because he knew he'd be flogged if he returned to camp without it, they would shoot him on the pretext that he'd tried to escape.

Because of the guards' sadistic activities, there were always dead bodies to be carried back to camp at the end of the day. Exhausted after the long day's hard labour, starved and aching after the strain of lugging the corpses, the prisoners were often ordered to stand motionless for several hours while the guards counted them. Any movement was savagely punished.

Only after the counting was completed were they allowed to return to their barracks for food, often to find that there was very little, if anything, left.

When he finally lay in the hard, narrow bunk he shared with another prisoner, his body wracked with hunger and exhaustion, Fred felt a faint flicker of satisfaction. He had managed to cross the minefield and survive one more day.

It was no wonder that some of the young boys accepted the protection of the Kapos, who, in return for sexual favours, allocated lighter work or handed out an extra piece of bread. Although Fred never considered this option himself, homosexuality was rife in the camps. Sex was the only commodity that prisoners had left in a world where everything else had been stripped away.

On Saturday afternoons, Dr Mengele would arrive with his doctor cronies at the Buna camp which was known as Auschwitz III and order all the prisoners to strip naked. Everyone trembled when Mengele appeared. He was a handsome man with a disdainful expression who had perfected a way of looking through them as though they were transparent, which in their emaciated state was not far from the truth.

During selections he would stand on a box to appear taller and more powerful while he and his acolytes scrutinised the bodies to decide who would live and who would die. No matter how ill they were, they tried to stand up straight and look strong because if you were sick and couldn't work, you were no longer any use and went up the chimney. Sometimes Mengele would ask for volunteers for some special task, but it was whispered that they were used for medical experiments. One of the older prisoners took Fred aside one day. 'Never ever volunteer for anything, no matter what they promise,' he warned.

On Sundays, Mengele carried out another type of inspection. Although the Nazis professed a horror of germs, in fact it was the overcrowded, unsanitary conditions of the camp, where no soap was issued and thousands of bodies were crowded in together, that caused infections to flourish. When an epidemic of pustular dermatitis broke out, the prisoners who sorted the clothes of the new arrivals were the first to get infected. Fred's ship-mate André Wayne was one of the clothes sorters who had to line up every week and show their hands to Mengele, while he peered for signs of the tell-tale pustules. If he spotted blisters on their hands, they were doomed.

They might get away with it one day by swiftly turning their hands over but the following Sunday there would be no way to hide the infection because it invariably spread. The unfortunate men being dragged away tried to feign indifference to their fate and appear strong, but a nervous tic on their cheek or a throbbing vein at their temple would betray their emotions. An hour later, smoke would billow from the crematorium.

Fred survived the selections until the day hunger made him reckless. When he heard that a hundred men were needed to volunteer for kitchen work, the idea of being closer to food and the possibility of getting an extra ladle of soup from the bottom of the pot where the precious vegetable peelings usually settled, made him forget the older prisoner's admonition. He was already lining up with the other volunteers when his mentor yanked him away from the group.

'Remember what I told you? Never trust their promises!' Fred was angry that this interference had deprived him of extra food, but the following morning the camp was buzzing with news. 'Those hundred guys went up the chimney last night,' someone told him.

Fred dragged himself from one endless day to the next. There was no hope, no faith and no God, and yet in the depths of his being he discovered the stubbornness to endure the dismal existence and deprive his tormentors of victory. But his grip on life was about to be severely tested. One Saturday in the summer of 1944, Dr Mengele pointed his well-manicured finger at Fred and before he had time to realise what was happening, the Kapos had hauled him off to the most dreaded barracks of all: Block 24, where the medical experiments were conducted.

They pumped fluid into his stomach, rubbed him all over with some foul-smelling liquid and poured kerosene down his gagging throat. Six men held him down while the surgeon started to slice open his groin without anaesthetic of any kind. Unable to move or make a sound as they cut him up in the name of medical science, Fred was in agony, remaining completely conscious throughout the torture. When the butchers of Auschwitz had completed their surgery, they rubbed some chemical into the raw wound and left. Three days later, when the incision had begun to heal, they returned, ripped his flesh open and injected him with a different chemical.

The experiment was devised ostensibly to find a swift method of healing wounds. Ever since the disastrous German campaign in Russia the previous year, when the Wehrmacht lost over 600,000 men, it was obvious to everyone except Hitler that Germany had lost the war, but he continued to send young soldiers on their hopeless mission. As the German losses increased, it became essential to discover some way of making soldiers recover from their wounds so that they could return to the front quickly. The inexhaustible supply of expendable Jewish prisoners made them ideal subjects for sadistic experiments which, it was later revealed, had served no purpose whatsoever as the doctors usually fudged the results.

As Fred's gehenna continued, he lost track of time. Lying nearby, other victims were yelling, screaming or moaning. All around them hung the indefinable scent of terror which was more palpable than the metallic smell of blood or the putrid stink of pus. Pain that no one would alleviate seared Fred's body day and night and he wished he could die. On a freezing November day, when the guard wasn't looking, he stole a sharp knife, concealed it in the bunk and sliced his wrists. As dizziness overtook him and consciousness slipped away, he waited for death to bring him peace at last. But when he opened his eyes and looked around, he realised with a shock that he was still alive. In that moment of epiphany, Fred knew that he was meant to survive and with that knowledge came a surge of strength.

Even though it was already January 1945, Fred still needed a great deal of strength to survive the last few months of the war. With the Russians advancing, the Germans were determined to erase all evidence of their crimes. After killing off those who were too ill to walk, they proceeded to herd the rest across Poland and into Germany, five abreast. Fred had typhus and infected wounds and some of his fellow inmates, who themselves were dying, placed him on a makeshift trolley which they pulled along the frozen road in the snow. When they reached Gleiwitz in Silesia, they were pushed into open cattle cars. By the time they arrived at Nordhausen in Germany, Fred's hearing had been irreparably damaged by the frost. The bodies of those who had frozen to the sides of the waggon or had starved to death were flung over the side.

As they were taken through the town to a small camp near the Luftwaffe airport, German civilians hurled stones and clods of dirt at them, called them dirty Jews and blamed them for the war. It soon became clear that they had been sent to this camp to die. Fred's job was to pick up all the dead bodies in the morning. He would load them onto trucks bound for the crematorium at the nearby Dora concentration camp, where the Germans made V1 and V2 rockets beneath the mountain.

Although these missiles were meant to attack England, few of them ever reached their target because the prisoners sabotaged them. Whenever the rockets failed in their mission, the Germans would hang 200 or 250 prisoners in reprisal. It was already March, they were given very little food, and hangings and floggings continued unabated. Those who became ill were dragged into a green-painted truck that was a mobile gas chamber.

Just when Fred thought he had seen and experienced every type of abuse and degradation, in the last weeks of the war at Nordhausen he witnessed cannibalism. Maddened with hunger, some prisoners cut up the bodies of those who had starved to death, but occasionally they administered the *coup de grâce* to the dying themselves, with a blow to the head. Fred watched as they lit a fire, put the pieces of stringy flesh on a stick and cooked them. He wondered if the following day they would be cutting him up, because he was too weak to defend himself. But no matter how ravenous he was, he never took part in these ghoulish meals. It offended his sense of human dignity.

By early April, the American army was coming closer and the sky was black with planes flying to Magdeburg or Dresden. During the bombing of Nordhausen, Allied planes hit the concentration camp by mistake and killed about 2500 prisoners who had survived the Nazi atrocities. When the bombardment ceased twenty-four hours later, Fred lay seriously wounded under the rubble of a collapsed building. Crawling out on his hands and knees, he was caught by a German, beaten up and left to die.

Two days later, he managed to escape. Staggering like a zombie, frozen to the marrow, injured and starving, he kept moving towards the town until he saw a green helmet and a rifle in front of him. Panic-stricken, he raised his arms and waited. When he realised that it was an American soldier, he collapsed. In the bushes behind them, about thirty Nazi soldiers were tearing off their uniforms and feverishly pulling on stolen civilian clothing.

When he woke up in a German hospital he did not believe that the Nazis had lost the war and did not trust the young German doctor who wore black jackboots under his long white coat. Several months later, when he was discharged from the hospital, he ran into an inmate who had also escaped from Nordhausen. The man looked at him as though he'd seen a ghost. 'Fred, you're alive!' he exclaimed.

'I may not look it but I am,' Fred replied.

'We held a funeral for you!' his friend said. 'After the camp was bombed, we assumed that you'd been killed with the others. Forty people came to your funeral!'

When General Eisenhower entered the camp, he ordered the townspeople to clean it up and bury the bodies in a mass grave before they were issued with ration cards. Fred stayed in Nordhausen for three months but after it was turned over to the Russians, he moved back to Berlin to search for his family. Not knowing that his parents had been killed, he kept waiting for them to find him.

In Berlin he joined the American Military Police and searched for former concentration camp guards. Some of them had obtained false papers from Jews they had killed and tried to get into the DP camps. One guard he picked up said, 'You know what Germany needs? Ten thousand Jews to come back and build the country up again!'

Another told him, 'Next time we'll be smarter, we won't leave so much evidence behind!' Some guards were bashed or killed by survivors, but Fred could not get over his horror of them and refused to touch them. Besides, he had faith in the democratic process of the Nuremburg trials, which he was invited to attend. It was a triumphant moment, to know that he had outlived his tormentors and was able to help convict the war criminals. Only the top twenty Nazis were on trial, but Fred had a profound sense of satisfaction at seeing Goering and Hess marched into court. And it gave him particular pleasure to note that some of the American soldiers escorting them were black.

Although he was disappointed that Goering eluded justice by committing suicide, and that thousands of perpetrators were still at large, he felt that the trial vindicated democracy.

Now, as he twirled his sweetheart Magda around the deck in a tango, Fred recalled a very different dance he had attended shortly before leaving Berlin to board the *Derna*. He was chatting with some friends in a nightclub run by the Americans, when an attractive young woman came over, addressed him by name and asked him to dance. With a shock he recognised her as Irmgard Hauser, who had lived next door to him before the war. Like other German youngsters, she had joined the Hitler Youth and relished using her power to torment and humiliate Fred. When he declined her offer to dance, she looked brazenly at him and said, 'Maybe you can help me find an American so I can migrate to the United States?' Fred slapped her across the face and walked out, feeling better than he had felt for a long time.

His dancing partner on the *Derna* did not know what nightmares his smiling face and witty comments concealed. But Magda had nightmares of her own, as the blue number tattooed on her forearm revealed. That dated from her internment at Auschwitz, where she had looked after an adorable girl called Esther.

Esther Fiszman was taking a rare stroll around the deck with Sam. Attracted by the happy sound of young voices singing to the accompaniment of a guitar, she drew closer, then stopped and stared. Sitting beside a fair-haired fellow was the young woman who had saved her life in the camp. She often thought about Magda but never expected to see her again.

With an excited cry, she rushed over to her and the two young women hugged each other. 'I can't believe it's you, that you're here on this ship!' Esther kept saying, tears filling her eyes. 'I've thought about you so often!' She began to recall the time Magda had saved her life by hiding her in the camp laundry when she had typhus, but Magda did not want to talk about it. She was determined to put the past behind her.

Most of the concentration camp survivors on the *Derna* felt the same way. The tattooed number that was the legacy of the camps belonged to a world that they had left behind, along with the ashes of their parents and the humiliation, terror and pain they had locked away and marked 'never to be opened'.

There were no words, when it was all over, to describe what they had seen and suffered. No language could express what you felt when you saw your mother and little sister led away, to emerge as sweetish smoke from a tall black chimney. No words to explain how it felt to be forced to watch young boys having a noose slipped over their thin necks, or to see young women tortured and humiliated in public. To survive, you were forced to sort the clothes of the dead or cart people from the gas chambers to the crematoria, even when you could detect a faint pulse threading beneath the bluish skin. The shame you felt because you hadn't been able to stand the gnawing pain of hunger and became a Kapo's favourite for an extra piece of bread.

And if they were willing to talk, who would want to know the hideous way the Nazis had redefined human nature, the depths to which human beings could sink, and how easily apparently normal people could become monsters of cruelty? They were the messengers who had returned from hell, and their message was that those in charge were not devils with horns, but people whose ordinariness was their most chilling characteristic. If they'd been willing to examine the meaning of their own survival, they would have realised that it also illustrated the strength of the human spirit to endure and triumph over evil, but to find the strength to face the future they had to refrain from looking back.

Yvonne Engel had a softness and vulnerability that everyone responded to. Plump and affectionate, she was a girl everyone felt comfortable with. Which words could she use to describe what it had been like for her, when, at the age of twelve in Auschwitz, she had been pushed into the gas chamber? Naked, trembling, her thick hair shaved off, she was squeezed among screaming, terrified women and children, waiting for the gas to be piped through the ceiling and knowing that this would be the last place she would ever see.

Suddenly the door had opened and she was pushed from death into life because the usually efficient killing system had broken down. For once, Zyklon B had failed to blow through the vents.

No one guessed that Bob Grunschlag, who appeared so strong and confident, fought with the demons of the past every night and woke up covered in sweat and terrified of losing control of his bladder. In the nightmares, he was back inside the forest bunker in Poland, maddened by hundreds of lice, or staring at the faces of his dead companions crawling with fat white maggots. Sometimes he was running across the rooftops again to get away from village boys chasing him with pitchforks.

If André Wayne were to study philology all his life, where could he find the words to convey the anguish he felt when he saw his seventeen-year-old sister sent to the left? She had offered to hold a child for the tired woman next to her, not knowing that women with small children were automatically consigned to the gas chamber.

The boys on the *Derna* gazed longingly at Ella,* a spirited girl with a mass of strawberry blonde hair and a slim figure. No one knew that behind her carefree manner lay a snake-pit of memories she wanted to forget. At thirteen she'd been ordered to stand on a platform in the yard of the Gestapo headquarters in Slovakia while German guards pointed rifles at her. A prisoner had escaped and she was to be shot in reprisal. In front of her stood her father, his eyes a terrifying red, being held back by his companions from rushing towards her and sharing her fate. And while she was thinking, with a surprising lack of emotion, that this was the end, the execution order was rescinded and she was sent back to the cell.

A young man started singing and some of the orphans joined in. As a Russian folk song sounded all over the deck, Verner Puurand bristled. This singer had to be a Communist, sent to spread Bolshevik propaganda overseas. Harold Kapp, who had served with the auxiliary SS corps in the Wehrmacht, glanced over at the Jewish youngsters. Many of them had numbers tattooed on their arms, but he was sceptical about them. They had probably done it themselves, to make people think they'd been in a concentration camp.

---

* Her name has been changed at her request.

13

Like a cripple hobbling along an endless road, the *Derna* dragged itself through the waves. Captain Papalas dismissed complaints about the state of the engine and blamed our slow pace on the poor coal taken on in Aden. But when Verner Puurand looked around the engine room and saw the sluggish pistons and the amount of coal being shovelled by the sweating stokers, he didn't agree. 'It's the boiler,' he told his sons. 'They say the engineer is trying to fix it, but he hasn't got a hope. They'll have to wait until we get to Colombo.'

The children were bored with cards, bakelite dolls, Bibi books and the few games they'd brought with them. Vassiliki Fatseas and her brother Petro found a child's pram and wheeled each other around the deck at breakneck speed. This kept them amused until Vassiliki strained a muscle and doubled up in so much pain that her sister Mary was alarmed. While they waited for the doctor to appear, someone suggested that a light broth would help. Hours later Doctor Themelis put his head around the door of the cabin. Seeing that the patient was sitting up eating soup, he shot Mary a scathing look. 'I see you're all doctors now, so you won't be needing me!' And with that he turned and strode away.

While Vassiliki was recovering, Petro agreed to play hangman and noughts and crosses, even though he felt humiliated because she always won even though she was two years younger. To make the games more interesting, Vassiliki suggested playing forfeits with a naughty twist. Each time one of them lost a game, they had to take off an item of clothing she said, her dark eyes sparkling with mischief. Before long, Petro's shorts, shoes, shirt and underpants lay in a pile in front of his sister. 'Give them back!' he shouted and crawled into his bunk in embarrassment because she had hidden them all and wouldn't return them. Petro was forced to stay in bed with the sheet pulled up to his chin until one of their sisters rescued him.

With so little to distract them, even the slightest incident varied the monotony. Sometimes small silvery fish leapt out of the sea and landed on the worn timber deck at Peter Kraus's feet. The skinny six year old with his round glasses watched fascinated as they tried to lift themselves up, occasionally managing a low jump until they lay exhausted on the timber, their sheen fading as he watched. The ship's baker Michael, who liked Peter and his little brother Paul, often brought them freshly baked rolls because they hated the meals in the dining room. He even managed to produce a birthday cake for Paul when he turned four. Sometimes Michael twisted bits of bread on the end of fishing lines and the boys sat patiently at the stern, hoping to catch a fish.

Their mother Clara tried to keep them out on deck as much as possible. The child in the cabin was coughing more than ever and she was worried that her sons would become infected. 'You really must take him to a doctor as soon as we get to Colombo,' she told the mother, but the neglectful woman only shrugged and yawned.

'It's just a cough,' she said.

In between games of bridge that absorbed him for most of the day, my father would pore over an English textbook, trying to teach himself the tenses of verbs. *Catch, caught. Bring, brought. Teach, taught. Make, made. Do, did.* How could anyone remember a language that had more irregularities than rules?

Although he had never been in business and didn't know how to go about manufacturing buttons, he wasn't worried. Having survived the Holocaust in Poland against seemingly hopeless odds, he was confident that we would manage in Australia. He often bolstered up his bridge partner Leon Ament, who didn't know anyone in Australia and felt apprehensive about arriving alone in a strange country. Dr Ament had a rare combination of attributes — a spectacularly handsome appearance and an unassuming nature. With his fiery dark eyes and a small cleft in his chin, he bore a striking resemblance to the film star Tyrone Power, although according to my mother, that was a compliment to Tyrone Power.

Everyone talked about the future, but those who were skilled in a trade, like Harry Braun, felt more secure than the rest. Harry, who was one of the orphans, felt confident about earning a living as a dental mechanic.

'Everyone knows that the streets in Australia are paved with gold,' he used to joke with his friends André Wayne and David Weiss.

'But if this ship doesn't pick up speed, someone else will get to the gold before us!' one of them retorted. Many thought they were coming to a backward place where European skills and ideas would guarantee success, especially as they had heard that Australians didn't like to work hard and preferred to take things easy. Trying to outdo each other, they would boast, 'We'll teach those Australians a thing or two!'

'I don't care about making money,' Bill Marr would say. 'You know why I'm coming to Australia? Because it doesn't have any borders!'

The older Polish crowd thought that Max Ferszt had an enviable career because a photographer could always make a living. Max had been a society photographer in Warsaw, and Cyla had fallen in love with him at first sight while she was on holidays.

'He looked like a film star when we met,' she recalled. 'I was seventeen at the time and I couldn't stop looking at him. I'd never seen anyone so dashing in all my life. Luckily for me, there weren't any other girls staying at the hotel at the time, so he asked me to come for a sleigh ride in the woods. I don't know what got into me, but I started reciting love poems! After we parted, I wrote him silly schoolgirl letters but never expected him to reciprocate.'

Cyla always had a group around her, eager to hear her stories. She was a sensual young woman of ample proportions who attracted people with her zest for life and ringing laugh. She was an excellent raconteur, and her slow, lilting voice kept them fascinated as she described their courtship. On the day her hero stepped out of her dreams and appeared in Lodz, her home town, to visit her, she wore her best coat with a fur collar and waited at the station surrounded by her girlfriends who couldn't wait to see the paragon they had been hearing about for the past year. Two years later, when he proposed, Cyla was ecstatic.

But their married idyll was shattered soon afterwards, when war broke out. Shortly after invading Poland, the Germans had signed a mutual non-aggression pact with the Russians, dividing the country between them. Along with many other Jews in Warsaw, Max had been press-ganged to sweep roads, and after being savagely beaten up by the guards, he decided to flee from Nazi rule.

The western region remained part of the Reich while eastern Poland was occupied by the Russians. This pact was Hitler's masterstroke. It ensured that Russia would not declare war on him while German boots trampled over Europe. Meanwhile in Poland, where the Nazi persecution of the Jews had already begun, there was a mass exodus eastwards towards the Russian zone which offered some hope of survival.

At first, life for Cyla and Max under Russian occupation in Bialystok was relatively uneventful, but everything changed when they refused to accept Russian citizenship. Shortly afterwards, two agents from Russia's dreaded secret police, the NKVD, banged on their door at midnight and told them to pack a small case because they were to be sent back to Warsaw. Assuming that they would only be travelling for a few hours, Cyla brought a bag of sweets for the journey. But the following day, the crowded train was still lumbering through an unfamiliar landscape that didn't look anything like the Polish countryside. There were no sanitary facilities in their crowded waggon, no food, and only boiled water called *kipiatok* to drink while they sucked the sweets.

Three weeks later, the train ground to a halt. Standing bewildered at a desolate station surrounded by miles of wasteland, Cyla blinked in the unaccustomed sunlight and tried to get her bearings. They had come to a remote province of Siberia not far from Archangelsk where her ship-mate Anna Szput had been deported. But the journey was not over. For hours they sailed in a raft along the Wologda River until they arrived at a wilderness called Poldarsa. There was no sign of human habitation, only dense forests of birch, pine and alder stretching in every direction. 'This is where you will live and work from now on,' the camp commander announced. 'You will never see your beloved Warsaw again.'

Cyla and Max became slave workers at a labour camp. 'They handed us axes and told us to go into the forest and chop trees. If you didn't work, you didn't eat, that was the rule. None of us had ever held an axe or saw, and the ones they gave us were blunt so we all got terrible blisters,' Cyla recalled, stroking her hands as she talked. 'Every evening an overseer checked to see how many trees each working group had cut, and if you met your quota you were entitled to a plate of herring soup.'

Suddenly she laughed. 'Some of the prisoners became very crafty. The overseers put a notch on the bottom of each log they counted, but the following morning some of the inmates would saw off the part with the notch and pass those same logs off as the next day's work!'

After the men had sawn the logs, Cyla and the other women had to chop up the branches. As the forest gradually receded under their saws and axes, they had to trudge further and further to reach the trees and eventually she had to walk for eighteen kilometres to reach the birches and pines. The words that try to convey past sufferings are always inadequate. As she sat on the deck of the *Derna* near the equator, wiping the perspiration from her neck and dreaming of cool breezes and iced drinks, it was hard to recapture the torture of hands chapped and frozen, and bodies shivering under their padded cotton jackets in the merciless Siberian winter, as they wondered whether they would ever see their home again.

But although her eyelashes sometimes frosted over as she sawed, her feet felt numb and her bones ached with cold, Cyla's soul responded to the grandeur of that white landscape when snowdrifts covered the forest floor and plump pillows of snow glittered on the birch boughs. In summer, after the ice had melted, the forest bloomed and they picked blueberries and mushrooms from the soft loam.

Like Cyla and Max, and Anna Szput and her husband, many other Polish Jews on board the *Derna* had been deported to Siberia to become forced labourers in a harsh environment where medical aid was non-existent and no one cared if they lived or died. They struggled in freezing cold with hunger and disease, but the Russian guards were apathetic rather than cruel. Despising all the prisoners as either bourgeois exploiters or Nazis, they meted out the same punishment to everyone, not singling Jews out for annihilation as the Nazis did. The Baltic passengers who accused the Jews of being Communists did not realise that many of their Jewish ship-mates had been deported to Siberia for opposing Communism and had suffered the fate that they themselves had fled to avoid.

By the time Cyla and Max had built their barracks at Poldarsa, Hitler had crushed most of Europe and no longer needed Stalin's neutrality. Eager to begin his conquest of the hated Bolsheviks, he broke their non-aggression pact and invaded Russia in 1941.

Now that they found themselves fighting on the same side as the Allies, the Russians released the Polish prisoners. Although they were free to leave the labour camp, they received no food or money, only rough *mahorka* tobacco, and were ordered to remain in the Soviet Union as the war was still raging. Cyla and Max had no idea where to go. Everyone spoke of travelling south where the climate was more clement, but getting on a train was almost impossible. After walking for three days, they reached a station where thousands of people were crowded on the small platform, desperate to board the train. Although it was already jammed with people hanging out of the doors and windows as it pulled into the station, somehow Cyla and Max managed to push in. On the long journey, the train pulled into equally crowded stations where they traded their *mahorka* for bread.

Central Asia was splitting at the seams with refugees and each place they came to seemed more hopeless than the last. In Tashkent, Cyla was horrified by the mass of wounded, homeless people begging for a crust of bread, so on they went to Bukhara. Once a wealthy trading post for caravans laden with silks, spices and precious jewels on the ancient Silk Road, Bukhara had become a chaotic slum of desperate people as tens of thousands converged there from Siberian camps. With no means of supporting themselves, they slept in alleys, begged for food and when all else failed, they stole and cheated.

Like the other refugees, Cyla and Max had been forced to live by their wits to scrounge enough food to survive. When berries were plentiful, Cyla squeezed them, diluted the juice and sold glasses of cordial at the market. Another time, she made a few cucumber sandwiches to sell. 'I was always hungry and longed to bite into a piece of meat!' she recalled.

'Sounds just like the *Derna*!' quipped one of her ship-mates. A faraway look came into Cyla's eyes and she drew little Slawa closer. Three-year-old Slawa had been born in Bukhara with a twin brother who only lived for twelve days. When the war was over, and they were finally able to return to Poland, it hurt to leave the tiny grave so far away in Central Asia.

While Cyla talked, Max pointed his Leica at Slawa sitting on a deck chair with a pair of sunglasses perched on her little nose. Cyla was smiling again. 'That's the camera he bought in Bukhara,' she said. The Leica had rescued them from poverty and hunger, as soldiers would queue up to be photographed. Snub-nosed boys called Ivan and Boris would pose self-consciously in their shabby uniforms and later marvel at their own image on the paper. They all wanted their photos taken.

Another Polish passenger confident about the future was Hanka Pilichowski. Her eyes, Scarlett O'Hara green, were accentuated by titian hair twisted into a French roll and by an eau-de-nil scarf knotted at the throat. She was a couturière whose deft fingers were never still. She spent most of her time on board sewing stylish dresses by hand and embroidering silk lingerie. Her suitcases bulged with exquisite Parisian laces, buttons and fashionable accessories she had bought, knowing that these luxury items would be in demand in Australia. While chatting with her Polish companions, she made a pair of shorts for her ship companion Bronia Glassman, who didn't have anything cool to wear. Everyone said that Hanka would do well in Melbourne because its fashion-conscious women were said to be crying out for a high-class dressmaker.

Hanka and her husband were a striking couple who looked as though they'd been born to enjoy a privileged life. But only a few years before, Hanka had discovered a steel core inside herself that kept her alive. When she thought about it later, she realised that she had done some crazy things and taken enormous risks, but anger had given her courage. In the first few months of the war, she'd watched a German soldier beating up an old Jewish man in a Warsaw street. That's when she had resolved to fight the oppressors and never give up.

When her Catholic friend Jasiek, a resistance fighter, was wounded during the Warsaw Uprising in 1943, she put him on a barrow and pushed him through the ruins. They wandered from one town to another, right under the nose of the Germans who were searching for anyone who had fought in that doomed rebellion. Through the terrifying bombardment, she continued to wheel her friend around and managed to protect him from the Germans, even though she was on false papers and risked being caught herself.

During their wanderings through the devastated countryside, her skill with the needle helped them survive several times. By transforming Jasiek's white shirt into a nurse's uniform, she was able to obtain work at a hospital, which provided a roof over their heads and a little food, mainly carrots. Another time, she kept them alive by selling blouses and nightdresses she made out of tablecloths she found in a village church.

After the war, while working as a dressmaker in the Polish city of Lodz, she met the debonair Henryk Pilichowski and fell in love. Although their shipboard companions assumed from the gold band on her finger that they were married, they had never gone through a formal ceremony. She couldn't see the point. If two people loved each other, they didn't need a piece of paper to prove it. But she didn't disclose that to her friends on the *Derna* as she held up the white shorts she had just finished. They elicited a chorus of admiration for her talent, and assurances that she would be the most sought-after couturière in Melbourne.

Sitting a small distance away, Matylda Czalczynski was also optimistic about her employment prospects because she had completed a beautician's course in Paris. While her nine-year-old daughter

Karmela played with Haneczka and some of the other children, Matylda tried to comfort her cabin-mate Halina Kalowski who was worried about the *Derna's* slackening speed. She felt nauseated by the rocking, weary from the heat and anxious about her pregnancy, but Matylda's pleasant conversation helped to pass the time. Now she was chatting about that nice old Mrs Weile who was distraught because she had lost her wedding ring. Rousing herself from the deck chair, Halina joined in the search and, to the owner's relief, spotted the well-worn gold band in the washroom.

In the three weeks they had spent together, Halina had told her friend about her first husband who had saved the lives of his family, but had been killed in the last week of the war. Her heart ached for him because he had been such a good, unselfish man.

'I didn't even know where he was buried, but you won't believe it, one night the answer came to me in a dream,' she said in her quiet voice. 'Guided by my dream, we started searching until a gravedigger in a Polish country town remembered burying him!'

Dreams had also sustained Matylda through those terrifying years. Separated from her husband at the very beginning of the war, she had managed to keep herself and Karmela alive by posing as Christians, while she worked as a field hand in the Polish countryside. The one thing that had kept her going during those years of danger, fear and maltreatment was the certainty that, when the war ended, she would be reunited with her husband. She would fall asleep dreaming that his strong arms were enfolding her once more and that they would spend the rest of their lives together.

After being separated for six years without any contact, Matylda miraculously did find her husband, and felt as ecstatic as she had always known she would be. But her dream was shattered. Convinced that she must have died, he had formed a relationship with another woman who had recently given birth to their child. The shock Matylda had felt when she discovered this showed on her strained face as she spoke, staring blankly at the ocean. In a dull voice she said, 'He offered to leave the other woman so that we could be together again, but I couldn't accept that. I was too hurt. And I couldn't bring myself to build my happiness

top: About to board the *Derna* in Marseilles, 30 August 1948: (*r-l*) Cyla Ferszt, Slawa Ferszt (*in front*), Max Ferszt, Fela Feigin, Danny Feigin (*in front*).

bottom: Leaving Europe.

top: Anna and Henryk Szput, about to board.

bottom: Author's parents Bronia and Henek Boguslawski with Danusia (the author).

Sunbaking on the deck.

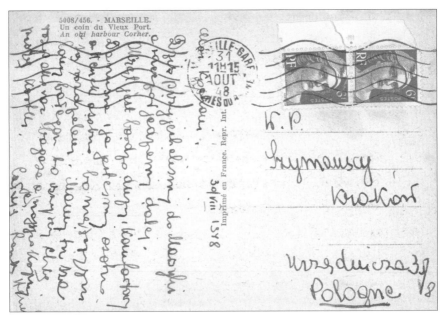

The postcard the author's parents sent from the ship in Marseilles, 30 August 1948.

top: Passengers from Kythera.
Front row: *(l-r)* Stan Travasaros,
Mattie Travasaros, Vassiliki Fatseas,
Petro Fatseas, John Comino. Back row:
(l-r) Mary Fatseas (*second from left*),
Stamatina (*last name unknown*),
Koula Travasaros, Katina Travasaros,
Betty Fatseas (*second from right, with
white collar*).

left: Sam Fiszman in Russian army
jacket with medals.

right: Miss Derna (Ginette Wajs) with first officer John Papalas during the Crossing of the Equator ceremony.

bottom: Archbishop Theodore Rafalsky.

(l-r) Charlie, Dick, Guta and Stelios Boundalis.

top: Bill Singer and Anton.

centre: The Italian girl (*left*) and Dorothea.

bottom: Front row: (*l-r*) Maurice Zilberger, Alice Zalcberg, Abie Goldberg. Back row: (*l-r*) Jindra (Kitchi) Heller, Yvonne Engel, Bill Singer, Ginette Wajsbrod, George Rakusan.

top: Helle Nittim with her brother Rein.

bottom: Fire drill on the *Derna*. Front row: *(l-r)* Bill Singer, Bill Marr, Eugene Grunstein, Peter Rossler. Back row: *(l-r)* Joe Neustatl, Jindra Heller (*third from left*), Anton.

Part of the orphan group in Perth with officials from the Jewish Welfare Society.
Front row: *(l-r)* Christine Frant, Ginette Wajsbrod *(third from left)*, Alice Zalcberg,
Kitty Lebovics, Topka Barasz, Bella Barasz, Ruth Barasz, Miriam Barasz. Back row:
(l-r) Walter Brand — General Secretary of the Australian Jewish Welfare Society
(second from left), Magda Reich, Marketa Kraus, Irene Grunstein, Zofia Frant, Ella,
David Absatz — Honorary Secretary of the Jewish Welfare Society in Melbourne,
Dr Henryk Frant, Ruth Klausenstock, Yvonne Engel.

Anita Freiberger, 1948.

High jinks on the *Derna*.

Cyla Ferszt and Slawa relaxing on deck.

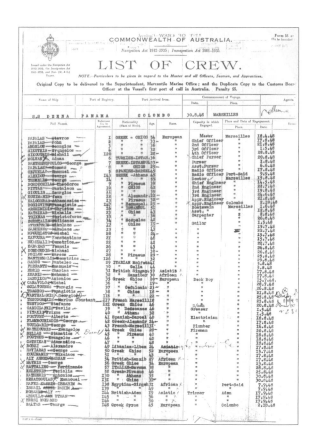

right: Part of the list of the *Derna*'s crew members.

bottom: Some of the crew.

top: Dorothea and Ogden Hershaw at a café in Port Said.

left: The Hon Lt-Colonel Ogden Hershaw (from IRO file).

left: First officer
John Papalas.

left: Silva Rae with purser George Parthenopoulos.

right: Ella.

top: The Estonian choir in Colombo. Front row: *(l-r)* Uno Mardus, Aino Liivat, Karl Liivat, Alide Kapp, unidentified boy, Maret Nittim, Selma Julie Nittim. Back row: *(l-r)* Heljo Valdas, Harold Kapp, Maria Nieman, Lydia Vink, Lea Ohtra, Oskar Jarvisto.

left: Captain Stavros Papalas, Dorothea Ritter and Alfred Weile in Colombo.

top: Skylarking on deck: Bob Grunschlag and Iziek Frenkiel.

bottom: Ready to disembark, 5 November 1948: Sala Salcberg (Szantal) and Morris Skorupa (Shell).

on the misery of another woman and child.' Her eyes filled with tears while Halina stroked her small cold hand in silence.

Was it possible for anyone to be completely happy again after this terrible war? Even though Halina had waited for eighteen months to find out what had happened to her first husband, even after she discovered that he had been killed, guilt tugged at a corner of her heart. Although she was happy with Mietek, in some irrational way she felt disloyal, as though she had abandoned her first husband and started a new life with another man.

The longer the voyage lasted, the more oppressive the heat became, causing more quarrels among the passengers. In the claustrophobic cabins, people complained that the other occupants were taking up too much room, scattering their belongings all over the place, or ruining their clothes. In the washrooms, women shouted at those who pushed ahead of them, left the showers and toilets filthy, or let their desperate children urinate on the floor. The plumbing in the toilets had never worked properly, so within two weeks the flushing mechanism didn't work, and the doors that didn't hang properly were sometimes wrenched off by passengers in frustration.

Out on deck, two enemy camps had formed and the adversaries eyed each other with suspicion, looking for evidence to support their criticism. A Jewish passenger sweeping in front of his deck chair sent clouds of soot onto an Estonian sitting downwind. An altercation ensued along ethnic lines, with the Jews complaining about the anti-Semitic Balts, and the Estonians muttering about pushy Jews.

Although this antipathy developed between the older generations, the young people were drawn towards each other despite their parents' warnings. Like Helle Nittim, some Estonian and Latvian girls found the Jewish boys attractive and lively with their guitars and songs, and the dances at the back of the deck led to romantic strolls and secret embraces on starlit nights. But any discussions about the war usually ended in stalemate. The Jewish youths, who had experienced the brutality of some Baltic guards in the concentration camps, wanted their ship-mates to at least acknowledge their nations' responsibility for collaborating with Hitler, but their arguments were met with defensive replies and a counter-litany of the atrocities committed against the Baltic states by Stalin.

Among the girls who attended the dances and enjoyed the company of the Jewish youngsters were Olga and Nina Matussevich. Although their parents spent most of their time in their cabin, they heard the ship gossip from their countryman Boris Arkadievich Sapojnikoff, a bear-like man with a deep voice who kept them enthralled with colourful stories from his days in the French Foreign Legion.

'They've found some of those Jewish youngsters cuddling in the lifeboats,' he boomed one day. The Matussevich parents resolved to keep a stricter watch on their daughters.

What they didn't know was that some nights Nina sneaked out to dance. She was a fun-loving sixteen year old with a full mouth turned up in constant laughter and fair hair braided on top of her head, and she enchanted Emil Kopel, one of the Czech orphans. The impetuous Nina was equally smitten and couldn't wait to see him. Sometimes she was accompanied by her older sister Olga, who liked talking to Kurt Reich and his sister Magda. But when the girls rushed back to their cabin at the end of the evening, afraid of being found out, Emil hoped that his sweetheart's father would not find out she had been socialising with a Jewish boy. The mysterious Russian couple who seldom left Cabin 14 and rarely mixed with their fellow passengers aroused curiosity among the other passengers who speculated about possible reasons for their aloofness. There were rumours that the girls were afraid of their strict father who beat them if they disobeyed him.

Rita Lindemanis had spent the past few days in her cabin because she had a boil on her nose and didn't want anyone to see her looking so ugly. Back on deck again, she found her friend Helle bent over some sewing. Helle was making some white shorts to set off her tan and couldn't wait to tell her friend about the romantic evening she'd had at the dance the previous night. The stern had been lit by three lanterns, tango music had sounded through the loudspeakers, and everyone was swaying to the slinky rhythm. One of the Italian stewards, Luciano, who was twenty-six and had been giving her soulful glances for some time, had grown bolder. Not content with eyeing her longingly, he had actually touched her hand. Helle was aglow with romantic possibilities.

But she wasn't the only one with news that day. From Rita's beaming face it was obvious she also had a story to tell. 'I've met this fantastic boy!' she burst out, hardly able to sit still. Philippe was tall, dark, handsome and very French. So exotic. And those smouldering eyes! Helle was intrigued. Where did this fellow spring from? Who was he? Moving closer to her friend, Rita whispered, 'He's a stowaway! Three of them sneaked on board in Aden. The captain knows about them. They're allowed out while we're at sea but they'll be locked up when we get to Colombo.'

Philippe Sauvage had been standing beside Rita one afternoon as she held onto the rail. Although she seemed to be gazing out at the ocean, she was lost in a daydream. She saw herself in Queensland, wearing a nurse's uniform, trim in her starched cap and apron, looking after patients the way those wonderful German nurses in Munich had looked after her. On her day off, she saw herself picking tropical fruit in her aunt's orchard.

She turned and smiled at the young man standing next to her, but couldn't follow much of what he said. She knew only a few words of French and English, while his German was equally poor, but mutual attraction overcame their linguistic deficiencies, and in a halting way that made them both laugh, they managed to communicate.

'He's very worried about what will happen when we get to Australia,' Rita confided to Helle. 'He's illegal, so they won't let him enter. They'll send him back.'

Helle remained unmoved. 'He should have thought of that before he stowed away,' she said.

But her soft-hearted friend shook her head. 'He had a terrible life there. He can't possibly go back.'

By now the romantic hothouse created on the long voyage had affected many of the passengers who had paired off, providing salacious gossip for their compatriots. The Estonians watched the glamorous Silva Rae strolling around the deck with the attentive Greek purser she was working with. Dorothea was spending more and more time with the first officer. Salezy Potok was regaled with comments about his daughter Alina from his censorious Polish acquaintances, who pointed out that her behaviour was giving her a bad reputation. But when he confronted her about spending too much time in the fourth officer's cabin, Alina was indignant. She insisted that Michael Sikoutris was just a good friend who let her iron her dresses in there.

Some of the married women, anchored to fidelity by the presence of their husbands, envied the freedom of the single mothers and nudged each other whenever one of them emerged from an officer's quarters after a rendezvous.

'You'd think that with a young daughter, she'd set a better example,' they sniffed. A Polish woman composed a ditty on the subject and circulated it among her friends.

> 'For an extra bowl of soup
> Or a slice of bread,
> Our female compatriots
> Will sometimes go to bed.'

On the afternoon of 24 September, the passengers were summoned for their first lifeboat drill, shortly after the crew had held theirs.

'That's a fine time to hold a drill, when we've been at sea for over three weeks!' Colonel Hershaw scoffed. Vassiliki and Petro rushed to their station, thinking this was going to be fun, when they ran into an old Greek woman who latched onto them because she was frightened. She was too old for this kind of exercise, she lamented. What if she fell into the water when they lowered the boats? A blind woman travelling with her daughter had become ill on board and was too debilitated to come out onto the deck. What would happen to her in an emergency? someone wondered.

To Helle's disappointment, the drill lasted only a few minutes. After showing them the assembly point for each cabin, a crew member demonstrated how they should put on their life vests, and dismissed them. By now it was common knowledge that one of the engines had broken down. 'We have to pray that the other two keep working so we never need those vests and lifeboats,' people muttered as they dispersed, wondering whether they could depend on this antiquated equipment and indifferent crew to save them if the need arose.

'They didn't even lower the boats or test the tackle,' Colonel Hershaw commented to his companions afterwards, shaking his large head in disdain. 'I only hope that the lifeboats are more seaworthy than the *Derna*!' But some of those who had already examined the lifeboats at close quarters when lying concealed inside them with their sweethearts, had noticed chinks of light shining through parts of the gunwale, and doubted whether they'd stay afloat.

'Nothing would surprise me about this ship,' Colonel Hershaw would comment, puffing on his meerschaum pipe. The carelessness of the crew defied description. He'd often had to call a seaman over and point to a hatch left open close to a ladder or to a companionway where children were playing. He often noticed booms and derricks swinging free, which could have given unsuspecting passers-by a nasty thump and sent them flying. And even when they were secured, it was only with a flimsy bit of cableyarn. Poking around the ship, he noticed that funnel stays were tied on with rope thinner than that used for clotheslines. When he pointed out an open space in a railing, where he'd recently grabbed hold of two small children who could easily have gone overboard, someone later closed the gap with a piece of twine! It took some forceful language in an officer's ear to get it securely fixed. The inexperience, laziness and irresponsibility of most of the crew were disgraceful, and he intended to submit a detailed report about it at the end of the voyage.

While ruminating about the appalling state of this vessel, Colonel Hershaw looked up and saw that young Jewish couple talking to the two sailors again. Verner Puurand agreed that there was something very odd about them. And as for those Communist propaganda songs that they had been hearing lately, he'd certainly have something to say about them in his report.

14

Colonel Hershaw and Verner Puurand were correct in observing that the only people Guta* and her husband Dick spent their time with were two seamen. The young couple sat there day after day, hardly moving from their spot on the portside deck, talking only to Stelios Boundalis, the young Greek carpenter, and Charlie, the grey-haired Asian deckhand. Their friendship had begun when Stelios noticed them sitting by themselves under the blazing sun. He had been hammering away on deck, fixing one of the many loose planks that passengers often tripped on, and was intrigued by the wistful expression of this young woman with crinkly ash-blonde hair and a nose with a curiously flattened bridge.

Stelios was an outgoing fellow in his mid-twenties with a big smile. He bawled maudlin Greek songs at the top of his voice while he fixed doors, nailed planks and repaired lifeboats. With a combination of slapstick, mime and goodwill, he managed to convey his offer to erect a little awning for this forlorn couple, and was rewarded by a grateful smile.

Day and night Guta and her bespectacled husband sat on the forward deck to escape not only their stifling cabins but also their

---

* Her name has been changed at her request.

fellow passengers. Wiping the perspiration from her neck, Guta gazed around with the bewildered expression of a child who is lost in a dense forest and can't find her way home.

According to her birthdate she was eighteen, but sometimes it seemed as though she had lived for a hundred years. She breathed in the bracing smell of the sea and pinned her gaze onto the rocking waves whose motion soothed her mind. As the buzz of conversation from the Polish group sprawled out on deck chairs wafted towards her, she reflected that she no longer spoke the same language as her compatriots. They seemed so confident, capable and articulate that she didn't even have the courage to try. She had lost the art of communication just as she had lost so many other skills that life required, and felt as though her inadequacies were emblazoned on her forehead for all to see.

But she didn't feel inferior to Stelios the carpenter. He always stopped to talk to her and Dick as he passed, and treated her as though she was quite normal. Sometimes at night when he was off duty, he brought his guitar and sat at her feet, serenading her. He made it his job to bring a smile to her face by bellowing his favourite Mexican song and changing the heroine's name to Guta.

Stelios's mate Charlie became the fourth member of their close-knit unit. One of the oldest seamen on board, he had skin like polished mahogany and a roguish grin. Charlie's origins were a mystery but, like a character from a Conrad novel, he'd spent his life sailing to exotic places on freighters and steamers, and had lived through enough escapades to fill a dozen adventure books. Charlie had slaved on the Panama Canal at the turn of the century, and told them terrible stories about the hardships he'd suffered during the construction which had claimed thousands of lives.

Guta was grateful for the company of these two men. At times she felt like that wolf-boy they had found in Poland after the war, who had lived for years with a pack of wolves and could only crawl on all fours, grunt and growl. The women's talk of cake recipes, clothes, hair styles and love affairs all seemed as incomprehensible to her as the laws of gravity would have been to the glittering fish that sometimes jumped out of the sea and landed at her feet.

In the bestial world from which she had recently emerged, speech had been reduced to its most primitive elements. Stripped of all ornamentation, delicacy and nuances of meaning, basic communication consisted of abbreviations, vocal short-hand, grunts and curses. Nothing existed except survival, and that demanded total concentration. In a world where evil reigned unchecked, the refinements of language had been irrelevant.

Nine years had passed since the carefree nine-year-old girl from the Polish city of Poznan, whose indulgent parents had provided her with piano lessons, a Brownie camera and a belief in the innate goodness of human beings, had been transformed into a quivering mass of instincts focused solely on survival.

Her induction into the underworld had begun in 1941 in the Lodz Ghetto where, instead of going to school, the Nazis forced her and the other inmates to watch public hangings. After enduring two years of starvation and daily terror in the ghetto, Guta, along with her parents and several hundred strangers, was pushed into a cattle car that began a slow and terrible journey into the unknown. During a brief stop, one of the guards discovered a newborn baby whose mother had tried to conceal its existence. He tore it from its mother's arms, held it by its tiny legs and smashed its soft skull on the floor. It lay there like a broken waxen doll while the mother uttered a hyena laugh that Guta would never forget. For the next three days, as the train rattled along the endless line, the sound of her deranged laughter resounded in their ears. Guta could hear it now, over the rhythmic slapping of the waves.

She had tried to cling to her father when the waggon door finally slid back, but someone pulled them apart and herded her into the barracks with her mother. Things happened so fast that there was no time to think above the inhuman yelling, the ferocious snapping of the dogs and the cracking of whips that slashed faces. One shock followed another as incomprehensible orders were screamed at them. 'Faster, faster! Deposit your parcels on the trolleys. Line up! Strip!' Their teeth and fingers were searched for gold.

What did it all mean? What was this place? Cringing with embarrassment, Guta tried to hide herself but a woman with hard, unfeeling hands grabbed her, shaved off all her hair and left her staring at the mountain of human hair, blond, red, chestnut, black and grey, plaited, rolled in a bun or tied in a ponytail, heaped on the floor, disembodied and bizarre. Someone smeared a pink viscous disinfectant all over her, even in the most private places. Just when it seemed there could be no worse humiliation, they were prodded like cattle and made to parade naked in front of hard-eyed men who separated them into two groups. She kept looking around. Where was her father?

The shocks at Auschwitz–Birkenau kept coming. Fortunate to be assigned a job instead of being gassed on arrival, Guta was ordered to unload the corpses from the carts and pile them up in front of the insatiable maw of the crematorium.

Occasionally as she touched an arm or leg before pushing it through the oval iron door, she could feel a weak pulse struggling to assert its right to live. After their bodies had been pushed into the oven on a long plank of wood, flesh, skin and bone emerged as anonymous ashes that were carried to the Birkenau swamp and used as landfill.

Guta had become part of the Tod Kommando — the Death Task Force. In time, she learned to suppress her horror and dissociate herself from the job that kept her and her mother alive. Only by plunging her hands into the bowels of death day after day was she able to earn that clay-like muddy bread that she shared with her mother. As her mother had not been assigned any work, Guta would rush back to their barracks every evening, terrified in case she had been carted away with those who were no use to the Nazis. Like an animal, Guta learned to depend on her instincts and to sense danger in distant sounds and sudden silences.

A few months later, when the icy wind slashed her emaciated body in its thin striped jacket, she and her mother were loaded onto another train. A three-day journey brought them to a smaller camp surrounded by a pine forest. This was Stutthof, near Danzig on the Baltic coast. There were no bunks, only lice-infested straw scatttered on the floor, a raised platform for public hangings, electrified fences and hardly any food.

Stutthof was the realm of the dead and dying. It surpassed the horrors of all written and visual images of hell. Bodies swung from gallows like scarecrows, sprawled against electrified fences like bats, and lay in piles in the yard and the barracks each morning, dead from typhus or starvation. Inside the barracks, they lived among stench and filth. One day one of the sadistic female guards was showing an army officer around the camp. '*Da haben wir unsere Untermenschen*,' Guta heard her say with a delicate shudder of distaste. 'Here we have our subhumans.'

The only hope of surviving this last rung of hell was to absorb its lessons. Yelled at, cursed and abused every day, they spoke mostly in grunts and curses. Whenever new prisoners were brought in, Guta only had to hear them speak to know whether they would survive. When a group of Hungarian women arrived at Stutthof, they still spoke in complete sentences and used polite expressions. She knew they didn't stand a chance.

What use were fine words when the tracery of her mother's spine was visible from the front and pus oozed from the sores on her body? The sore on her mother's elbow had eaten away all the flesh and exposed the bone. Too weak to fetch snow to clean up the arm for her, Guta sucked the putrid flesh out of her mother's sores so that it wouldn't spread and rot her entire body.

Near her on the deck, a pregnant woman in a navy pleated skirt and bare feet walked past on swollen legs. That brought back another incident. One of the women in her barracks doubled up in pain and gasped that she was about to miscarry. They all knew that if the guards found out she was pregnant, they'd kill her. One prisoner tore a strip off her ragged skirt to tie around the woman's mouth to stifle her screams while she laboured in agony to expel the tiny body, a bud wilted before it had time to blossom. They had no knife or scissors and, desperate for something to cut the umbilical cord before she bled to death, someone smashed the window and used a shard of glass. A moment later she ran towards the latrine with an unusual bulge under her skirt. She returned without it. When the whistle blew next day at roll-call, their blood froze. Someone must have found the foetus. But the announcement was about a broken window. As punishment for damaging property belonging to the Reich, they were ordered to stand outside in the snow for several hours. Some dropped to the frozen ground and never got up again.

Without realising it, Guta ran her finger along the flattened bridge of her nose. To vary the monotony of camp life, the guards would beat prisoners with rubber hose, plaited wire, clubs and long leather whips studded with metal balls that crushed flesh and broke bones.

The camp commandant had a special talent. He'd perfected a karate-like blow to the jaw that never failed to make the victim topple over and fall backwards, exposing the soft and vulnerable places he enjoyed kicking with his lovingly-polished boot. During one of those beatings, Guta heard the crunch of bone as he smashed her nose, the base of her skull and her ribs. It was two days before she regained consciousness. Bruised and broken all over as she was, she had to stand still at the interminable daily roll-calls.

'If only you didn't glare at the Germans so much,' her mother used to lament over Guta's mangled body. 'I'm sure they beat you so often because you make it so obvious that you hate them. Why attract attention to yourself?'

But Guta mumbled, 'I can't help it. I'm not looking for trouble, but they disgust me so much that I can't hide my feelings.' But the fury that fuelled her defiance also strengthened her resolve not to give up.

Hoping to hear some news of her father, whom she hadn't seen since the day they arrived in Auschwitz, Guta became proficient at throwing secret messages over the fence to the men on the other side. To send one of these missives required overcoming two almost insurmountable obstacles: finding a scrap of paper and a pencil. If she was determined enough to give away some of the precious watery soup, a prisoner would let her use his pencil stump. She would wrap the precious message around a pebble and tie the small parcel with a thread pulled out of her dress.

Usually her messages landed without being spotted, but on one occasion she was caught by the camp guard. A whistle shrilled through the camp to announce a public flogging. The camp fell silent as all the prisoners, including her mother, were forced to watch while Guta was made to stand on a box and flogged forty times with a leather strap. And yet, throughout all the suffering, pain and humiliation, one thing they could never crush was her sense of her own strength and dignity, or the hope that one day this would end and life would be beautiful once more.

Despite her agonised pleas for her mother to hold on just a little longer, Guta heard her mother's last fluttering heartbeat two days before the Russians arrived to liberate the camp. Two days later, when one of the soldiers picked Guta up and carried her tenderly to the field hospital truck, she looked up into his face and saw tears flowing down his cheeks. He saw an emaciated girl, ill with typhus, a smashed face and a frostbitten leg rotting with gangrene. She was fifteen.

The road to recovery was slow and spiked with pain. She endured one operation after another as surgeons tried to rebuild her nose and graft flesh onto her mutilated leg. When she was strong enough, she worked in a medical laboratory by day and studied at night.

Guta had never intended to leave her native land. She wanted to help rebuild her ravaged country and play her part in creating the new egalitarian society that was supposedly taking shape. While enrolled in a crash matriculation course, she befriended a fellow-student whose courage she admired. Barbara had fought with the partisans and had scars and medals to show for her heroic deeds during the war. The two became close friends and often sat up late, cramming science and algebra and discussing the just society they were going to create in Poland.

One evening Barbara looked up from an equation they were trying to solve. 'You know those *matzos* Jews eat at Passover? How come they're white?' she asked. Guta didn't understand the question. 'Well, you'd think that the blood from Christian babies would make them dark,' Barbara explained. Guta stared at her friend, too stunned to reply. Barbara's hand flew to her mouth. 'I didn't mean to upset you. Please don't be offended,' she cried, 'It was just a question of chemistry, that's all. After all, blood turns dark when it's heated.'

Guta finally found her tongue. 'I can't believe that an intelligent person could believe such vicious nonsense. You're repeating superstitions from the Dark Ages!' she exclaimed.

Barbara flushed. 'When I was a little girl, my mother always said that if I was naughty the Jews would take me away, so I believed they were capable of anything, even using the blood of Christian babies,' she said. Flinging her arms around her friend, she sobbed, 'Guta, I don't know what to say, I feel terrible. Please forgive me. I'll never repeat such stupid things again.'

Although they remained friends, the incident had left a profound mark on Guta. She was shocked to realise that she was living in a country where even basically decent people were still being brainwashed to believe that Jews were the Devil incarnate. How many more centuries would it take for this deeply ingrained prejudice to disappear? Six years of persecution by the Nazis and the blood of ninety percent of Polish Jews hadn't washed away this age-old hatred. She was depressed to think that she had survived the Nazi camps only to return to medieval prejudice in her own country.

Several months later at the Jewish welfare office in Lodz, while scanning lists of survivors in the hope of finding a relative, Guta met a pleasant young man who was doing the same. Dick was twenty-five, dependable and caring. Like so many young people who found themselves alone after the war, the two clung to each other in an effort to replace the love and warmth they had lost and create a family again. They married soon after they met, and not long afterwards boarded the *Derna* for Australia.

The other passengers saw a tall young woman in a cotton print skirt, socks and laced-up shoes, but what stayed with them was her air of vulnerability. Like someone who has just emerged from a coma, she seemed dazed by everything around her. In the camps she had learned the skills she needed to survive, but in peacetime they were no use. She wondered whether she would ever make up the time and social skills she had lost.

But with Stelios and Charlie she conversed without any problems. They hated the Italians because they had sided with Hitler, betrayed the Greeks and marched in at the bidding of their opportunistic Duce. The two seamen often talked about the fights that erupted below decks between the Greek and Italian crew who lay in wait and lashed out at each other in the galley, the dining room or in their cramped quarters.

Tensions simmered and exploded. It took only an angry glance, an accidental shove, a curse or a comment casting doubt on someone's paternity or impugning their nation's courage, for flick-knives to click open and white-faced antagonists to confront each other, fists clenched and weapons raised. Supporters would rush into the fray and soon there was a free-for-all, as seamen shouted, punched, lunged, kicked and slashed their despised opponents. Occasionally alarmed passengers ran out of the way of seamen chasing each other around the decks and shouting curses as knife blades gleamed in the moonlight. Late one night, Heniek Lipschutz was out strolling when he witnessed a tense stand-off that lasted until Kosmos, the captain's portly son, advanced to disarm three Italian crewmen wielding chains.

Late at night, after these encounters, Stelios and Charlie would creep towards Guta with some of the injured Greek combatants. They knew that she had completed a first aid course and had brought iodine and gauze with her, and, more importantly, that she was on their side. Pushing forward his companions with their slashed arms or bloodied noses, Stelios would whisper, 'Can you bandage this one?' After she had dabbed the wounds with iodine and bandaged them, they would murmur their thanks and disappear below. Secrecy was paramount because they didn't want the captain to find out they'd been fighting again, but they trusted Guta whom they regarded as an honorary Greek. In gratitude for her help, they often brought meals out on deck so that Guta and Dick didn't have to go down to the stifling dining room, adding some extra treat that wasn't available for the other passengers.

Guta and Dick's relationship puzzled the seamen because they seemed more like friends than lovers. They were not physically demonstrative and never even held hands. Stelios couldn't understand it. 'Are you sure you're really married?' he would ask in his ingenuous way that always made her smile. Thinking that it was lack of privacy that kept the couple apart, the sailors suggested various places where they could be alone, but the idea of making love with so many people around appalled Guta.

Although Dick tended to be serious and withdrawn, he had an aura of mystery that women found attractive. He didn't indulge in small talk but when he said something it was usually witty and memorable, and Guta liked the way he looked deep into her eyes and listened closely to every word she said. She supposed that their depressed, introverted state would wear off once their life became more settled and the traumas of the past had receded.

Occasionally on the other side of the deck she would watch the Estonians rehearsing their national songs. Something about them and their dark-shirted conductor disturbed her. Perhaps it was their rigid, regimented demeanour, or the unsmiling faces that gave no indication of what they thought or felt and reminded her of some Baltic camp guards whose cold brutality she had experienced. And now one of their group, the middle-aged man who sometimes played the accordion, was giving her a long, cold stare that made her shiver even though the sun was blazing.

15

Landfall was imminent. As seagulls screeched around us, the ship buzzed with excitement. For the first time in four weeks we were going to step on land. The day before we docked, men brushed suits and polished shoes, women ironed dresses and pinned their hair up, while the proud mothers of Anna Sznur and Haneczka Poczebucka twisted their daughters' hair in strips of cloth to make Shirley Temple sausage curls in honour of the occasion. My hair stayed plaited as usual.

The *Derna* dropped anchor in Colombo Harbour in the noon-day heat on 27 September, as the city shimmered in a misty haze. Determined not to waste a moment, everyone rushed to the purser's office to have their passports stamped so they could disembark as soon as the first tenders arrived to ferry them ashore. My mother couldn't wait to taste normal food again and feel the ground firm beneath her feet.

'I don't know how I'm going to stand another two weeks of this voyage,' she sighed as we stepped into the tender which sped towards the city and left a widening wake of foam behind us.

After the monotony of the ship, Colombo burst onto our dulled senses with the joyous impact of a fireworks display. The vegetation, exuberant and moist, looked as though it had been lacquered with paint of a startling green that seemed to drip off the wide leaves. There were fairytale croton bushes, their leaves speckled with yellow, scarlet and tangerine, and perfumed plants with flowers like crimson saucers. Agile boys, whose white loin cloths dazzled against their chocolate skin, monkeyed up the tall smooth trunks of coconut palms with astonishing speed, machetes in their mouths. They slashed the tops of the rough shells, but I didn't like the thin musty liquid that spurted out or the rubbery flesh that they cut into strips for us to taste.

Running along the street, skinny men with sharp cheekbones and legs as thin as chicken bones weaved in and out of the traffic, pulling rickshaws. On the tattered seats reclined Singhalese women with gold bangles clanking on their plump wrists. Beggars whose eyes blazed in deep sockets held their birdlike hands together in supplication, while Europeans drove past in the back of opulent cars with expressions indicating that all was right with their world. The gulf between the affluent and the destitute was distressingly deep. It troubled my father, who pointed out the contrasts as we wandered along avenues lined with palm trees that we had only ever seen in picture books.

The women with smooth jet-black hair and vermilion dots on their foreheads were like exotic blooms, the brown flesh of their midriffs exposed between their fitted short-sleeved tops and the shimmering saris so cleverly pleated that they didn't need buttons or zippers. Little Pauline Seitz tugged at her mother's arm as a bejewelled woman walked past. 'That lady had a red stone in her nose!' she shouted, twisting her head round for another look. 'Look, they're eating in the street!' Crouched on the pavement stirring a pot on a primus, a woman in a wraparound cotton skirt doled out dollops of rice onto large banana leaves for men who scooped the food up with deft movements of the right hand and didn't spill a grain.

Men squatted on the pavement selling figurines. '*Memsahib*,' they called out to Vala, holding up their handiwork. 'Please look. Nice elliphant.' Pauline wouldn't let her mother rest until she had bought a matching pair with neatly curved ivory tusks. When my parents stopped to admire some statues carved by a white-haired vendor whose own face resembled an ebony carving, he kept nodding and pointing at me. It took my startled parents several minutes to realise that he wanted to buy me. For the rest of the day my mother kept a tight grip on my hand.

In a lush clearing in front of a government building ornate with pillars and arches, an elderly man in a loin cloth sat cross-legged on the grass, a pipe in his hand and a woven basket in front of him. While a crowd gathered, he began to play the pipe and as he did so, the lid of the wicker basket lifted up. I stepped back. Uncoiling itself out of the basket was a striped cobra, its malevolent citrus eyes defying anyone to turn away before leaving a coin for the snake charmer.

The smells of Colombo were intoxicating. I breathed in the overpowering scent of sandalwood and camphorwood, unable to decide whether I liked it or not. From colourful shrines and temples, the sweet smoky smell of incense teased my nose, while the strange odours of cummin, coriander, cinnamon and garam masala wafted out of shops and market stalls, along with purple, saffron and crimson powders and fabled plants like frankincense, tamarind and myrrh.

All Colombo was buzzing with the news that the ship which had just docked in the harbour was carrying over 500 migrants to Australia. When a Czechoslovakian Jew who had settled in Colombo heard about the Jewish orphans, he hired a bus and rushed to the port to take the children to the zoo. Although he was taken aback to discover that most of the orphans were in their late teens, he bought them all ice creams, showed them around and then invited them out for a lunch they would never forget.

On top of a hill looking out over the city and the ocean, the orphans came to a gleaming white palace set in a tropical park. This was the Galle Face Hotel, whose colonial opulence took their breath away. Although Ceylon had gained its independence from British rule in February that year, within that colonnaded façade the traditions of the Raj were firmly entrenched. In a dining room, slow-moving wooden *punkahs* creaked above their heads while teak floorboards creaked under their feet. Reclining in rattan armchairs, fair-complexioned women in linen dresses, broad-brimmed hats and superior expressions nibbled at dainty cucumber triangles and sipped tea served by brown-skinned waiters, while an orchestra played music from the Palm Court.

On the starched white tablecloth, fruit they had never seen or tasted before was arranged in gilded bowls: pineapples, mangoes, passionfruit and the translucent segments of tangy mangosteens. No one knew how to eat the passionfruit, and some spat out the gritty seeds. Mangoes had a strange odour that some found delectable, others nauseating. And behind every high-backed chair stood a waiter in white livery, waiting to pass a finger bowl or whisk away a plate. Beside Topka sat Ginette, a big bow tied on top of her head, picking at the food. 'Those men with the brown faces keep staring at me,' she whispered, not realising that they were admiring her delicate little face and fair hair.

Like a swarm of maddened bees in pursuit of nectar, everyone from the ship rushed to the restaurants. After four weeks of a monotonous diet light on meat but heavy on starch, tomato sauce and pickled vegetables, we couldn't wait to have a proper meal. The passengers who dined at the Galle Face Hotel that evening were astonished when the head waiter handed the men false shirt fronts and black ties so that they wouldn't lower the tone of the establishment. As they entered the ornate dining room, Bronia Glassman and her ship-mate Cyla Ferszt noticed that some of the English ladies looked in their direction and pointedly began spraying themselves with eau de cologne. 'You'd think we had the plague,' Bronia whispered in Cyla's ear. The musicians who entertained the diners that night had a familiar accent and when Bronia went over to talk to them, she discovered that the group were from Warsaw and were also on their way to Australia.

In the more modest establishment where my parents and I were dining, the food kept coming: strange, exotic and flavoured with tantalising spices. Tiny fish fried in batter, crab in spicy sauce, curried vegetables, and chicken roasted to perfection. Unfamiliar with Ceylonese food, we bit enthusiastically into the mouth-watering chicken. Almost immediately our throats started to close up. We coughed and choked, our faces red and eyes streaming as we tried in vain to cool our burning mouths with glasses of iced water. 'So much for normal food!' my mother gasped.

Probably the only passenger who relished Colombo's hot curries was Elsie Pataky. She had grown up in India and felt nostalgic in Colombo for the family and the way of life she had left behind. Because of her pregnancy she had stopped smoking during the voyage, but collected the cigarettes that Dorothea distributed every week. By selling them, she and Ignac could afford to eat on shore. Communicating was no problem for her either, because she spoke English. While strolling around the city, she stopped to gaze at a jeweller's window and soon became engrossed in a conversation with the owner, who invited her inside. She laughed heartily when he placed several unset rubies and sapphires in her palm and explained that she had no money. To her astonishment, he presented them to her as a gift.

The profusion and low price of precious stones in Colombo's shops made them irresistible. The few passengers who possessed a little cash bought several stones, while the rest could only stare and dream. Wandering around the streets, Fred Silberstein and his friend Fred Weile saw some of the officers going into one of the jewellery shops. 'That shop must have the best prices, because those guys would know where to go,' Fred Weile reasoned. He seemed to have a good business sense and convinced his companion that it was worth buying some stones to sell in New Zealand at a big profit. After the owner had sworn to the high quality of the stones, they left with their little pouch, slapping each other on the back at the terrific deal they'd made, not suspecting that they were destined to be bitterly disappointed.

Nearby at the crowded bazaar, they were sucked into the kaleidoscope of noise, colour and movement. Fred Silberstein bought a pair of shorts from a jovial hawker, but when he returned the following day to exchange them because they were too tight, the atmosphere changed. The stall holder yelled at him and an angry crowd gathered. Sticks were brandished and violence hovered in the sultry air, so Fred put the shorts down and left the market in a hurry.

Helle went ashore together with the Puurands and some of their friends, pleased that she'd thought of having her Girl Guide card stamped as a memento of her visit to Ceylon. She was astounded to see so many of the locals walking barefoot on asphalt that scorched her feet, even through the sandals. Parched in the enervating weather, they entered the cool lounge of the Metropol Hotel and ordered drinks, hoping that they'd be able to afford the prices. The women were sipping iced orangeade and their companions were drinking Dutch beer when the Singhalese man at the next table leaned forward and struck up a conversation with Verner Puurand. After paying for their drinks, he called for two taxis and showed them around the town. Their benefactor owned a tea plantation where they watched women sitting cross-legged on the factory floor, sorting, sifting and packing tea leaves. After presenting each of them with a pound packet of the best Ceylon tea, the man asked Verner to deliver a letter to his brother in Australia.

Helle couldn't wait to get back to the *Derna* to tell Rita about her excursion, but a flurry of gossip greeted her as soon as she boarded. Karl Kassmann, a former Estonian wrestler who had been living in Colombo for the past twenty years, was coming to the ship with his Dutch wife the following day. The big news was that he'd arranged for the choir to give a concert on Radio Colombo.

Next morning, they tried to calm their nerves as they gathered round the microphone in the recording studio and sang the songs they'd rehearsed on board. First the men sang 'Mu Esstimaa ja Kuldrannake' (My Estonia and Golden Shore). This was followed by the whole choir singing 'Lahkumislaul' and 'Nooruslaul' (Farewell Song and Song of Youth), and they concluded the concert with a nostalgic rendition of 'Koduotus' (Home) which brought tears to their eyes.

Although Helle didn't think their voices had harmonised as well during the performance as they had during rehearsals, the radio audience was so delighted that they phoned in requests, and the station manager ran into the studio to ask them to keep singing. They didn't know any other songs, so after a hurried consultation they gave a repeat performance. When a journalist from the *Colombo News* arrived to interview them and take their photograph, they felt like celebrities. To cap it all, the station gave each member of the choir four rupees. Helle bought thirty-three lemons and fifty bananas with hers: for the first time in her life she was able to eat her fill of bananas.

Passengers who had no money traded their belongings with the locals. By selling his American army jacket to one of the hawkers, Bruno Tohver was able to go ashore, but some passengers remained on board for the entire four days we were in port. They included Mattie and Katina Travasaros and their cousins John and Stan. After her ordeal at the railway station in Cairo, when she had almost lost the boys in the crowd, Mattie's mother was adamant that she would not risk that happening again in a foreign country. No matter how fervently they argued and pleaded, she refused to give in. They were staying put and that was the end of it. While most of the passengers spent the day ashore, the four youngsters watched local boys diving for the coins that some passengers tossed into the sea. When they disappeared from view, Mattie held her breath until they emerged from the depths, sleek as young seals, the coins clamped between their strong white teeth.

Many youngsters found the water of Colombo Harbour irresistible. Some of the orphans dived in, but when they tried to swim back they found that the current was so powerful they could hardly make any headway. When twelve-year-old Nick Matussevich and one of his brothers dived in, they looked up into the stern face of the first officer who signalled them to come out immediately. Swimming in the harbour was dangerous, not only on account of the current, but also because of the sharks. As they clambered on board, the boys hoped that their father wouldn't hear about their escapade.

Meanwhile some of their sisters had almost been caught by the treacherous tide while ashore. Their parents chatted with a Russian artist they had met, while the girls strolled along a palm-fringed beach that seemed to stretch forever. As they paddled in the water, stooping occasionally to pick up shells, they heard shouts and turned to see a gang of local boys running towards them, waving their arms and shouting. Unable to understand what they were saying, the girls became frightened until they realised that the boys were pointing to the waves which were crashing onto the shore. The tide was rushing in and if they didn't run they would be cut off.

Lars Meder's experience was far more enjoyable. When the Estonian engineer of the Swedish tanker moored in the harbour boarded the *Derna* to scrutinise the passenger list, he found the Meders whom he knew from Estonia, and invited them on board his vessel. Excited, Lars poked around the freighter which, unlike the *Derna*, was clean and cool. He noted its diesel engine and air-conditioning, and wolfed down the best meal he'd had in the past four weeks.

Two of the Jewish orphans, Peter Rossler and Joe Neustatl, decided to make the most of their opportunity to explore Colombo. Peter was thrilled to be able to capture the bustle of the port, the city streets and the rickshaw drivers with his movie camera. Among a group of locals he was struck by an old man with a finely moulded face and a carved walking stick.

'Take a photo, *sahib*!' the man's companions urged him, but as soon as the camera stopped whirring, he was surrounded by insistent men holding out their hands and demanding payment. As Peter and Joe backed away, the mob came after them, shouting and gesticulating. They raced along a narrow alley, darted behind some stalls and managed to escape.

On the last day in Colombo, Peter and Joe decided to catch a local bus to Kandy and visit the famous Buddhist temple. But after the bus had trundled along the pot-holed, congested road for over an hour, they discovered that Kandy was still a long way off. They jumped out at the next stop and caught the bus back to the harbour, worried in case the *Derna* left without them.

Dr and Mrs Frant, with their daughter Christine and one of their young charges Alice Zalcberg, enjoyed a welcome break from shipboard life when a French doctor and his English wife invited them to their luxurious villa. The wife was charmed by Alice and astonished the Frants by offering to adopt her. At fifteen, Alice was a sparky girl with a dimpled left cheek and a wide mouth that was never still. Her exuberant personality constantly got her into trouble, especially with the older passengers who accused her of being rowdy. The other orphans often played pranks on her by short-sheeting her bunk or hiding her towel, but she got her revenge by rigging a bucket of water over the door to drench one of the culprits when he came back to the cabin.

After years of deception and fear, at fifteen Alice was learning to be herself. As a spoilt, sickly seven year old, she had been smuggled out of the Czestochowa Ghetto where her parents and older sister remained. For the next five years she was shunted from one reluctant stranger to another, from one town to another, in search of a sanctuary. In each new home, she had to learn another name and memorise a different life story so that no one would discover she wasn't Catholic. Alice lived on a knife edge of fear and tension, as one family after another abandoned her. Those experiences left such a deep imprint on her that even after the war ended, she was too frightened to admit that she was Jewish.

But now that she was among other young Jews and had a good-looking boyfriend in Abie Goldberg, her fun-loving personality began to assert itself and she felt happy for the first time in years. It was this exuberance that had appealed to the couple in Colombo, but the Frants explained that their assignment was to bring all the orphans to Australia and, in any case, Alice was travelling to join some relatives in Sydney.

We had now been in Colombo for several days and the novelty was wearing off. Rumours began to proliferate. Perhaps they had been unable to fix the broken engine. And where was the captain? As he hadn't been seen for some time, people speculated that he had jumped ship. Others said that he was drunk but Uno Mardus, who had seen him lying white-faced in his cabin several times, thought he might be ill. Four weeks of our five-week voyage had already passed. How could we possibly make it to Melbourne by 12 October?

Every day in port the loading continued. The *Derna* took on 1200 tonnes of coal in Colombo, as well as other cargo including rice, lentils and onions, and now sat much lower in the water than she had at the beginning of the voyage.

Finally on 1 October, our fifth day in port, we were notified that we would be sailing early next morning and had to return to the ship by midnight. Some of Dr Frant's charges decided to have one last slap-up dinner ashore. When Bob Grunschlag, André Wayne, Harry Braun, David Weiss, as well as Abie Goldberg, ordered chicken, the waiter asked, 'Hot chicken, sir?' They looked at him in surprise and laughed. Of course. Who'd want to eat cold chicken? But when they took a mouthful of the curry and proceeded to gasp and splutter, they understood the significance of the question. Taking pity on them, the waiter brought a milder dish and they paid the bill with the last of their rupees, saving the exact amount needed for the tender back to the ship.

But this time the boatmen demanded a much higher fee than usual due to the late hour, and for once they refused to negotiate. Finally, close to midnight, the boys realised that they had no choice but to pay the exorbitant fee. As they didn't have enough money, Abie Goldberg, the only one with sufficient cash, took the tender back to the ship alone and returned soon afterwards with money to pay their fares.

Dawn was breaking when Helle awoke to hear her admirer Luciano shouting from the doorway, 'Sopra! Sopra!' Go up on deck! Along with the other yawning passengers, she made her way up to the front deck where crowds had already assembled. We were about to leave port and Adnan Molvan, the chief purser, was sitting at a table ticking off names to check that everyone was on board and there weren't any more stowaways. The line stretched up and down the wide internal stairs between the foredecks to the cabins, right up to the landing where he sat with his back to the wall.

The process took so long that the sun was already beating down on our heads while we waited. The boys who had returned to the ship late at night were still half asleep and became increasingly rebellious at having to get up so early just to wait in an endless queue. It reminded many of them of the pointless roll-calls in the concentration camps. Bob Grunschlag was furious that the chief purser was throwing his weight around as usual and treating them like dirt. A few days earlier, when Bob had complained that the food was inedible, Molvan had sneered and said, 'People who don't pay for their passage should be grateful for anything they get.'

When it was finally Bob's turn to stand in front of the purser and be checked off the list, instead of giving his name, he glared in menacing silence, as did the youths behind him. Without saying a word, they inched forward, coming closer and closer, until the purser looked uneasy. When it looked as though they would push his table and ram it into him until he was jammed against the wall, he leapt off his chair, sprang aside and abandoned any further formalities.

As the *Derna* sailed away, the Estonian passengers were in turmoil about an article they'd read in the *Colombo News*. According to the report, their benefactor who had shown them around town and organised the radio concert was the secretary of the local Communist Party. Everyone was reeling with shock. They had allowed themselves to be entertained by a Communist! They had entrusted their letters to him! Someone even whispered that Mr Kassmann had made his money trafficking in women. 'Jealousy is speaking, and sour grapes,' Arnold Ohtra noted dryly in his diary as the ship left a slowly widening wake in the dull green water.

Relieved that the engine had been fixed and that the next port of call was Fremantle, we all settled down for the last two weeks of the voyage. At last we were on the home stretch.

16

The day after we set sail from Colombo, some of the passengers were intrigued by the goings-on in the library. The Jews had congregated there, men and women in separate groups. The men, their shoulders draped in fringed shawls, were swaying backward and forward, murmuring chants in a strange tongue. They wore skull caps: small ones perched on the back of the head, or larger ones planted square on top. Although some of the women were murmuring fervently over their prayer books, others whispered to their neighbours or looked around for their children.

It was Rosh Hashana, the Jewish New Year, which ushers in the ten most solemn days in the religious calendar, culminating in Yom Kippur, the Day of Atonement. On this occasion, however, there was no ram's horn to herald the holy day and remind the worshippers of their covenant with God and their obligation to man. No one missed the shrill, fractured sound made by blowing the *shofar* more than fourteen-year-old Leon Wise. As he prayed with the other orphans, his thoughts returned to his mother and father.

He'd last seen them at the Gare de Lyon in Paris where, together with hundreds of other heartbroken parents, they had said goodbye and sent him with his brother and sister to the safety of a Jewish children's home in France's unoccupied Vichy zone. Leon's most precious possession on the ship was a scrap of paper torn out of an exercise book. It was the letter his father had written in the concentration camp at Pithiviers, where he was interned.

Several years later, in 1943, when Leon and the 120 other children staying at the home were in danger of being caught and deported, they escaped. They tried to cross into Switzerland but had to turn back because the Germans were stationed near the border. That evening they slept at the railway station in Limoges, where Leon heard the sound of marching boots and looked out of the window to see Germans rounding up the town's Jews. Next day they travelled to the border again and clambered onto the trucks that were waiting to transport them to safety. But when they reached a forest, they were told to scatter quickly to avoid a German patrol that was scouring the area with dogs.

Later Leon discovered that two of his closest friends had been caught and shot. The survivors were fortunate in being allowed to remain in Switzerland, because many other refugees were sent back over the border to certain death. His group was interned in a camp located in the Ecole de Charmilles near Geneva for eight months. They slept on straw on the wooden floor of a large classroom, guarded day and night by Swiss guards and not allowed out.

He was still in the Swiss camp when Rosh Hashana came round, but they had no *shofar*. Leon, who was a feisty ten year old at the time, was playing in the yard when he saw a young man walking past in the long coat and prayer tassels of Orthodox Jews. 'Can you get us a *shofar*?' Leon called out. The young man soon returned with the ram's horn and passed it under the wire fence. Leon became a hero.

During the service on the *Derna*, which in the absence of a rabbi one of the passengers conducted, a little girl wandered into the library and stood fascinated among the swaying, murmuring worshippers. It was little Veronica Matussevich, unaware that her frantic parents were searching for her all over the ship. Distraught at being unable to find her, they had gone to the captain who was considering turning the ship around in case she'd fallen overboard when one of the congregation brought her back to her relieved family.

For the Jews who had not admitted their religion when filling in their application forms, the Rosh Hashana service posed a dilemma. Even those who were not religious wanted to take part in a service that stirred unbearably painful memories of parents, home and family life. Not to pray on this solemn occasion was unthinkable.

One of these passengers was Zosia Rogozinski, who was travelling with her husband and two-year-old daughter Edie. Zosia was already panicking at the thought of life in Australia. Although her optimistic and resourceful nature had helped her to survive the Holocaust, the rigours of the voyage made her doubt their decision to migrate to a country they knew nothing about.

After seeing Colombo, her worries redoubled. Would Australia be equally primitive and strange? Her friend Fela Feigin, who was travelling with her husband and small son, was also wringing her hands. She should have waited for the American visa from her sister instead of accepting the Australian permit just because it had arrived first.

Seeing so many Jews gathered in prayer aroused considerable discussion among some of the other passengers. Since the Jewish quota was supposed to be small, how come there were so many of them on board? Archbishop Rafalsky, however, had no such qualms. He wished the Jews, including his troubled young friend Sam Fiszman, a happy New Year and urged his compatriots to do the same. Curious about this festival, Arnold Ohtra asked one of the Jews what year it was according to their calendar, but the man did not know. The observant Jews knew that it was the year 5708.

On the morning of 5 October, the sun's rays shining through the clouds formed a silvery stripe on the horizon, like a silken ribbon tied around the belly of the world. As my father had told me that we would soon be crossing the equator, I wondered whether this was it. Although raindrops fell, shirring the water until it resembled grey taffeta, the weather was as sultry as ever and everyone trudged around the deck or slumped on deck chairs, mopping their necks and foreheads.

Our only distraction was the Miss Derna contest, which had been the main topic of conversation among the likely candidates for the past few days. Rita was convinced that Helle was the most beautiful girl on board and was certain to win. But although secretly she would have loved to be chosen, Helle was too proud to enter such a contest. It was demeaning, she thought, for any self-respecting girl to push herself forward like that. It would be like saying, 'Here I am, choose me!'

Rita was still meeting her stowaway in secret. He only had to gaze at her with those passionate dark eyes and her knees would start to wobble. But she noticed that he often looked worried. Australia was the next port of call, but since he had no permit to enter the country, he had no idea what would become of him, and dreaded the prospect of being sent back to his miserable existence in North Africa.

As he confided his problems in that seductive accent, his eyes never leaving her face, Rita's heart ached for him. If only there was something she could do to help.

Now she rushed up to Helle, beaming. 'I've got it all worked out!' she said. 'It was Philippe's idea. He said if we got married, he'd be able to enter Australia legally!' Ignoring the concern on Helle's face, she continued. 'I agreed. Philippe is going to ask the captain to marry us.'

Helle was aghast. 'How can you possibly think of marrying someone you don't really know, just so he can get into Australia?'

But Rita was too impetuous to be dissuaded by the cool voice of reason. 'If it doesn't work out, we can go our separate ways. I just want to help him.'

After breakfast, the two girls followed the other passengers to the top deck to hear who had been chosen as Miss Derna. Helle's heart beat faster as they waited for the announcement. John Papalas, the first officer, stepped forward and led a wisp of a girl by the hand. Placing a paper crown with the letter D on her smooth fair hair, and draping a Panamanian flag around her thin shoulders as a cloak, he announced, 'Please welcome our Miss Derna!' It was Ginette.

Although she had started off being a lonely waif, Ginette had by now become everyone's pet. Mrs Frant adored her and Dr Frant's usually sharp glance softened whenever he saw this affectionate little girl who often snuggled into his lap. The captain had taken her under his wing and sometimes invited her to come to his cabin or sit at his table, which made her feel special. Thrilled at having been singled out from all the passengers as Miss Derna, Ginette beamed as she curtseyed to enthusiastic applause. Looking on, her little friend Haneczka pouted. She was just as pretty and her bow was bigger than Ginette's. Why hadn't she been chosen?

Although Haneczka wasn't aware of it at the time, she and Ginette had more in common than pretty faces and big bows. Like Ginette, she too had spent the war years being cared for by Catholic foster-parents. After having been palmed off to several people in Byelorussia, including a priest, she'd spent the past two years with a family she had become attached to. In 1945, when her mother found her, her foster-mother asked: 'Do you want to go with that Jewess?' Haneczka had no idea she was Jewish and didn't want to leave, so the foster-mother abducted her, hid her near a river and refused to let her go. For a time, Haneczka's mother went along with her demands and bought the foster-mother a sewing machine and whatever else she asked for, but in the end she decided to put an end to this charade and collect her child. Shocked at being forcibly reunited with her mother, Haneczka was shattered shortly afterwards when someone tore off the cross she wore around her neck and flung it into the fire. As a result of her traumatic experiences, she couldn't eat for two weeks. That was when she discovered that food was a weapon she could use to control people. On board the *Derna,* however, most of us lost our appetite and Haneczka was no exception.

After the coronation of Miss Derna, an announcement in several languages invited both young and old to don bathing suits and meet on the forward deck at three o'clock to celebrate the arrival of King Neptune. The captain, sporting a festive paper hat, arrived with his acolytes, the tiny Miss Derna and Colonel Hershaw, who urged everyone to salute King Neptune. As they walked along the thin red line that led to the mythical monarch of the seas and bent to kiss his hand, they were struck by a jet of water from a hose wielded by the crew. After everyone had performed their obeisance, the crew took great delight in catching the pretty young girls and pushing them into the tarpaulin swimming pool. Although most of the young people enjoyed the distraction, Helle noted in her journal that evening that the whole event had been pathetic.

The following day Rita experienced a distraction of a less pleasant kind. Her mother had discovered her plan to marry the stowaway and was horrified. Ordering Rita to stay in the cabin, she went to discuss the situation with her brother. Shortly afterwards the captain, to whom Rita had never spoken before, sent for her.

Trembling with apprehension, she entered his cabin and found it surprisingly austere. Although the captain's German was basic, his meaning was clear. In a quiet but forceful voice he said it had come to his attention that she planned to marry a stowaway. 'I'm speaking to you as your father would have spoken if he had been here,' he said. At the mention of her dead father, tears sprang to Rita's eyes and she looked down at her tightly clasped hands. 'You are a kind-hearted girl, but you can't marry this fellow just because you feel sorry for him. I won't hear of it!'

Now that we had crossed the equator, the monotony of the voyage returned and the old irritations reasserted themselves. Evening thunderstorms came regularly, but although the gusts of torrential rain that ricocheted off the waves cooled the air for a while, the rain only increased the humidity. While some passengers wanted the portholes opened to catch the momentary breeze, others slammed them shut to prevent moisture from seeping into their bedclothes and making them damp and mouldy. As it was, the sheets were rarely changed. Helle waged war with a steward who kept running into her cabin to close the porthole that she kept opening. Leon continued to berate his cabin-mates for stepping on his blanket instead of using the ladder.

Fred Silberstein was exasperated by the lax standards of hygiene on board. No one seemed to clean the washrooms, scrub the toilets or change the bed linen. Whenever he wanted fresh bedclothes, he had to pull them off his bunk himself, carry them to the steamy laundry where the walls ran with moisture, and argue with the belligerent laundry staff.

Colonel Hershaw was annoyed with the captain. Despite his stated intention, Captain Papalas had not discharged Dr Themelis in Colombo after all.

'What to do?' The captain's thick eyebrows arched above his mild brown eyes while he spread his pudgy hands in a gesture of helplessness. 'He came to see me the night before Colombo and begged to stay. He had tears in his eyes. He said, "I am not young any more. Who will give me a job? What will become of me?" But I am sure that we will see an improvement from now on,' the captain said. 'He promised.'

Colonel Hershaw couldn't conceal his contempt for the captain's weakness. It was naïve to put any credence in this incompetent medico's self-pitying tears, and irresponsible to place the health of the entire ship in jeopardy through misguided pity. As it was, he felt the *Derna* had been extraordinarily lucky that no epidemic had broken out as yet, and that no one had been poisoned by the rotten lamb. But to hope that this good fortune would continue for several more weeks was tempting fate.

It seemed to Captain Papalas that the problems he had to cope with on this voyage were never-ending. Gloomily, he surveyed the number of worshippers celebrating the Jewish New Year. He had nothing against Jews but even a cursory glance at this crowd revealed that he was carrying far more of them than regulations allowed. Turning to Silva Rae at the dining table he sighed. 'I wonder what will happen when we get to Australia and they find out that we've exceeded the quota. We might as well turn the ship around and go straight to Israel!'

Not long after the *Derna* had crossed the equator, Ella's brother Anton* became ill. He had been strumming his guitar on deck when he suddenly doubled over and winced as a spasm jabbed his stomach. When the pain grew worse and the colour drained from his face, Ella ran to Dr Frant for help. 'It's probably food poisoning,' he told her. 'He should eat as little as possible.' But instead of improving, Anton deteriorated. His face was the colour of the ashes the crew flung overboard and he vomited and groaned with pain. Summoned again,

---

* His name has been changed at Ella's request.

Dr Frant took his temperature, looked at his thickly coated tongue and palpated his tender abdomen.

There was little doubt that the lad had appendicitis, and that posed a serious problem. He was not a general surgeon and had no surgical instruments with him, not even sutures. There was no point even considering the ship's doctor, to whom he wouldn't have entrusted a sick cat, and in any case the *Derna* had no operating facilities. And Fremantle, according to the officers, was still about ten days away. All he could do was reassure the brother and sister and hope that the inflammation would subside.

Some of the Greek seamen who had befriended Anton offered their advice. They were fleeing the oppressive right-wing government of their country and emerged on deck at night to breathe the salty air and sing the heroic songs of the partisans. Although they had no common language, Anton had responded to the mood of their songs and accompanied them on the guitar. 'Your brother must eat something or he will die,' they told Ella. Every day they smuggled something nourishing out of the kitchen for him: two tiny eggs, a little broth or some barley.

Anxious not to alarm Ella, Dr Frant continued to make reassuring, non-committal remarks which only infuriated her. Although he was their guardian on the ship, he was just stalling, playing for time, refusing to take responsibility, she fumed. And what about that other doctor on board, the Greek one with the bulbous nose? Why didn't he do something? She sat beside her sick brother all day in the shady area near the bridge where the officers had let him spread out his blanket, her mind churning. Had they survived the Holocaust for him to die on this accursed ship? She couldn't bear to think of having to tell their mother in Prague that her adored son had died on the way to Australia because no one had known what to do. Her mother would probably blame her.

Ella stared moodily at the sea as she shielded her eyes from the light glancing off the waves. The clear green colour of the Indian Ocean reminded her of the night she had arrived in Auschwitz. It must have been around two in the morning when the cattle truck jammed with prisoners had finally reached its destination. With guards yelling, whips cracking, dogs barking, she and her father were herded along an alley lined with poplars silhouetted against an emerald sky. For one moment time stopped, the terror in her heart subsided and the ugliness around her vanished as she stood transfixed by the surreal beauty of the scene. Even when she discovered that this vision owed its existence to the fumes of the Zyklon B used in the gas chambers, its eerie radiance stayed imprinted on her mind.

Within minutes of arriving at the Nazis' death factory, Ella was separated from her father and never saw him again. When she asked an older prisoner about the smoke that poured out of the chimney and the nauseating sweetish smell that permeated the camp and saturated your clothes and skin, she didn't believe the answer.

Some time later, she was thrilled when she heard on the camp grapevine that a transport had just arrived from her home town and that her mother was among the new arrivals. The thought of seeing her again, of being held in her arms and comforted, gave her hope for the first time. She wouldn't be alone any more.

As soon as she was able to sneak away from the watchful eyes of the guards, she crept out, hid behind her barracks, crawled on her stomach underneath the wire and flattened herself against walls to avoid being caught in the watchtower's searchlight. Inside her mother's barracks, she walked straight past a bony woman with a scrawny neck, lined face and broken nails. It was only when the woman called her name that she realised it was her mother. There was no trace of the beautiful, vivacious woman who had once been so proud of her complexion and white hands.

But there was a bigger shock in store. The joy and outpouring of motherly love that the thirteen-year-old girl had anticipated were absent. There was no jubilation, no enthusiasm, no warmth. Debilitated and depressed, her mother was absorbed in her own misery. The longed-for hug felt perfunctory, and Ella couldn't feel any love in her mother's resigned arms. She was heartbroken. Although she was dying of starvation herself, she had risked her life to see her mother and hold her again, only to find a stranger who was too deeply sunk in her own misery to give any comfort or affection to her daughter.

Before being deported, her mother had been entrusted with the care of her nine-year-old nephew. Her sister had sent him over the border to

Slovakia for her to look after, thinking the boy would be safer there than in Hungary. Not long afterwards, however, as Eichmann's Final Solution accelerated and Jews in Slovakia were rounded up, Ella's mother was deported to Auschwitz with her son Anton and her small nephew. When the three of them stood in front of Dr Mengele awaiting their fate, he ordered her and Anton to the right, but her nephew was sent to the left.

Powerless to save him, she watched the child being taken away. Even though she knew that going with him would not have saved his life, she could not forgive herself that he was killed while in her care. The child was dead but she was still alive. Listening to her mother's dead voice, Ella felt totally abandoned.

From Auschwitz, Ella was sent to Ravensbruck and then to a salt mine at Bendorf. There she polished tiny ball bearings with micrometric screws in the bowels of the earth, while inhaling salt dust that encrusted her paper-thin skin. By April, the Allies were closing in. Determined not to leave a single Jew alive, the Germans dragged this surreal army of starved, disease-ridden skeletons through the German countryside, shooting those who could not continue their grotesque march.

Surrounded by Wehrmacht soldiers, they were left in a forest clearing one night where they resorted to nibbling plants to try and fill their empty stomachs. Some of the plants were poisonous and those who ate them died in agony. The next day the guards pushed them on, but by the time they reached the outskirts of Hamburg, two-thirds of the group had died. When they came to a dynamited bridge one of the guards helped Ella down the riverbank so she could relieve herself. 'When the enemy comes, please tell them that we were humane,' he said. These were the first kind German words she had ever heard.

A few days later, abandoned by their captors, she was lying on filthy straw in a closed waggon, too weak to move. Suddenly the door slid open and she heard the words that she had almost given up hope of hearing: '*Ihr seitz frei.*' Dazed, she tried to grasp the idea of freedom and wondered whether she had died, because angels in white veils were leaning over her, speaking in soft, soothing voices. They were Danish Blue Cross volunteers. She was about to be taken to Sweden as part of a deal that Himmler had struck with Volker Bernadotte to exchange some prisoners for personnel-carrying trucks.

Even now, three years later, Ella could remember how difficult it had been to believe that she was really free, that the humiliation, hunger and suffering were over. Some of the prisoners broke into a store and stole as much food as they could carry, because they were convinced that this was just a trick. On the boat to Sweden, when they were told to throw away their old clothes because they would be given new ones, no one believed it. They stuffed their rags into the crevices of the boat, just in case. When the Swedes tried to build them up with cod liver oil, they spat it out when their benefactors weren't looking. You could never tell if you were being poisoned.

In the Swedish town of Lund, Ella took months to heal. She had weeping sores all over her body, weighed thirty-five kilos and tottered on ostrich legs. When she had recovered sufficiently to return home, she was reunited with her mother in Prague, but their relationship was thorny. Festering beneath the surface, but never referred to, was their shattering reunion at Auschwitz which had caused a rift that was difficult to heal. Apart from that, her mother had trouble adjusting to this defiant young woman who had been fending for herself for the past few years, while Ella resented her mother's criticism and demands. They were at cross purposes, because the girl who didn't want to be treated as a child still wanted her mother to look after her.

Rebellious and resentful, Ella couldn't settle down at school. She still hoped that her beloved father would return and his last words to her in the cattle train to Auschwitz still rang in her ears. 'Be a good person and never lower your standards.' Although she was lively and popular with the other students, she felt alienated. Her school-mates laughed, joked and played the guitar, but she couldn't see anything to laugh about. What her mother called her wild streak was anger and grief that couldn't find an appropriate outlet. With her fluent Swedish, English, French and German, Ella worked part-time interpreting radio news bulletins, a welcome relief from the tedium of school. Occasionally she was employed as a guide for international groups visiting Prague, but when her schoolwork suffered her mother forbade her to do it any more.

Ella's rebelliousness sometimes manifested itself in dangerous ways. Whenever Communist propaganda was blared through loudspeakers in the street, she would make critical comments and mock the slogans. Strangers would sidle up and warn her to be careful or she'd end up in jail. When two of her equally outspoken friends disappeared from the gymnasium, she finally realised that if she wasn't careful she'd meet the same fate. The sudden death of Foreign Minister Jan Masaryk darkened the skies over Prague. The Nazis had been defeated but another kind of dictatorship was looming.

At about that time Ella's mother heard of a scheme to send orphans and youngsters with only one parent to Australia, and urged her children to take advantage of it and leave.

Although Ella suspected that her mother wanted to get rid of her because she was so difficult to handle, she knew that it was a good idea. Her resentment intensified, however, when she found out that while she was to be smuggled across the border illegally, her mother had obtained legal papers for Anton at considerable expense.

His moans broke in on her reverie. He was mumbling through fever-scabbed lips and when she looked at his face, she was alarmed to see that it had a greenish hue. Something had to be done urgently. Perhaps Jean-Pierre the barman would think of something. She jumped up and started running towards the stern, past rows of sunbaking passengers. Surrounded by his friends, Otto was strumming his guitar and composing raunchy lyrics to familiar songs. 'Hey, Ella! Come and join us!' one of the boys called out, but she shook her strawberry blonde curls and kept going while their admiring glances followed her. There was something foxy and self-contained about her that men found intriguing. She was friendly but inaccessible. They envied the young barman whose company Ella preferred, although they found it ironic that the only guy she was keen on was unlikely to reciprocate her interest as his sexual orientation was towards men. But she felt relaxed with him because he was easy to talk to and had no personal agenda. Her brother needed help urgently and since the doctors on board weren't doing anything, perhaps this street-wise barman would suggest something.

Apart from Dr Frant, there were two doctors on board. One of them was my father's bridge partner Leon Ament. Many women on board had designs on Dr Ament, but their hopes were never realised because he remained faithful to his fiancée, a Swiss nurse he had met in Germany after the war, who was later to join him in Australia.

The other medico was Irene Abrahamsohn, an attractive brunette. Irene had studied medicine in Berlin when Hitler came to power. It was a dark time in her life that she tried not to think about.

Ostracised by the other students because she was 'tainted' with Jewish blood, she had felt like a leper and it had taken every gram of strength to hold her head high and concentrate on lectures in such a hostile environment. But after she graduated, she wasn't allowed to practise. The only work she could get was in a forensic laboratory, assisting the pathologist. She loathed the dead bodies and the sickening smell of formaldehyde, putrefaction and faeces, but there was no choice because she was her family's sole breadwinner.

Stripped of his business and assets and forced to wear the yellow star, her father had sunk into a profound depression. Like so many German Jews, he loved his native land and considered himself a German patriot, but he was so shocked at being deprived of all his rights and treated like an enemy of the state that he stopped going out altogether. His rations were so meagre that if it hadn't been for a Quaker from the local pharmacy bringing them food in secret and the butcher's wife occasionally leaving some meat on the roof of the neighbour's shed, they would have starved.

After her father died of a heart attack in 1943, Irene and her mother lived through the terrifying bombardment of Berlin, and then through the Russian occupation which was so dangerous for women, especially lovely young ones like her. Fortunately the Russians respected doctors, so she pulled on an armband with a big red cross and proceeded to treat the soldiers, most of whom were suffering from gonorrhoea.

Irene's only friend on board was another young German woman, Herta Birnbaum, who was also a lone mother travelling with a small child to New Zealand. Afraid that their children would fall out of the bunks, the two women spent most of their time on deck under an awning that Irene had rigged up to protect them all from the sun. One day, the stresses of the voyage, the pain of loneliness and anxiety about the future overwhelmed Herta who broke down and sobbed. Moved by her friend's plight, which she shared, Irene resented the self-centred attitude of the other passengers. They were all out for themselves and had no compassion for anyone else. To add to her own anxiety, one morning her mother slipped and fell over on deck and broke her leg. Irene splinted it and took care of her for the rest of the voyage.

It was Irene who advised Ella to prepare nourishing but easily digestible food like barley broth and light sponge cake for her brother. Although Ella had no idea how to cook and had never been in the galley before, she ran down to the bowels of the ship. She shrank back when she looked into the cavernous hall where an army of kitchen hands with sweating faces were stirring huge pots, beating doughy mixtures and flourishing long sharp knives as they chopped onions and opened tins of tomatoes, shouting and cursing each other across the work bench.

They stared at the young girl asking in a nervous stammer if she could cook something for her sick brother. Beckoning her inside, they showed her the Ali Baba sized jar where they kept the barley, gave her an enormous pot to cook it in and burst out laughing when she asked for a small saucepan. The catering requirements of the *Derna* made small utensils quite unnecessary. By then the kitchen crew had become used to passengers coming into the kitchen to supplement their diet, because mothers often came in to prepare semolina for their babies.

While Ella was struggling to make barley broth for her brother, which despite all her best efforts burned and stuck in lumps to the bottom of the pot, Archbishop Rafalsky fell ill with gastroenteritis. When Ella emerged from the galley one afternoon with her bowl of barley broth, Dr Frant asked if she could also boil some rice for the archbishop. A few hours later, carefully balancing the two bowls, she climbed the stairs gingerly, one at a time to steady herself against the rolling of the ship. She knocked on the door of the cabin which had been converted into a sick-bay for the archbishop. The gaunt man managed to smile when she brought his rice and blessed her kindness, and even though they had no common language, she felt uplifted by his blessing.

When Ella returned to her brother with the broth, he was writhing in pain. She was through with being helpless. The doctors had said that performing an operation was out of the question and there was nothing they could do, but their inaction made her blood boil. She would take matters into her own hands. When Jean-Pierre suggested enlisting the radio officer's help, she burst into the radio room. George Alexiou, for whom she had occasionally translated Swedish news bulletins, listened while her angry words tumbled out.

'Something has to be done to save my brother,' she blurted out. The radio officer was sympathetic. 'Perhaps I could send an SOS to see if there is a ship nearby with surgical facilities that can take your brother on board, but you have to speak to the captain first. Go and plead with him, throw yourself on his mercy. Kneel and beg if you have to, because I can't send an SOS without his permission.'

Ella rushed to the captain's cabin three stairs at a time and stood in front of him, hardly able to catch her breath. 'My brother is dying,' she gasped, trying to suppress the tears that were welling up. 'Please, let them radio for help. Or turn back to Colombo.' But the captain shook his head. He was deeply sorry but the ship was already behind schedule and he couldn't delay the voyage by turning it around, or waiting for another vessel to catch up. Ella felt that she was choking on her fury. 'You are nothing but a murderer! If my brother dies, I will hold you responsible!' she shouted and slammed the door behind her.

As suddenly as it had appeared, Anton's crisis passed. The pain disappeared and the colour returned to his face. The relieved doctors on board the *Derna* were left to reflect on the mysterious workings of the human body, which so often succeeded in healing itself without their intervention.

17

The fact that the *Derna* had the same type of expansion engine as the *Titanic* did not escape the notice of passengers who had looked around the engine room and noted the condition of its antiquated machinery. 'It's a good thing there are no icebergs in the Indian Ocean,' someone joked after a visit to the bowels of the ship. The broken engine had not been fixed in Colombo and the ship was crawling along even more slowly than before. The triple expansion engine had three cranks which drove steam at high pressure into the crank shaft and cylinders in turn, but the boiler was not generating enough steam. One engine had already broken down and now the second was failing.

The gravity of the situation became obvious when the chief engineer asked some of the young men, including Bill Marr and his friend George Rakusan, to go down into the engine room and shovel coal. 'We need help to keep the engine going, because the stokers are worn out,' he said.

With its suffocating heat and the grinding din of the machinery, the engine room resembled Vulcan's forge. Pistons laboured, thick coal dust coated everything and blasts of smoky air made their eyes water. The stokers shovelled coal as fast as their muscular shoulders could manage, but despite their efforts the steam did not build up and there was talk of a leaking valve.

Bill and George emerged on deck with faces as scarlet as chili peppers and backs streaming with sweat, while other boys took turns shovelling. Even such gruelling work was preferable to the usual lethargy of shipboard life. When the chief steward asked Verner Puurand's older son Hans to help in the galley, the sixteen year old jumped at the offer. Too shy to approach the girls or mix with the boys, he was bored. Besides, he welcomed the prospect of earning some money so that he wouldn't arrive in Brisbane with empty pockets.

Meanwhile Captain Papalas continued to tell anyone willing to listen that only the poor quality of the coal they'd taken on in Colombo had caused the *Derna* to slow down. About a week out of Colombo, Verner Puurand woke up and looked around in astonishment. 'We are going backwards!' he exclaimed. During the night, a number of people had heard two hollow thumps and then an ominous silence. The second engine had ground to a halt. Exhausted from thirty years of hauling cargo across the oceans of the world, the *Derna* was close to collapse.

The dawdling pace of the ship was a constant source of jokes, but beneath the jollity there was genuine concern. We were floundering in the middle of a vast ocean on a ship with two broken engines. It had been obvious for some time that we couldn't possibly reach Melbourne by the scheduled date, but now our chance of reaching it at all seemed remote. When it was suggested that the captain send out an SOS in the hope that some nearby ship would come to the rescue and tow us to the nearest port, he shook his head. He knew only too well that his boss, Stavros Livanos, would oppose such a costly operation. It would eat up the profit from the fares. 'We must keep trying to repair the engines,' he said.

The mechanics who had tinkered with the leaking valves in Colombo had patched and soldered as best they could, but the patient was old and had too many diseased organs. Down in the engine room, the engineer, greaser and stokers toiled in a losing battle. It was the worst possible situation in the tropics, where temperatures in the engine room could soar to over a hundred degrees, dehydrating their bodies at a pace that outstripped the fluids they drank. The stokers knew the danger: they had all heard stories about colleagues who had leapt overboard to their deaths, confused and crazed by heat, thirst and the loss of salt through the pores of their sweating bodies.

Although he was too young to help, Petro Fatseas sneaked into the engine room whenever he could. He was fascinated by the machinery, especially the huge pistons that slid up and down, and watched them until the stokers chased him away. He had noticed that the man in charge of the engine room was the second engineer they called Johnny. Older and more corpulent than the others, he was bald with a curiously pale skin and experienced eyes that darted everywhere as he barked instructions and directed the work.

Petro was scrambling down the ladder that led to the engine room one afternoon when he looked down and stopped, glued to the spot. Johnny was lying on the floor. His face, always pale, had a waxen look, his eyes were closed and he was as motionless as the plank he was lying on. From the hushed conversation of the stokers, Petro figured out that a leak in one of the valves had extinguished the fire that kept the steam building up inside the boiler. It appeared that Johnny had crawled inside to find out which tube was leaking so he could plug it with a metal seal. Working in the heat, smoke and fumes, he had collapsed and died in an effort to prolong the *Derna*'s life.

Those who rose early the following day witnessed a scene they would never forget. Sunrise at sea is a spiritual experience in which the dawn of creation is staged anew each morning. The dark horizon gradually lightens, as though illuminated from behind by an invisible celestial lamp, tinting the sky with wisps of rose, apricot and lemon. As the sun climbs above the vast horizon, it licks the crests of the waves with a silver light. But on this particular dawn, the attention of the passengers was distracted from the miracle in the sky. Gathered at the stern of the ship, several officers stood on either side of a plank on which the rotund body of the second engineer lay wrapped in the Panamanian flag. Beside the captain, Archbishop Rafalsky, an imposing figure with his long black robe and big silver *panagia* on his chest, was intoning a prayer to bless the soul of the departed engineer.

Wide-eyed with awe, Pauline Seitz clutched her mother's hand. But another little girl found this ceremony strangely comforting. It was

Ginette, whose heart beat faster when she heard the cadences of Christian prayers. They transported her to those happy days when she had been part of a loving Catholic family and would sit on polished wooden pews with her foster-parents on Sundays, listening to the chanting of the priest. Watching curiously from the top deck where she slept every night beside her mother and step-father, Ginette's friend Haneczka was puzzled by one aspect of the ceremony. Why had they retrieved the flag instead of leaving it wrapped around the dead man to keep him warm?

After the archbishop had finished praying, the captain and officers stood at attention while the seamen tipped the plank up. As the body slid into the sea, the water parted with a reverberating splash to receive it and quickly closed up again.

The finality of the burial at sea haunted those who witnessed it. Rita, who watched beside her mother, felt hot tears roll down her cheeks. 'That poor man,' she said. 'Now he'll be eaten by sharks.'

Her mother nodded. 'That's how it is,' she sighed. 'When you're dead, you're dead.'

Although the burial had cast a momentary gloom over the passengers and evoked philosophical reflections about the ephemeral nature of life, the presence of death reaffirmed the joy of being alive. Soon they regained their spirits and resumed their preoccupation with more worldly topics. Since Colonel Hershaw's seduction of the Italian girl, Dorothea's relationship with her boss had become restricted to her secretarial duties. Brisk and businesslike, she only entered his cabin to type letters and notices, collect the soap and cigarettes to distribute among the passengers and to make announcements over the megaphone.

But as she strolled along the deck with the first officer, she sometimes passed Colonel Hershaw deep in conversation with some of his Baltic friends and the comments she overheard made her bristle. Although she was not Jewish herself, she felt angry whenever she heard the derogatory remarks. It seemed to her that instead of trying to foster harmony among the people in his charge, as befitted the escort of a multi-racial group, Colonel Hershaw was actually stirring up racism and encouraging the formation of two enemy camps on board.

A recent incident had increased her mistrust of him. In the report he had written and sent to IRO Headquarters from Colombo, which she had typed, he had described the overcrowded, unsanitary conditions on board the *Derna*. Before sending the report, he had shown it to Dr Frant, who concurred with his views. As soon as the IRO received his report, they passed it on to Stavros Livanos who sent a wire to the captain straightaway, inquiring about the source of the complaints. At the dinner table one evening, Dorothea was shocked when Captain Papalas told her that when he had asked Colonel Hershaw about the report, he had categorically denied writing it. He said that it had probably been written by one of the Jewish passengers.

At about this time, one of the youngsters in Dr Frant's group was transfixed by something he saw in the washroom. As the German in the next shower raised his arm to soap himself, he saw the tattoo in his armpit. The German army tattooed SS officers with their blood group so that if wounded in battle, they could be transfused without delay. Everyone knew that after the war many SS men had tried to excise this mark, claiming that the resulting scar had been caused by a shrapnel wound or an abscess, so that they would escape investigation and be accepted as migrants. Having been persecuted by the Nazis, who had tattooed their emblem of slavery on his left arm, he was outraged. Within half an hour, the ship was buzzing with the news that a German SS officer was sailing to Australia with them.

Like most of the others in Dr Frant's group, Bill Marr was shocked that after all they'd suffered at the hands of the Nazis they now had to share a vessel with them and their collaborators. The Jewish boys felt that from the moment the voyage had started, the escort officer had been stirring the Baltic group up against them. He was always watching them, accusing them of vandalising the upholstery and furniture, and complaining to Dr Frant about their noise, untidiness, loud singing and rudeness. It was time he was stopped.

Restless for action, some of the orphans held a meeting on deck one night and plotted to get even with the hated colonel. 'We should throw him overboard one dark night!' one hothead suggested, but he was shouted down. Sensing that their frustration was rising, Dr Frant urged them to remain vigilant, but warned them against taking matters into their own hands. In an attempt to defuse their anger, he assured them that he would send a letter to the colonel's employers in Geneva, informing them of his predatory and divisive conduct during the voyage. Dorothea, with whom Dr Frant discussed the letter, typed it out and added her own observations about Colonel Hershaw's behaviour.

Frustration and anger continued to build up in Sam Fiszman as well. Esther had remained in sick bay, and although my mother and Mrs Frant helped to take care of little Maria, he felt agitated the whole time. Worried about Esther's emaciated state, he cornered the ship's doctor and pleaded for something to stop the seasickness.

Wiping his wife's clammy forehead and stroking her arm, which was so skinny that the tattoo stood out, he said, 'After all she's gone through, she shouldn't have to suffer like this.'

With his impassive expression, the doctor said, 'I've heard the passengers saying that some of you people had the numbers tattooed just to get a passage.' Sam clenched his teeth and gripped the edge of the bed until his knuckles were white to stop himself from punching this despicable man.

One night, in an attempt to pressure the captain to give him and Esther a cabin to themselves, Sam camped in the passageway outside the captain's quarters and lay the baby on a blanket beside him. Perhaps if her crying kept him awake he would agree to give him a separate cabin. But the captain was not impressed by this tactic. It merely confirmed his initial impression that this young man was a troublemaker.

'If you don't pick up that baby and go back to your cabin, I'll have you locked up,' he growled.

Sam delighted in irritating the passengers he perceived as Nazi sympathisers by hanging the blood-red Russian flag with its hammer and sickle near his bunk, above a group photo taken while he was in the Soviet army. On deck he often wore the army jacket with all the medals. Provoking glares and hostile mutterings helped to defuse his tension.

He was having breakfast one morning when a Jewish passenger reached across the table for the marmalade. Without any warning, one of the others at the table, a thick-set man of about forty whom Sam believed to be Estonian, grabbed the dish and smeared the marmalade in the Jew's face. Sam leapt to his feet, jumped up onto the table and lashed out at the attacker, but others pulled him away and stopped the fight.

At dinner a few days later, while some of the Jews were speaking Yiddish, the same man said to one of his companions, 'Pity we can't feed them to the sharks.'

Sam was boiling. Hitler had gone, the Holocaust was over, but the ancient hatred was still there. 'You scum,' he hissed. 'You fascist scum. If you've got the guts to fight it out, I'll teach you a lesson.'

The man shrugged. 'You talk big because you're sitting on the other side of the table,' he sneered. 'I'd like to hear what song you'd sing if you ever met me man to man.'

Sam's eyes blazed. 'Suits me,' he spat back. 'Whenever you're ready, I'll fight you.'

The following day, one of his adversary's cronies came looking for Sam. 'He wants to meet you up on the top deck around midnight when it's quiet and there's no one around,' he said.

Sam nodded, teeth clenched. 'I'll be there.' Later that day he told two young Greek sailors about the impending fight. They had a common bond because the sailors had fought with the partisans during the civil war that was still raging in Greece. When they heard about his midnight rendezvous, they offered to keep watch in case his opponent brought reinforcements.

It was quiet on the upper deck that night. The only sound was the dull hum of the sea and the plashing of the waves against the hull, but in the past few hours, the sea had become rougher and the ship was rocking from side to side. A new moon with edges so sharp they might have been carved from marble cast a pallid light over the bulkhead and lifeboats when Sam arrived at the appointed place ahead of his opponent.

He was pacing the deck when the man emerged from the shadows. Eyes locked, they walked towards each other and started throwing punches. Although Sam was shorter and less solid, he was younger and more nimble. He had learned hand-to-hand combat as a boy from an uncle who had been a jujitsu champion in Warsaw and had coached him. Later, while in the Russian army, he had consolidated his martial skills.

But it was Sam's fury that gave him the biggest advantage. When he looked at his adversary, he saw not one man but a whole battalion of Germans advancing towards him. Punching, darting, slapping and kicking, the combatants grappled to gain an advantage. As Sam later described the fight, after they had thrown a few punches, his opponent knocked him down. Sam lay on the deck on his back with his opponent poised to strike. He put all his strength into his legs and, taking his opponent by surprise, lashed out and kicked him off. At that moment, the ship lurched and the man toppled backwards. Unable to stop his momentum, he fell over the rail.

Motioning for Sam to disappear, the sailors gave the alarm. Whether his opponent had fallen overboard or onto the deck below, Sam couldn't tell, but he never saw him again.

On 12 October, the day that the *Derna* had been scheduled to dock in Melbourne, we were still wallowing in the Indian Ocean. As soon as the first star appeared in the evening sky, it ushered in Yom Kippur, the Day of Atonement, the most solemn day of the Jewish year. At this time, Jews are encouraged to take stock of their lives, accept responsibility for sins committed against God and man, and ask forgiveness of those they have wronged. Given their recent sufferings, the worshippers demonstrated admirable forgiveness towards the Creator who had allowed their families to perish on account of their faith.

On the Day of Atonement, observant Jews all over the world fast for twenty-four hours, to focus the mind on prayer and reflection. The fast usually concludes with a festive meal. Although the Jews knew that the traditional food was not available on board, the prospect of breaking the fast with the usual spaghetti and tomato sauce was dispiriting. A small delegation asked Colonel Hershaw, in his capacity as liaison officer between the passengers and the captain, to request that a more satisfying meal be prepared for them when Yom Kippur ended.

Colonel Hershaw surveyed the group in front of him with obvious distaste. These self-styled God-fearing Jews always complicated life with their unreasonable demands. Bristling with sarcasm, he said, 'I'm sure you're aware that the ship's menu is somewhat limited and that the chef can't procure special dainties in the middle of the ocean. But of course you'll be given every consideration.' With that he ushered them out, irritated to hear them muttering something about intolerance.

The next day, once again prayers were held in the stern, but by the time the first evening star brought the fast to an end, those who had abstained from food and drink for the past twenty-four hours could hardly wait for dinner. When the waiters started bringing around the usual spaghetti and tomato sauce, there was an uproar.

Some banged down their cutlery, others pushed their chairs noisily away from the table and left the food untouched. Later that evening a group protested to Colonel Hershaw about the lack of consideration they had been given. 'We politely requested a different meal after our religious fast but were ignored. Look at the inedible meal they served us! It's an insult! It's discrimination!'

Appalled at what he perceived as undisciplined, unruly behaviour, Colonel Hershaw decided to let them have it. He had played the role of the Good Samaritan long enough. 'The food on the ship is nourishing and substantial, but there are 545 passengers on board and we are not in a position to prepare special treats for special groups. You people just have to fit in and make do with whatever is available,' he told them. He noticed that the most outspoken members of the group were former IRO employees who had made a nuisance of themselves from the beginning of the voyage, wheedling favours and showering him and the officers with unsolicited and unwelcome advice.

The colonel decided to include his observations about these aggressive types in his report on the voyage, because from their expressions as they left his cabin, he could see that he hadn't heard the last of it.

18

While we were drifting towards Fremantle, the *Derna* was the subject of urgent memos being circulated within Australia's Department of Immigration. The letter from the information officer in Cairo about the 'headache ship' with its overcrowded conditions and excessive number of Jews aroused great concern in Canberra. If his report was true, it meant that the quota they had imposed was being flouted. To compound the problem, they knew that once the press got hold of this information, it would exacerbate public antagonism towards the immigration program. In order to find out the truth, a departmental memo asked the IRO for particulars about the nationality of the passengers, especially the number of Jews aboard, to be supplied urgently and added, 'Minister anxious that no undue publicity be given in the press re overcrowding.'

Several days later, a reply arrived from IRO Headquarters in Geneva, stating that out of 219 passengers travelling under its auspices, 61 were 'of Jewish extraction, thus approximating to the agreed figure of 25 percent'. The IRO telegram concluded with words that set alarm bells ringing in the offices of the Department of Immigration: 'We must disclaim any responsibility for composition of groups placed aboard by other agencies.'

As Canberra well knew, only two agencies were responsible for transporting most of the passengers, so the 'other agencies' referred to could only be JOINT. Noting the disturbing implication, the Department of Immigration official in Canberra scrawled at the bottom of the IRO telegram: 'The agents for the *Derna* were advised that the Jewish quota of passengers must not exceed 25 percent of the total passengers on the vessel. It would appear from this telegram that the vessel may have more than 25 percent Jewish passengers and that IRO is aware of this.'

The following day, after a hurried consultation with Mr Calwell, Mr J Horgan of the Department of Immigration wrote a memo in his exemplary copperplate handwriting. 'We received advice that the Jewish quota had been exceeded but the Minister did not desire any Jews on board to be restricted.

'Those disembarking at Fremantle will be allowed to land. It was also mentioned that we had received a report that the ship might prove a "headache" case, as it was definitely overcrowded. The press might play this up and we would like an early report as to conditions on ship generally.' It was arranged that a Commonwealth migration officer would board the *Derna* as soon as it arrived in Fremantle to investigate the situation.

But although our scheduled arrival date had come and gone, Fremantle was nowhere in sight as we continued to drift in the Indian Ocean.

'If we got into one of those lifeboats and started rowing, we'd get to Fremantle before the ship!' David Weiss joked.

'With our luck, there'd be a hole in the boat and we'd sink!' André Wayne retorted.

The others shrugged. 'We'll probably sink anyway, the way we're going.'

In the meantime, everyone peered at the horizon in the hope of seeing another ship.

To while away the endless hours, Gilda Brouen sometimes sang operatic arias on deck to the delight of the Italian stewards who loved music and sometimes joined in. With her musical training, Gilda felt that singing against the wind would strengthen her voice and help her get work when she auditioned in Melbourne. She longed to sing in opera, but was willing to accept any singing role she was offered to resume the career that the Nazis had cut short.

Whenever Dorothea walked past, they exchanged a few words, but although the two young women had travelled together from Berlin to Marseilles, they had drifted apart soon after the voyage began. Already in Marseilles Gilda had decided that her lively travelling companion was very flirtatious, but after Dorothea had moved in with Colonel Hershaw they saw little of each other. Following the episode with the Italian girl, Dorothea had taken up with the first officer, and her old friend felt that she had been dropped in favour of more rarefied company.

Gilda, who spoke Italian, occasionally chatted with the young Italian girl who was still distressed about the incident with the colonel. Ashamed and humiliated, she gnawed her nails with worry. What if she became pregnant? What would her relatives say? The disgrace was unthinkable. Gilda tried to comfort and reassure her, furious that this unprincipled man had taken advantage of her vulnerability and was now strutting around the deck, ogling other potential victims.

The idea of writing a verse about the voyage had been germinating for some time and on a particularly tedious day, Gilda started to jot down some ideas. After poring over her poem for several days, she passed the 'Ballad of the *Derna*' to her cabin-mates Ilse and Elfriede, who laughed appreciatively at the way she had captured the boredom, gossip and distractions of shipboard life.

When she wrote, 'There's water, water all around, but little on the ship is found,' she was not exaggerating. Water had been rationed ever since we left Colombo. Whether this was due to the unexpected length of the voyage or to the fact that the captain had underestimated the amount we would need, the shortage became so acute that all the showers were turned off and water was only available for several hours each day. The captain's claim that passengers had been profligate with the supply only served to increase the general anger.

In the tropical heat, the water shortage caused desperate hardship, especially for mothers with babies. Rationing increased congestion in the washrooms as hundreds of passengers converged on the cramped area and had to queue for their turn. Babies screamed and toddlers whined while exasperated women shouted, jeered and abused each other.

'Wait your turn!'

'Didn't they teach you to stand in line?'

'What primitive hole in the ground did you crawl out of?'

'Look at her, Lady Muck, thinks she doesn't have to clean up after herself. Whoever saw such a disgusting mess?'

To avoid the chaos, Topka would wake the younger children late at night to wash their hair, because she discovered that there was a trickle of hot water at that time. Every few days Halina Kalowski would creep into the dining room to steal a few jugs of water and give Stefan a good wash. Hardly able to move in the heat through her advancing pregnancy, she spent most of the days slumped in a deck chair, a moistened handkerchief on her haggard face. For the thousandth time, she wished that she had gone ashore that first day when the captain had told the pregnant women to disembark.

The water shortage took Bill Marr back to the Death March from Auschwitz across Germany to Dachau three years before. They had already been marching for about ten days without food or water. The hunger was terrible but it was nothing compared to the excruciating thirst he felt when every cell in his body had screamed for water. Occasionally Bill would snap young shoots off the trees and suck the blessed moisture onto his parched tongue. When by some miracle it rained, some of the prisoners could not control themselves and threw themselves on the ground to scoop puddles of dirty water into their thirst-scabbed mouths. Near Kutno, when they reached a river, some were so crazed with thirst that they leapt in and drowned.

Somehow Bill had found the strength to keep going. Perhaps it was sheer bloody-mindedness, a refusal to let the enemy triumph now when the end of the war was so close. A few days later, they were stumbling across a potato field. Desperate for something to drink, they started digging through the clods of earth with the metal mugs they'd brought from the camp. They had almost given up hope when water suddenly spurted up. Artesian water, but water just the same. The rabbi who was hobbling along with them said, 'Today is the holy day of Tish B'Av. This water is a miracle from God!' Bill wasn't religious but when he heard the rabbi's words his gaunt face was split by a grin as he said, 'All right, I'll accept that!'

* * *

After the Yom Kippur incident, tensions continued to rise not only between the passengers, but also among the feuding crew who still lashed out at each other. The air at night was thick with conspiracy and hate, as dishes clattered in the kitchen above hurried whispers and meaningful looks were exchanged over platters piled with macaroni, mutton and chocolate blancmange. After the last passengers had straggled out of the dining room and all the plates had been washed and slammed back into the cupboards, the galley doors were closed and the combatants confronted each other with murder in their eyes.

They were advancing towards each other, eyes locked, when an unexpected chink of light widened in the doorway and distracted their attention. It was Captain Papalas. Instead of his usually mild, worried expression, his eyes were hard and his face was set in anger. In his hand was a snub-nosed pistol. The combatants dropped their rigid stance, backed down and slunk away. The stand-off was over and for the time being authority had been restored.

Cheering and shouting broke out as soon as we caught sight of the rugged Australian shore, baked ochre by the brilliance of the sun. In the general scramble for a place against the rail, we craned and twisted our necks for our first view of the great southern continent we had finally reached. The *Derna* sailed into Fremantle Harbour, edged her way into the channel and berthed. 'We're in Australia now!' my father said in a voice ringing with significance.

'Thank God!' my mother sighed.

I couldn't see anything of interest on the wharf below and wished I could go back to my knitting. My skeins of coloured wool had all been knitted into separate pieces destined to become jackets and skirts, but they looked messy. Before going ashore I wanted to fit them together and stitch them as seamlessly as I could.

Soon after the *Derna* docked, two immigration officers boarded the ship. Their informality endeared them to the passengers. They had reddish hair and boyish freckled faces, and didn't throw their weight around or bully anyone. If they were typical of Australians, then we had come to the right country. With good-natured smiles that few of the passengers had ever seen on the faces of government officials, the officers ticked off names from their long lists, made sure that people had the right documents, checked medical records and handed out landing cards. Inevitably, some passengers had mislaid their papers or had no record of vaccination against smallpox or x-rays for TB, and these omissions were reported to Canberra.

Introducing himself as the escort officer appointed by the IRO to accompany the migrants, Colonel Hershaw handed the officers a letter written by one of the passengers in his group.

Dear Sir,

May I bring to your attention the following matter concerning possible infiltration of Communist agents with immigrants to Australia.

1. Background.

Before and during German invasion of Czechoslovakia and Poland, the Jewish element fled to USSR.

During the war, they became ardent Bolsheviks and took active part in Red army as well as in war industry as commissars, political supervisors and NKVD agents, being admitted to Communist Party; the youth to 'komsomol' (Communist youth).

After V-Day thousands of these persons returned from USSR to Germany in possession of Polish, Hungarian, Romanian and Czechoslovakian (Soviet satellite government) passports and claiming themselves Displaced Persons.

It may be noted that not a single Christian have left those countries in possession of an official passport!

2. Communist activity among immigrants on board SS Derna.

Information shows: of 451 IRO and AJDC passengers a great majority (about 3/4) are of Jewish origin and most of them with Soviet satellite passports, claiming citizenship of these countries.

Many of these persons during the voyage from Marseilles made Communist propaganda by 1) favouring Soviet regime and totalitarian system, 2) singing Soviet propaganda songs, 3) causing unrest among the crew as well as passengers, 4) making favourable comments concerning foreign policy of Soviet Union, 5) playing Russian gramophone records over the ship's loudspeaker system.

Who can tell how many Soviet agents are there among these persons? What are their objectives? How they could flee with official passports from behind the 'Iron Curtain'?

The following facts can be corroborated by many co-passengers who wish to remain unmentioned in this report but are available for any further evidence if required:

1. ORENSTEIN, immigrant Jew, about 25, has been noticed to be a leader of a group about 20 youth, lauding Soviet system, singing Soviet songs, played Russian gramophone records, contacted the crew of Derna for the purpose of Communist propaganda causing unrest among them.

2. FISZMAN, immigrant Jew, about 28, openly declaring and favouring Soviet totalitarian regime, admitting his Communist views. Twice had a quarrel with co-passengers on political ground.

3. Unidentified immigrant Jew, about 40, singing Soviet propaganda songs, caused unrest among co-passengers, afterwards tried to explain these songs being Ukrainian national songs and himself as Ukrainian.

Yours very truly,

Verner H. Puurand. Commander Estonian Navy, ret.

The immigration officer who passed the letter on to his superiors little suspected that it was to create a furore in government circles, create headlines and make the *Derna* a household name throughout Australia.

* * *

Before we were permitted to disembark, two policemen boarded the ship and made straight for the captain's cabin. Ever since we had entered Australian waters, Captain Papalas had been wondering about the repercussions if Australian authorities discovered the real number of Jews on board, so he had anticipated a visit from immigration officials, but not from the police.

Everyone was mystified by the presence of the policemen. Those who had spent much of their lives waiting for the dreaded knock on the door speculated that they were Australia's secret police. When a succession of people were seen entering and leaving the captain's cabin, other theories were put forward. Some surmised that the officers had come to arrest the German with the tattoo, while others wondered whether they had come for the Communists.

Verner Puurand was the first to be interviewed because it was his letter that had triggered the investigation. Questioned at length about his allegations, he reiterated his claims that subversive elements on board had sung Soviet songs, spread propaganda and fomented unrest among the crew. During the interview, he added two more agitators to his list. They were the Polish couple, Guta and Dick, whose crime, in his view, was that they had spent all their time on deck talking to two seamen. But despite their searching questions, the officers were unable to elicit a shred of evidence to substantiate his claims that this couple, or the others he had named, were Communist agents.

Immigration and police officers spent most of the day on the ship. After all the documents had been checked and the passengers cleared for disembarkation, one couple was ordered to remain on board until further notice. The officials decided that the allegations Puurand had made against Sam Fiszman were serious enough to warrant further investigation, but Guta and Dick were permitted to go ashore. Not even in the post-war Communist paranoia that gripped Australia in 1948 did talking to sailors constitute dangerous subversion.

When Guta was informed about the accusation, she was worried in case it placed a black mark against their names even before they had set foot in Australia. Would their names be recorded in the police files forever? And would this cause trouble for their sponsors? It upset her to think that in return for their kindness, they were to be hounded by police or placed under suspicion. To add to her anxiety, someone told her that the Australian Intelligence Service was as implacable as Fouchet's secret police during the French Revolution, and once they started hounding a victim, they never let up.

Unaware of the problems of some of the other passengers, my parents and I disembarked to find Bronek and Pola Stein waiting for us on the wharf. Although my parents had never met the Steins, they were connected through other distant, and equally unknown, connections in Brisbane who had sent our landing permit. While our parents spoke to each other in Polish, six-year-old Gary Stein and I sat in awkward silence on the low wall that ran beside City Beach, swinging our bare legs while a blustery wind whipped my face and neck with needle-sharp grains of sand.

My parents were charmed by Perth, its brick bungalows fronted with neatly clipped lawns and bright gardens that resembled idealised scenes in picture books, complete with a cat or dog on every doorstep. 'That must be what they mean by saying that "an Englishman's home is his castle,"' my father said, quoting a phrase from his English textbook. With obvious pride, the Steins drove us around the sunny town along the banks of the Swan River where they had settled shortly before the war. Any apprehension my parents had felt about coming to Australia melted away with the Steins' warm welcome and the relaxed atmosphere of this city where people smiled and greeted strangers in the street.

Other passengers were also discovering the delights of Australia. For many youngsters it was literally the land of milk and honey, as they drank frothed-up milk flavoured with chocolate or strawberry, licked ice cream cones and bit into chocolate bars. After the privations of the war and the rationing of post-war Europe, the casual abundance of food in the shops astounded everyone. Inside the butcher shops, men in blue striped aprons smeared with blood slapped great slabs of meat the colour of rubies down on the scales, while at the greengrocers cases overflowed with oranges that cost only two shillings a bucket. A Greek milk bar owner beckoned to shy Mattie Travasaros and her sister and handed them strawberry ice creams. This time they ate them before they melted.

With the ten shillings each of the orphans received from the Australian Jewish Welfare Society, most of them rushed out to buy milk shakes which they had never tasted before. Topka, who received two pounds for herself and her sisters, hovered outside a cake shop, peering at the prices speared into each cake on stiff triangular signs: 2/-, 1/3. What did those numbers mean? As she stood trying to figure out the prices, one of the engineers she knew from the ship walked past, a good-looking young Greek with a glossy black moustache. Speaking in German so she would understand, he asked her to come inside and started pointing to coconut slices, cream buns, cup cakes and lamingtons. When the salesgirl had wrapped them up, he handed the bulging parcel to Topka and refused to let her pay. 'For you and your sisters,' he said.

One of the orphans bought several tins of plums and apricots with his ten shillings, only to discover when he later opened them that he had been misled by the illustrations on the labels and had purchased jam instead of fruit. But it made a welcome change from the marmalade they spread on their bread every morning.

When Perth's Jewish community heard that the ship in the harbour had brought sixty-one orphans to their city, they converged on the *Derna* with boxes of apples and oranges and distributed them among all the children on board. They invited the orphans into their homes and treated them like long-lost children. It was Sukkoth, the harvest festival, and after the synagogue service a party was given in their honour. They stared at a table piled with white bread sandwiches with the crusts cut off, sponge cakes, fruit slices, cup cakes, chocolate crackles, biscuits, jellies and orange drinks. No one had seen such a spread in the past ten years or met such warm-hearted, generous people who couldn't seem to do enough for their young guests.

The affection was mutual. Many Perth families were so taken with these youngsters that they didn't want them to leave. Mingled with their admiration and compassion was a twinge of guilt that they had escaped from Europe before the war, while these teenagers had suffered so much. They longed to give them a home and find partners for them among the closely knit Jewish community which certainly needed an infusion of new blood. The warmth of this community was so seductive that some of the orphans wanted to stay there rather than continue on to Melbourne, but Dr Frant reminded them that they had to complete the voyage, as arranged by the Jewish Welfare Society.

Bill Marr was invited home by a family who had migrated from Palestine after World War I and had settled in Perth because they didn't have enough money to travel further east. As they sat on the balcony, eating oranges that were available here in such marvellous profusion and luxuriating in the sunshine, his hosts advised him to stay in Melbourne instead of going on to Sydney. 'The Jewish community in Melbourne has a heart, most of them come from Hungary and Poland. They'll welcome you, but the Sydney Jews are cold, mainly from England or Germany. They won't help you,' they warned.

The following day was Sunday, and those who wandered around Perth were amazed to see that the city had become a ghost town. In the suburbs, however, women wearing brightly coloured dresses and hats decorated with bows and flowers were strolling to church. For Elmars Kuplis, arriving in Australia was a milestone he wanted to mark with a prayer of thanksgiving. Inside the Anglican church in town, tears of gratitude misted his eyes as he looked at his little family. He had resolved never to be separated from them again, and God had helped him bring them safely across the seas. For Silva Rae, Fremantle had a special significance, because her little daughter Anneke took her first tottering steps on the wharf.

After having been cut off from friends and relatives for so long, it was thrilling to get letters again. Kurt Herzog received a letter from his sister in Sydney with a crisp five-pound note folded inside. Although this was all the money he owned, he immediately shared his windfall with his friend Elsie Pataky, whose ballooning stomach now made it obvious that confinement could not be far off. She had been waddling around barefoot ever since her flimsy sandals had fallen apart early in the voyage. As he gave her half his money, Kurt said, 'Buy yourself a pair of shoes.'

Emil Kopel, who turned twenty in Fremantle, also had a stroke of luck. His guardian, whom he had never met before, flew to Perth to meet him. For Emil's birthday he gave him his first Australian money, a one-pound note that lasted him for three weeks.

Helle's parents had also been sent five pounds in the mail. Feeling prosperous, Helle set off for the shops with one of her cabin-mates. She knew what she wanted to buy. After finding the English word for brassiere in the dictionary, she repeated it several times to make sure she got it right. Looking into the shop windows, she thought that clothes here were dowdy and old-fashioned, and that the women in their shorter, brightly patterned dresses lacked style.

As they strolled along the street, she noticed a man following them as though trying to eavesdrop on their conversation. Feeling uneasy, she was about to quicken her step when he caught up and started talking to them. He had apparently migrated from Estonia many years before and had almost forgotten the language, but hearing their conversation had stirred his memory. Helle was shocked. How could you forget your own language?

As they turned into a department store, she repeated the word she had learnt in the dictionary before entering the women's lingerie section. Brassiere. To her dismay, however, the saleswoman couldn't understand what she was saying, no matter how many times she repeated it. Finally, with a flushed face and cringing with embarrassment, she had to point to what she wanted. 'You mean a bra!' the saleswoman exclaimed.

Not all the letters contained good news, however. On their first day in Australia, some passengers discovered that relatives who had promised to take them in had changed their minds. Anna Szput could hardly believe her eyes as she read that her cousin had let them down. He was sorry that he would not be able to meet them when they arrived in Melbourne because he was exhausted and was going away on a holiday, but he had arranged for someone else to meet them instead.

While the rest of us went ashore, Sam and Esther Fiszman were forbidden to leave the ship because of Puurand's allegation. When Archbishop Rafalsky heard that Sam had been accused of Communist agitation and was being confined on board, he wrote a letter of support, denying that his young friend had engaged in any subversive activities and vouching for his good character. Thanks to the archbishop's intercession, as well as to the assurances of the Jewish community who guaranteed that Sam would return to the ship, he and Esther were allowed to go ashore. The authorities decided that there would be time to look into the allegations when the *Derna* reached Melbourne.

In the meantime, they had other problems to deal with. The master of the *Derna* reported seven stowaways who had no valid documents or permits to enter Australia. Their thumb prints were taken and forwarded to Canberra, but by the time we sailed from Fremantle, two of them had absconded. Warrants for their arrest were issued and a reward was offered for any information leading to their apprehension.

To the captain's relief, at the request of the Commonwealth migration officer for Western Australia no action was taken about the number of Jews on board. Better to keep it quiet, they reasoned, than risk controversy and create a public uproar.

Even before the *Derna* had reached Australian shores, there had been some concern in the Department of Immigration about the conditions on board migrant ships. On the day we sailed for Melbourne, an editorial in the *Adelaide News* called for an inquiry into the matter, claiming that unscrupulous European shipping companies were exploiting migrants. Although the subject of the article was the SS *Napoli*, the Department of Immigration suspected that conditions on the *Derna* were far worse and likely to attract even more criticism.

Among the officials who boarded the *Derna* in Fremantle to accompany her to Melbourne was Major William Weale. Although his function was ostensibly to complete the passenger cards and facilitate the registration of aliens before they disembarked, his task was to investigate conditions on board and report to the Department of Immigration. From the moment he set foot on the vessel he was appalled by the filth, neglect and overcrowding he saw.

Thirty-seven passengers disembarked in Fremantle to begin their new life on Australia's west coast. Among them was Arnold Ohtra, with his wife and daughters Tiia and Lea. Philip Georgiades and his wife

Germaine also left the ship at Fremantle. They decided to catch the train to Melbourne at their own expense rather than spend another day on the *Derna*.

As the *Derna* slowly pulled away from the wharf on the final leg of the voyage to Melbourne, everyone was discussing the investigation into the so-called Communists. Since the name of the author of the allegations hadn't been made public, passengers speculated about his identity. Some, like Dr Frant, thought it must have been the German with the SS tattoo.

But the man with the tattoo was no longer on board. Someone recalled seeing him go ashore in Fremantle with his attractive dark-haired wife, but he had not returned. People were furious that he had given them the slip and escaped justice. Only a few passengers knew the truth: although the German had been an SS officer, he had protected a Jewish girl during the war and saved her life. They had fallen in love and married, and after the war ended, she reciprocated by protecting him from retribution. They had come to Australia to start a new life far from the tragedies of the past.

No one was more impatient for the journey to end than Halina Kalowski. She was now seven months pregnant, haggard and listless. She had consulted a medico in Perth to check whether she should leave the ship and complete the journey by air. Despite her pale face, strained expression and the dark rings under her eyes, he saw no reason to worry. Her pulse was good and the foetal heart beat was strong.

'You'll be fine,' he assured her. 'There's no reason why you shouldn't continue the voyage. After all, you still have two months to go.'

19

Sitting on her bunk, Elfriede Hof was writing in the morocco leather diary in which she recorded every detail of the voyage in her neat, well-spaced handwriting. This time she was noting the natural phenomenon we had witnessed the previous day. After a morning of gusty winds and rough seas in the Great Australian Bight, at 2.18 in the afternoon the light suddenly began to fade. The moon's shadow swept across the sun and within a short time only a brilliant crescent remained visible at the edge. Primitive tribes interpret a solar eclipse as an evil portent signifying the anger of the gods, but even the passengers of the *Derna* shivered as darkness fell over the world. As the moon continued its path across the sun, the crescent of light gradually grew larger, and two hours later, the moon slid off and daylight returned. A sigh went up, part disappointment that the miracle was over, and part relief because the world had become familiar once more. For many passengers, however, this spectacle was soon to be eclipsed by another natural phenomenon which occurred just as unexpectedly the following day.

Having recorded most of the previous day's events, Elfriede glanced out of the porthole, put her pen down and called her sister. 'Ilse, come and look at this!' A stocky man was lurching up the gangplank, clutching a bottle in each hand. It was the chief stoker. They had often seen him emerging from the engine room, a sodden kerchief tied around his beefy neck. After leaning against the rail for a few minutes to gulp fresh air, he would return to the inferno. Accompanying the stoker onto the ship was one of his mates whose unsteady legs also buckled as he attempted to steer him along the gangway. They'd obviously had a merry time in Fremantle on their last day ashore.

Elfriede had spent her day sampling Australian food, the wonders of which she was recording in her journal. Big ham rolls, luscious ice cream and chocolate sold in blocks. Although she wanted her supply to last until we reached Melbourne, she couldn't resist and snapped off another square. As she munched, she felt more optimistic than she'd felt for weeks.

The clanking of the anchor reassured us that we were finally leaving Fremantle. As the ship started to move away from the shore, young Nick Matussevich looked down and saw a dead albatross lying on the deck. When he ran down to Cabin 14 to tell his mother, she said in a sepulchral tone that sent a shiver down his back, 'That means death'.

Several hours later, the little green island of Rottnest came into sight, and Clara Kraus pointed it out to Peter and Paul, holding them up for a better view. Although she had done her best to keep them away from the other children, they were both coughing. She smiled down at them. 'Not long now. Only a few more days and we'll be in Melbourne.'

Clara had hated the *Derna* from the moment she walked up the gangplank and she hated the old rust bucket even more now, but at least they were almost there. But as she watched the West Australian coast recede, she became aware of a peculiar motion. Surely it wasn't possible, but she could have sworn the ship was turning around. A moment later, she knew she hadn't imagined it. They had made a full circle and were heading back towards Fremantle. Within minutes, the whole ship was buzzing with the news. Stamatios Sellas, the forty-year-old chief stoker, had collapsed and died.

Forced to stifle their chagrin at this new delay because of the tragedy, the passengers speculated on the cause of the unfortunate man's death. Those like Elfriede, who had watched him stumble aboard with his liquor, had no doubt that he'd drunk himself to death. Some elaborated, adding that he and his mate had made a wager to see who could drink the most and he had been the unlucky winner. Hearing that the stoker had drunk himself to death, Vassiliki Fatseas listened wide-eyed and formed her own impression of the incident. 'He must have burst!' she told Petro. The image of someone exploding after he'd consumed too much liquor lodged itself in her imaginative mind and haunted her for years to come.

By seven that evening, the ship had returned to port, where it was met by a police launch carrying Sergeant Bunt and Constable Johnson. With the appropriate air of official gravity, they took the body to the Fremantle morgue. When the passengers discovered that the death certificate had been issued by the ship's doctor, they could not conceal their scorn. How could a medico who had succeeded in avoiding contact with live patients throughout the voyage possibly know what had caused death in someone who had expired?

After we had rounded Cape Leeuwin, everyone's spirits lifted. We were already in the Great Australian Bight and there seemed little between us and Melbourne's Port Phillip Bay. This was a great source of comfort to Halina Kalowski. She lay on the deck chair, her dark curls damp with perspiration from the humidity, and closed her eyes, wishing that when she opened them, she would see Melbourne.

She hardly noticed when her friend Matylda leaned over and wiped the beads of perspiration off her forehead. 'Can I get you anything to eat? You've hardly eaten anything for days,' she said. Halina shook her head. When she next opened her eyes, her husband Mietek and little son Stefan were looking at her with worried faces.

As Mietek handed her a glass of iced water, she tried to smile. 'I'll feel better as soon as the ship stops rocking. It's got worse, hasn't it?'

For the past few hours, the sea had been more churned up and flecks of foam crested on the rising waves. Mietek looked at his wife's dark-ringed eyes burning out of her thin face. Only three more days, he consoled her. She didn't want to tell him that for the past two days she hadn't felt the baby moving and that the stillness inside her womb terrified her.

By evening the ship pitched and heaved. The bow rose up as though trying to reach the sky, and after a brief pause plunged downwards as if diving to the bottom of the ocean.

Concerned about the children as always, Topka collected them up on her way to the washroom and urged them to hold onto the rails in the companionways. Her arm around little Ginette, who had never overcome her revulsion of communal washing, Topka gave her a hug. Poor kids. All they wanted was someone to love them and give them a cuddle.

At least now that the *Derna* had replenished its supplies in Fremantle there was ample water for washing clothes. Topka had washed out the children's underwear and had begun soaping the younger ones when the ship suddenly pitched and water sloshed all over the floor. 'Hold on tight so you don't fall over!' she called out.

The door opened and the woman who had complained at the beginning of the voyage about having to share a cabin with Jews stepped inside with her little daughter. At that moment the ship lurched again and they both slipped and fell. Topka helped the little girl to her feet and guided her to the basin so she could hold on. In the meantime the mother, sprawled on the floor, looked beseechingly at Topka and called out, 'Come and help me!'

Topka gave her a withering look. 'I wouldn't want you to catch some terrible disease,' she said. 'I'll look after your child but you can pick yourself up.'

Out on deck, Petro had found a child's abandoned three-wheeler. He'd never seen such a thing before and after watching its wheels turn, he sat on it and pushed off. Just at that moment, a huge wave punched the side of the ship with such force that the tricycle, with Petro on it, hurtled towards the railing. Unable to stop it, he could feel his heart thumping with terror, certain that he would be flung into the churning waves. At the last moment he was yanked off the bike. He looked up into the strained white face of his sister Mary.

For the older Matussevich teenagers, the wave-tossed ship provided the most exhilarating ride of their lives. Standing at the bow of the *Derna* as she plunged and rose, plunged and rose, they held on to the rail and shrieked with sheer joy, feeling at one with the roller-coaster ocean. This was freedom.

That night, as wild waves tossed the ship from side to side, there was a frightening crash. The cutlery had fallen out of the drawers in the dining room and most of the crockery had smashed. Broken glass and large pieces of the thick white plates covered the floor. In the cabins, tables toppled over, suitcases slid across the floor, bags flew off bunks and glass splintered everywhere.

In all the chaos, Elfriede started giggling helplessly. 'The pram!' she gasped, holding her sides with laughter. 'Look at the pram!' As though it had a will of its own, the pram rolled across the cabin, stopped against a wall, and rolled back and forth with each movement of the ship.

In the morning, under a bruised sky, the decks were lonely, windswept and dismal, as people with greenish faces crawled out of cabins clutching their stomachs, heaving over the rails and wiping threads of mucus from their mouths. Defying the rough seas, they grabbed at the rails just before the next lurch, edged against walls to avoid being tossed from side to side, and clutched at banisters to avoid being hurled headfirst down the stairs. With most of the cups and plates broken, the waiters were relieved that few diners turned up for meals. Those who did found that the coffee sloshed perilously in their cups and boiled eggs rolled from one end of the long table to the other.

All day long in the Great Australian Bight the barometer tumbled. The swell ran ever higher and the ship wallowed in the deep furrows of the sea. Everything swung, slid, slanted, tilted or reeled from side to side as the ship was buffeted by waves that pounded it, while the gale whistled through the decks. Sheeted sprays drenched the ship from bow to stern. Throughout the wild night that followed, the old timbers of the *Derna* groaned and shuddered as though the vessel itself was engaged in a life and death struggle with the ocean.

A loud thump woke Halina from a fitful sleep. In the cramped, fetid cabin that stank of vomit, sweat and too many bodies crowded into one small space, the door snapped off its hinges. She sat up with a start. Where was Stefan? Unable to see him, she jumped off her bunk in panic. Immediately she doubled up in pain. Holding her belly, she wondered whether the cramp was caused by something she had eaten, or perhaps she had pulled a muscle when she sat up so suddenly. A frightening thought squatted in the corner of her mind like an invisible toad croaking on the edge of a pond, but she dismissed it. It wasn't possible. She still had two months to go.

Next morning, the waves slapped the ship with less ferocity and the passengers began to clean their devastated cabins by picking up soiled blankets, shaving mugs and shattered glass. When Matylda glanced over at Halina, she stopped what she was doing. Halina's pupils were dilated and she was biting her lip in an effort to stop herself from crying out. 'Halina, what is it?' she asked, looking at her friend in alarm. Surely it couldn't be the baby, not now, with only two days to go before we reached Melbourne. Her mouth dry with pain and fear, Halina whispered hoarsely, 'Matylda, I'm in labour.'

She had recognised the spasms that were convulsing her body, and knew that with the second baby, labour wouldn't last very long. What she had dreaded was about to happen, without a competent ship's doctor or even a delivery ward and two months too soon. The captain's warning on that first day came back to haunt her. Where could she give birth? Who would help her? And could such a premature baby survive, especially on this ship?

There was no point going for the elusive Dr Themelis. When Matylda ran to tell Mietek that his wife was about to give birth, he rushed to find Dr Frant. As it happened, he was an obstetrician from the Polish town of Bydgoszcz. Although his authoritative manner and commanding presence inspired confidence in others, on this occasion he didn't feel it himself. As he knew only too well, even in well-equipped hospitals babies born at seven months had little chance of surviving, and the *Derna* had no facilities of any kind for confinement. He only hoped the birth would be straightforward, but what would happen afterwards, God only knew.

As Mietek's cabin was larger and airier than Halina's, Dr Frant decided that it would be the best place. The occupants were asked to vacate it and sheets were draped around the bunk where Halina lay to give her some privacy. Her eyes bulged in her pale face and her hands gripped the side of the bunk with each contraction, while Matylda smoothed her hair from her perspiring forehead and sponged her with a damp cloth. As the head crowned, Dr Frant said, 'Hold her chin down to help her push.' Halina moaned and dug her fingers into her friend's hand as the veins stood out on her temples, and with the last of her strength, she pushed out the baby. As the tiny body slipped out, Dr Frant cut the cord. Tears of joy, exhaustion and relief poured down Halina's face as she held her tiny daughter who looked like a bruised little bird.

The delivery over, Dr Frant promised to return later to check on them. 'This baby is very tiny,' he said to Matylda on his way out, shaking his head. The expression on his face made further comment unnecessary. Matylda looked at the baby, hardly bigger than a kitten, and knew that she shouldn't be handled too much. Recalling the way premature babies were swaddled in Poland, she placed her on a pillow and wrapped a sheet around the entire bundle, marvelling at this miracle of nature. 'Look how perfect she is,' she whispered to Halina, whose eyes shone with love.

Mietek, who had been hovering outside the cabin waiting for news of the birth, broke down and wept when he heard that it was over and his wife and baby were well. Taking charge, Matylda sent him to find hot water bottles for the baby. Glad to have something to do, he did the rounds of the ship and returned with four of them, which they filled with hot tap water and spread around the baby to keep her warm. Late that night, Matylda was startled from her sleep by a man's voice. 'I'm sorry to wake you but could you come and put the baby's arm back inside the pillow?' Mietek was whispering. 'I'm frightened that she'll catch cold but I'm afraid to move her arm in case it breaks!'

Later in the day, Halina had an unexpected visitor. 'So it's you!' the captain growled, recognising the woman who had presented herself on the first day of the voyage with the other pregnant women. 'You got yourself into this! I told you there were no facilities on board for delivery.' His gaze softened when he peered at the miniature human being cradled in her mother's arms, but he shut the door behind him with more force than necessary. Halina was too euphoric to care.

As the baby was too weak to suck, Halina expressed the milk and fed her with an eye dropper, while Matylda supplemented it with sugar and water. The baby weighed around one and a half kilos, had a blueish tinge and a cry like a sick bird. Hour by hour, she became more listless and Halina grew more apprehensive. Would love and determination be enough to keep her alive for the next few days?

She decided to call the baby Jennifer Fay Derna. Jennifer was an anglicised version of Mietek's mother's name and aptly meant 'white wave'. Fay was after her mother who had been murdered in the Warsaw Ghetto. Her father's last words to her had been, 'Whatever happens to us, you must survive.' Halina smiled at the tiny scrap of life in her arms, so perfectly formed, and born in Australian waters. She had survived. And so would little Jennifer.

20

By one of those strange quirks of fate that make fact more incredible than fiction, the *Derna* arrived in Melbourne on Guy Fawkes Day. Although few of the passengers had heard of the dissident who had attempted to blow up the English parliament back in 1605, it seemed appropriate to end a voyage marked with feuds, plots and intrigues on a day that commemorated the victory of law and order over mayhem and violence.

At dawn, when grey skies shed a grudging light over the water, the pilots came on board. As the ship nosed into the harbour, anxious faces clustered on the top deck for their first glimpse of the city which for many would become home. Impatience for the voyage to end mingled with anxiety. Despite its hardships, the journey had kept real life at bay, but now they would have to meet it full on. Even the most optimistic souls sighed when they looked out at land that crouched sullen and intractable under the drizzle along the damp Victorian coast.

Few passengers could sleep the night before the *Derna* berthed at 29 South Wharf. Kitty Lebovics emerged from her cabin red-eyed. Never had she felt so abandoned since the day the war ended and she discovered at the age of thirteen that she was alone in the world. The future she had contemplated with such equanimity had now arrived, and it terrified her. What did Australia hold for her? Why had she crossed the seas to live among strangers? Through friendships and flirtations she had become attached to her fellow orphans in Dr Frant's group. The close proximity, shared experiences and vicissitudes of the voyage had melded them into one big supportive family, but now they were about to be dispersed. Some were staying in Melbourne, others would travel to Brisbane, while she was bound for Sydney. What would happen to the bond they had formed?

Topka, always so strong for others, locked herself in the cabin and sobbed as the enormity of the situation overwhelmed her. She had brought her three young sisters to a foreign land and was responsible for them. How would she be able to take care of them? What would become of them when they arrived? Where would they go?

In her distress, she heard Dr Frant's firm voice outside the cabin. 'Topka!' he called in the peremptory tone that made opposition unthinkable. 'Topka! Pull yourself together! We have to get the children organised. Unlock the door!' She blew her nose, mopped her streaming eyes, straightened her slim shoulders and opened the door. He looked searchingly into her face and patted her shoulder. 'Don't worry. You'll see, everything will turn out fine.'

Too excited to finish breakfast, Lars Meder stuffed bread and marmalade into his mouth, gulped down his coffee and rushed out on deck so as not to miss a moment of this occasion. Only two more days and he'd see his father again. Reaching into his pocket he checked that the crisp pound note was still there. He was glad he hadn't spent it on one of those fizzy pink drinks he had coveted in the bar. Now he'd have a whole pound to spend in Auckland.

Suddenly he stared. Something was moving in Port Phillip Bay. Had he imagined it? He frowned and leaned over the rail, straining to see it again. He held his breath as a column of spray fanned out and a moment later a powerful black fluke sliced through the water, flipped over and disappeared beneath the waves. A whale! He rushed to tell his mother. It had to be a good omen.

Rain was pattering on the water at seven in the morning when Major William Weale, the Aliens Registration Officer who had boarded the vessel in Fremantle, returned with two members of his staff. While they checked passenger cards, x-rays and medical certificates, Major Weale had been asked by Tasman Heyes, the Secretary of the Immigration Department, to investigate the alleged infiltration of the *Derna* by Communist agents. In a departmental memo Mr Heyes expressed his personal doubts about these claims, saying that they had emanated 'from a person who gives evidence of anti-Semitic tendencies and some of whose statements are, to say the least, exaggerated'. Although they were obliged to investigate the matter, he urged Major Weale to take every precaution to ensure it was given no publicity and to warn all parties concerned against speaking to the press.

Major Weale lost no time in seeking out Colonel Hershaw about the allegations made in the letter he had handed to the authorities in Fremantle. 'You should speak to Verner Puurand,' Hershaw told him. 'He was the one who reported these Communist incidents to me.' Before leaving the cabin, he hesitated for a moment and lowered his voice. 'You should know that Puurand is fanatically anti-Communist,' he added.

A few minutes later, the cabin door opened and a stern-looking man of medium height with a bony face and a receding hairline stepped inside. First the major questioned Puurand about his allegations regarding the Polish couple, Guta and Dick, who according to him had spent so much time on deck talking to members of the crew and stirring them up. But when the major asked him specifically what they had said, Puurand was forced to admit that he had never actually overheard their conversations.

Next Major Weale asked for details about the so-called Communist propaganda that he had accused the Jews of spreading. Puurand replied that while discussing the merits of various types of government, some passengers had said they preferred the Soviet system. As proof of his allegations about Soviet songs that caused unrest among the crew and passengers, he mentioned that someone had played Russian records on a portable gramophone. When Major Weale probed for details to substantiate his claims about spreading propaganda, Puurand was unable to name the songs or give a single instance of unrest. In the end, all he could say was that some of the Baltic passengers had felt resentful when they heard those songs.

The next person interviewed by Major Weale was Dr Frant. When asked about the Jewish passenger who had upset Puurand by singing Russian songs over the PA system, Dr Frant explained that the man in question was a professional singer who had been asked by his companions to sing some folk songs to relieve the monotony of the voyage. Because of the vagueness of Puurand's accusations, Major Weale decided there were no grounds for interviewing Sam Fiszman, the Polish couple or the singer.

Proceeding with his investigation, Major Weale questioned the chief purser about various aspects of the voyage. As soon as he mentioned Colonel Hershaw, the vehemence of Adnan Molvan's reaction startled him. 'That man was the biggest and only nuisance we had on board!' he said.

The last person to be interviewed was the master of the *Derna*, who said that he had had a very long and tiring voyage as a result of poor-quality coal. He'd had to restrict fresh water supply as the passengers were wasteful, and he'd taken the necessary precautions not to run out of water. When questioned about the escort officer, he said that Hershaw had been divisive in favouring the Baltic people, voicing anti-Semitism on board ship and creating general ill-feeling. 'Hershaw came to me with a report about some allegations of Communist activity and asked me to sign it, but I said no,' Captain Papalas said. 'There was no such activity among the passengers that I or any of my officers ever noticed.'

Amid the chaos of departure, Liszt's *Hungarian Rhapsody*, which had become irritatingly familiar over the past ten weeks, was blaring full blast once again as the passengers lugged bags, baskets and hold-alls past companionways heaped with boxes and bulging suitcases. They rushed back to their cabins to pick up forgotten belongings, screamed at their children to stay close to them, scribbled last-minute names and addresses of their ship-mates, wished each other luck and promised to stay in touch. Cabins that for almost three months had seemed as confining as prison cells now appeared secure and comforting. Helle and Lea clung to each other. With tears in their eyes, they reassured each other that they would write and visit. Vala was grief-stricken when she said goodbye to Archbishop Rafalsky. An island of calm amid the shouting and jostling, the prelate raised his almost transparent hands over the heads of Bob Grunschlag and Abie Goldberg as he blessed them and wished them peace in their new lives.

The relationship between Colonel Hershaw and Dorothea had become so frosty that she left the ship without saying goodbye. As she walked down the gangplank, her curly hair bouncing around her eager face, her red leather bag in one hand and her Triumph typewriter under her arm, she didn't look back.

But now that it was too late, she wanted to kick herself for being such a fool and not demanding payment for the secretarial work she had done. He had never even broached the subject, but had behaved like a generous patron, buying her a skirt and blouse in Port Said when he should have paid her a salary. And he'd had the gall to ask for her little silver signet ring as a memento. What cheek. She was sad that she wouldn't see the first officer again, but as for Ogden Hershaw, if she never saw him again it would be too soon. At least he had written her a reference, condescending though it was.

'It is hereby certified that Miss Dorothea Ritter served as my secretary and executive assistant during the recent voyage from Marseilles to Melbourne with six hundred displaced persons from various European countries, a period of some two months.

'Miss Ritter showed herself most capable as a clerk, secretary, interpreter, troubleshooter and in numerous other ways, giving me invaluable aid during the extremely tedious and trying voyage. I was favourably impressed by her tact, resourcefulness and — rare in a female — her ability to think logically and act on her own initiative.'

Colonel Hershaw, however, was feeling particularly pleased with himself. He had just completed his detailed report about this appalling voyage, which he'd begun with the words: 'It is recommended most emphatically that this ship, being in its present condition entirely unfit to carry passengers, shall not be used by the IRO for transport of displaced persons.'

He had itemised the sloppiness of the crew, the criminal lack of medical facilities, the lack of hygiene, the abysmal incompetence of the doctor, and the uncouth behaviour of the chief purser whom he described as a bandit. Although he praised Dr Frant for his unstinting medical assistance, he criticised the Jewish passengers, especially those who had worked for UNRRA, citing the Yom Kippur contretemps as an illustration of their demanding nature and lack of gratitude. He mentioned 'undercover radical propaganda' and destruction of the ship's equipment by a group of Jewish youngsters. As though writing a military report, he concluded: *'Despite vigilant efforts on the part of my security forces, none of them were apprehended.'*

In contrast, the escort officer praised the wholehearted co-operation he'd been given by his Baltic group who had just presented him with a letter of appreciation he would always treasure. They wrote:

'The ninety-nine Baltic passengers en route to Australia under the auspices of the IRO wish to express their gratitude to the organisation which has made it possible for them to become resettled in security and freedom in this new homeland of ours...

'We have among us The Hon Ogden Hershaw who, thanks to his ability to foresee unexpected eventualities, and meet them with tact and kind understanding, has made easy for us this otherwise difficult voyage among these fifteen other nationalities.

'We Baltic people have forever in our hearts deep thanks and sincere appreciation to a fine Canadian officer and Gentleman. God bless Him!

'As a token of that appreciation, which cannot be properly expressed or interpreted we ask you, our Dear Colonel, to receive this small gift in the sincere spirit in which it is given, that it may always remind you of the Baltic peoples who love freedom and the democratic principles of the Western World.'

It was signed by Verner Puurand, Commander (retired) Estonian Navy, Pastor Friedrich Stockholm, and R Bode as the Latvian spokesman.

As Colonel Hershaw was about to disembark, he noticed Emanuel Darin, one of the former UNRRA employees he had crossed swords with during the voyage. Darin was one of the 'Jewish ringleaders' he had referred to in his report. Striding towards him, the Colonel extended his hand with a jovial smile. 'I do hope that we can put the unpleasantness of the voyage behind us,' he said in a hearty tone.

Emanuel's expression could have frosted boiling water. 'Your behaviour on the ship was disgraceful,' he retorted. 'I intend to write to the IRO about it. I hope they never employ you as an escort officer on a migrant ship again.' And with that, he turned on his heel and strode away.

It may have been this exchange that prompted Ogden Hershaw to add the final paragraph to his report. '*As a Public Relations man I am keenly aware of the sad fact that no amount of useful and constructive publicity issued by us can ever outweigh the odd bad mark against us in the public opinion. In the present case, where we carried several quite aggressive Jews, the effect of such publicity will no doubt prove dangerous to our goodwill, particularly in countries like the USA who, after all, pays the bulk of IRO expenditures, and whose public opinion is considerably influenced by Jewish sentiments and agitation.*'

Pushing for a spot against the rail, passengers leaned out from the ship and scanned the crowd on the wharf, desperate to catch sight of relatives or friends. Occasionally someone shrieked as they recognised a cousin or a friend they hadn't seen in years, rushed down to the wharf and ran into welcoming arms. People hugged each other, wept, and marvelled that they were together again. Some couldn't stop talking, while others could only stand in silence, too choked to speak.

An ambulance was waiting to take Halina Kalowski and her newborn daughter to the safety of a maternity hospital. The officers from St John's Ambulance made their way up the gangplank and with jolly voices tried to cheer up the worried little woman who clutched a baby no bigger than a doll. Everyone was eager to disembark, and in an effort to avoid a dangerous crush, the first officer ushered women with children down the gangplank first. As the St John's Ambulance officers came forward to help them carry the babies, several women screamed, panicked and started to run back on board. They were concentration camp survivors whose instinctive reaction was to flee from black-uniformed officials trying to take children from their arms.

As she walked off the ship holding little Anneke in her arms and Tarno by the hand, Silva Rae said goodbye to the purser. Apart from the glowing reference he had written in appreciation of her assistance, he had also given her a souvenir of their friendship. On the back of a photograph of them walking together on deck, he had written in tiny writing the first line of the romantic song from Lehar's operetta, *The Land of Smiles*: 'You are my heart's delight.'

Mattie and Katina Travasaros stood white-faced beside their mother, eyes straining to see their father. Would they recognise him from the old, worn photograph their mother had shown them so often? When she had talked about him he had sounded like a character in a story book, but now they were about to see him in the flesh. What would he be like? What would it be like to have a father? And, most important of all, would he like them?

As they scrutinised the people below, her mother suddenly pointed to a man in a felt hat staring up at them. 'It's your father!' she screamed. Grabbing their bulky packages, they rushed down and she fell into the arms of the man she hadn't seen for ten years. George Travasaros looked at the daughter he had last seen when she was swaddled in a blanket. Looking into her father's face, Mattie held out two sticky buns she had taken from the table at breakfast. 'I wanted to bring you something,' she said shyly. 'This is all I have.'

Ginette, a big bow tied on top of her fair hair, clung to Mrs Frant, who dreaded the moment when she would have to part with the child she'd come to love. A sense of desolation washed over Ginette at the thought of having to say goodbye to her friends and being alone among strangers again in a strange land. Her aunt's last words in Paris echoed in her mind. 'Tell your aunty in America what a bad girl you were and how much trouble you caused me.' But her aunt had tricked her. Ginette now knew that she had been sent to a place called Australia, and not America at all. A young man with curly hair smiled as he passed her, his Leica slung over his shoulder. It was Abie Goldberg who had comforted her that first day when she had sobbed in the train, and had later taken photos of her when she had been Miss Derna. 'Good luck!' he called.

A shrill voice rose above the din on the wharf. It belonged to a woman in a turban fashionably tied on with a scarf that trailed down over the shoulder of an elegant dress with padded shoulders. 'Ginette! Ginette Wajs!' she kept shouting.

But above her, at the rail, her dead sister's child was screaming, 'I don't want to go! I don't want to go! I want to go back to Paris!'

My father's bridge partner Leon Ament stood on the wharf alone, surrounded by passengers being greeted by friends or relatives. Watching all the reunions, he felt as though he was the only one who had nobody waiting for him. He didn't know a soul in Australia and had no idea where he was going to stay. He was looking around when a familiar face caught his eye. It was the man who had worked as his medical secretary in the Polish town of Stryj, who had wandered down to the dock to see if he knew any of the passengers. As soon as he saw his former boss, he said, 'Don't worry about a thing. You're sleeping at my place.' Suddenly Melbourne looked more welcoming.

Down on the wharf, reporters from Melbourne newspapers were already waiting, eager for first-hand accounts of the overcrowded hellship bringing Jewish Communist agitators to Australia. At a time of world-wide anti-Communist paranoia and Australian xenophobia, this story was bound to fuel the immigrant debate. Their grey felt hats pushed back from their sharp faces, spiral notebooks and cameras with big flash bulbs in their hands, the journalists besieged the ship in search of sensational stories, pretty girls and quotable quotes.

What they found exceeded their expectations. The gaunt bearded man in a black cassock with the photogenic aura of a Biblical prophet was Archbishop Theodore Rafalsky, who had been appointed to establish the Russian Orthodox church in Australia and New Zealand. The elegant old lady with the sad face was an émigré Russian aristocrat, Princess Nadezhda Meschersky, who was actually related to the doomed Romanovs. Crowding around her, they listened enthralled as she told them in a tragic voice that she was penniless. 'All I have left in the world is myself and my clothes,' she said. Looking around for attractive young women, they swooped on Dorothea Ritter and Gilda Brouen, and pens flew as they described the unsanitary, overcrowded conditions, terrible food and stuffy cabins.

One enterprising reporter found the young Greek couple, Philip and Germaine Georgiades, who had left the ship in Fremantle and taken the Adelaide Express to Melbourne instead. 'It was a disgusting voyage. The water was murky and it was rationed. They said we'd be travelling third class but it was really tenth class,' Philip said. 'We decided to spend our own money on the train trip rather than spend one more day on board!'

When questioned by the press, the beleaguered captain made some counter-claims of his own, accusing some of the passengers of damaging fittings and furniture and throwing food overboard. 'It is true that we had to ration water once, but food was plentiful and the ship's doctor inspected the cabins every day,' Captain Papalas said, and added defiantly, 'If you can find a migrant ship as good as the *Derna*, I will pay 2000 pounds!'

Despite all the efforts by the Department of Immigration to keep the topic of Communist agitators and the excessive number of Jews away from the press, this was the subject that the reporters were most eager to explore. They found a rich vein of indignation in Mrs Lidija Maulics, a university lecturer from Latvia who was heading for Auckland. Surrounded by reporters who scribbled down every word she said, Mrs Maulics accused young Jews of organising political meetings during the voyage. 'At least seventy-five percent of the passengers were Jews,' she declared, and repeated Verner Puurand's allegations about them singing Soviet songs, playing Communist phonograph records and coming to spread Communist propaganda in Australia. 'They told the passengers that life in Russia today was fine, criticised everything non-Russian and even spread propaganda among the crew,' she complained.

Within a few hours, the reporters and most of the passengers had dispersed, either by car or bus, but some of us were still waiting around for our luggage. The November light was as thin as a miser's smile. Buoyed by the expectation of Australia's sunny weather, we felt cheated by the rain that dribbled out of a low grey sky, as though our new country was greeting us with a scowl.

Elmars Kuplis and his family were impatient because their friends were already waiting to drive them to the coast, but the cases were still in the hold. Puzzled by the delay, Elmars went back on board to ask the captain about it.

'We're in Australia now!' Captain Papalas chuckled. 'It's up to the stevedores to unload. You can't hurry them.' Elmars walked into the shed where suitcases were heaped all over the floor, went up to a wharfie whose belly hung over his low-slung belt like a lop-sided balloon and asked about his cases.

Hands on hips, the man swung around slowly. 'Mate, are you blind?' he jeered. 'Can't you see it's raining?' In desperation, Elmars and his friend went into the hold and unloaded the cases themselves.

Melbourne marked the end of the journey for most of the passengers, but some of us had to travel to other Australian cities or to New Zealand. My parents and I were bound for Brisbane, where my mother would be reunited with her only surviving relative, her sister Mania. We stood on the bustling wharf, impatient for our luggage to be unloaded: two trunks and my father's button-making machine. Undisturbed by the huge pile of luggage or the anxious passengers waiting to leave the wharf, the wharfies unloaded suitcases, boxes, chests and crates with exasperating slowness, as though they were being paid by the hour.

Our bulky grey trunks, reinforced with wide wooden bands, finally appeared on the wharf. Everything we owned was inside them. My father's books, our few clothes and the eiderdowns. The bed linen that had been part of my mother's trousseau, monogrammed and embroidered with pre-war patience into curlicues, arabesques and flourishes, was especially precious because it had been a gift from her parents and was all that she had left from them. Clutching the knitting that had occupied me for the past ten weeks, I could hardly wait to hold my doll again to see if her new wardrobe fitted.

As he bent down to lift one of the cases, my father was puzzled by its lightness. He unlocked it to check the contents, and stood there staring as though his mind had trouble interpreting what his eyes were looking at. Hastily scrunched newspapers filled the case. Someone had removed our clothes, my father's books and my mother's monogrammed tablecloths, eiderdown covers and sheets. The button-making machine had also been stolen. Having lost most of the people she loved, my mother was not overly attached to possessions. After recovering from her initial dismay at the loss, she predicted with her usual perspicacity that one day my father would thank the thief who had stolen the button-making machine, and with it his plans to engage in business.

As for me, I was inconsolable because my doll was gone. I had spent the entire voyage unravelling the yarn and knitting it into ever more intricate designs, and was finally satisfied with the finished result. The dropped stitches were hardly noticeable and the sewing was almost seamless. Dolls represent a nostalgia for childhood, but I had virtually had no childhood and now I had no doll. Had all my work been a waste of time?

But despair was anathema to my parents. 'Nothing is ever wasted,' my father said. My mother, ever practical, said that I would undoubtedly find some good use for all the knitting.

While my parents and I were boarding the Trans Australia Airways plane for Brisbane, Fred Silberstein was checking in at the Melbourne YMCA, where he was spending the night before travelling on to Auckland the following day. The sputtering sound of gunfire woke him up. Panic-stricken, he sprang out of bed to see the sky lit up by flares as the shelling continued. Rockets hissed in the sky and people were shouting. World War III must have broken out. A moment later he looked down and saw children huddled around a bonfire, drawing glittering arcs in the air with their sparklers and jumping as firecrackers crackled, sizzled and exploded into the night. Fred laughed aloud. The period of gunpowder, treason and plot had ended and the good guys had won after all.

*   *   *

After most of the passengers had dispersed, 115 IRO passengers were left in the Customs Hall without any money or the means to reach their destinations, which included farms in Queensland, country towns in Victoria and South Australia, and cities in New Zealand. They hadn't eaten since breakfast, couldn't buy themselves a cup of coffee or a sandwich, had nowhere to sleep and no money for their train fares. Helle and her parents, brother Rein and little sister Maret, who were bound for Sydney, were among them, as were Rita and her family, who had to travel to the Queensland town of Monto. The Puurands, who were heading for Brisbane, were stranded too. Although before leaving Germany Verner Puurand had bought some diamond rings to sell in Australia, he had no cash. As for his son Hans, he felt cheated because despite all his hard work in the galley, he hadn't been paid a cent.

Having been informed about the passengers' plight, Miss Kidd of the Victorian Red Cross came to their rescue. Although Captain Papalas agreed to let them spend the night on the *Derna*, he refused to feed them, but the Department of Immigration agreed to pay their expenses in the hope of recouping the money from the IRO. Assisted by Major Weale, the indefatigable Miss Kidd chartered three buses to transport them to the Victoria Coffee Palace and organised a frugal meal for 2/6 each. The following day, after the women and children had eaten lunch at Travellers Aid and the men at the People's Palace, they were all transported to the railway station where Miss Kidd paid for their tickets.

Filing a report about this incident, Major Weale was scathing about Colonel Hershaw's incompetence. '*At no time was he able to give me figures as to the number of people wishing sleeping accommodation, meals, transport etc. I consider that during the 68 days spent on the voyage, this officer should have had every conceivable detail concerning these passengers and should have been in a position to give me any information I required in connection with the rushed arrangements I was forced to make late at night and during a weekend.*'

But the headaches caused by the *Derna* still hadn't ended. While Major Weale and Miss Kidd were organising food and fares for the stranded passengers, a self-assured young man boarded the ship, identified himself as Captain Merritt, a federal security officer, and said that he had come to see the purser about a missing stowaway. Armed with a torch, he proceeded to search the cabins and spent the night on board. When Major Weale arrived next morning to discuss the issue of the stranded passengers with Colonel Hershaw, he found Captain Merritt in the lounge, interrogating one of the passengers.

His suspicions aroused, the major asked him to step into the customs office. This time when questioned 'Captain Merritt' changed his story. He admitted that he was not a federal security officer at all but a builder's labourer with a compulsion to impersonate people. While wandering around the wharf the previous day, he had overheard customs officers discussing some missing stowaways and had embarked on his masquerade.

The *Derna* continued to make news. First there was the issue of eleven crewmen — eight Italians, two Greeks and one Syrian — who had deserted. The ship's agents, the Melbourne Steamship Company, who were liable to be fined 100 pounds for each deserter, offered a reward of ten pounds for information leading to their apprehension, while the Department of Immigration organised raiding parties to capture them. Only two were ever found and deported. Rita's boyfriend Philippe was not one of them.

And to add to the captain's woes, while the ship was loading wheat for Europe over forty crew members went on strike to protest against low wages and bad conditions. They handed him a log of claims, demanding that he improve their food and the primitive quarters in which they were forced to live like animals. When he refused, the winches fell silent and all activity on the wharf ceased. Mr W Bird, the secretary of the Seamen's Union who inspected the ship and met the strikers, stated that their conditions on the *Derna* were among the worst he'd ever seen.

The news that a ship full of 'reds' had arrived in Australia with the express purpose of disseminating Communist propaganda and destroying the fabric of Australian society continued to create a furore.

At a time when many in America and Australia believed that they were engaged in a deadly ideological war which threatened to obliterate democracy, reports about a ship bringing Communists into the country alarmed those who shared that belief. The notion that Jewish Communist agents had been admitted to Australia fell on fertile ground, despite the fact that many of the Jews aboard the *Derna* had been deported by the Russians to Siberia during the war, and most had left Europe to escape Communist regimes.

Australia in 1948 was ethnically homogeneous, politically conservative and racially xenophobic. Ninety-seven percent of the population was Anglo-Celtic in origin, and the majority was Protestant. Many of them regarded Catholics with mistrust bordering on animosity. Both groups agreed, however, that the creeping Communist menace was the greatest threat to society and religion since the barbarian hordes had invaded Europe. The Communist takeover of Eastern European countries in 1945 and the savage anti-West rhetoric issuing from the Kremlin justified their suspicions. From pulpits, podiums and platforms, priests, prelates, teachers and politicians thundered that eternal vigilance was the only way to combat the red menace, and the newspapers hammered home this view in articles and editorials. One enemy had been conquered, but a far more insidious menace now threatened the free world, ready to destroy those who were not on their guard.

On 10 November, five days after the *Derna* had docked in Melbourne, the controversy about its Communist passengers reached federal parliament when Mr Gullett, the Liberal member for Henty, stood up and asked the Minister for Immigration whether he had read the article in the *Argus* about the *Derna*. Had he investigated the claims made by Mrs Maulics about the Jewish passengers who had spread Communist propaganda? And were those Communists to be allowed to stay in Australia?

Mr Arthur Calwell, the Minister for Immigration and architect of Australia's post-war immigration policy, said that he hadn't seen the article but went on to say: 'One of the persons who inspired the criticism was a Lt-Col Hershaw who is an International Refugee

Organisation escort officer. Persons with whom he is associated made charges that certain people had indulged in Communist propaganda. Hershaw has an unsavoury reputation. Had he done in Australia some of the things which he tried to do on the ship he would have been sent to gaol for a long term. He was one of the first people who started the story about Communist activities aboard the *Derna*.'

At this point Mr Gullett began to interject and had to be called to order so that Mr Calwell could continue. 'Lt-Col Hershaw seems to be of the fascist type, and there are far too many people of that kind around today,' the Minister told the House. 'I asked my officers to make a complete check and I received a report from Major Weale who is the Aliens Registration Officer of the Department of Immigration in Melbourne. He conducted the fullest possible investigation into the allegation of Communist activities aboard the *Derna*.'

In a subtle attack on the agenda of those who had made the allegations, Mr Calwell said, 'There is no truth in the allegations of Communist activities on the part of some of the passengers but it is obvious that once these passengers were free from European police supervision, they naturally discussed among themselves various topics including European politics which, to a person looking for trouble, could easily be interpreted as propaganda.'

He concluded by saying, 'If I have to decide between accepting the report of some lady professor from Riga and the report of a responsible officer of my own department, I shall back Major Weale's opinion at any time.'

When he saw the reports about conditions on the *Derna*, Tasman Heyes, the Secretary of the Department of Immigration, was sufficiently disturbed to write to the Department of Shipping and Fuel, asking what action the government could take to improve conditions on foreign-owned ships bringing migrants to Australia. Several months later, Mr Heyes wrote to Major General C Lloyd of the IRO: *'The view held by the Department is that the Derna is not a suitable ship for the carriage of displaced persons.'*

*   *   *

The IRO did not renew Lt-Colonel Ogden Hershaw's employment. He returned to Canada and never escorted migrants again.

On her return to Europe the following year, the *Derna* was renamed for the fourth time. She made one voyage to Australia under her new name, the SS *Assimina*. Afterwards, she was sold for scrap metal and broken up in the Scottish shipyards of Blyth.

PART II
THEIR LIFE

PROLOGUE

A LETTER FROM BRISBANE

In the summer of 1995, I travelled to Poland with my daughter Justine. It must have been fate that led me, on the very last day of our trip, to Father Roman Soszynski, the priest to whom I owe my life. It was his steadfast support that had made it possible for my parents and me to survive in a Polish village during the Holocaust. After the tears had stopped flowing during our miraculous reunion, Father Soszynski rummaged through a drawer and handed me an old air letter stamped with the bust of King George VI. It was the letter my father had sent him almost fifty years before, shortly after our arrival in Australia.

'The voyage was long and arduous,' my father wrote. 'It lasted for ten weeks during which we passed Port Said, Aden and Colombo. Then we flew from Melbourne to Brisbane, a distance seven times greater than between Krakow and Warsaw. We were in the air for over seven hours. During that time a stewardess catered to all our needs and served elaborate hot and cold meals including meat dishes, fruit and dessert. Aeroplanes are comfortably equipped but very expensive. The flight cost thirty pounds.* The same distance by rail takes three days, and in all that time the train makes only three stops. Towns here are few and far between. The country is as big as Europe and Russia put together but has only seven million inhabitants.

---

* The basic weekly wage was five pounds.

The standard of living here is good, although there are not many wealthy people. The government ensures that all workers receive a basic wage on which they can live quite well. Food is reasonable even for the lowest income earners and pineapples and oranges are dirt-cheap. Meat, milk and bread are delivered to homes every day.

The cities are divided into business and residential areas. The centre of town, or the 'city', consists only of shops, offices, factories, workshops etc, while the suburbs, which are further away, have open space and greenery. Most families have a house and garden. Apartment blocks are rare. It's easy to buy or build a home. All they have to put down is one third, and the banks lend the rest which can be repaid over many years. The repayments cost no more than rent. Wages, rents and all bills are paid weekly.

People here are calm, courteous and industrious. Almost everyone works until five o'clock, even women, and after coming home from work, they prepare the evening meal. There is a five-day week. Saturdays and Sundays are devoted to household chores such as laundry, irrespective of religion, of which there are many. Various religions compete with each other and advertise in the newspapers.

Schools and hospitals are free, irrespective of income. Danusia* attended school for five weeks and received a good report. She is already communicating quite well in English. Schools are on holidays at the moment. The school year starts in the second half of January and ends at Christmas. In Poland at the moment you are probably having severe frosts but here it is summer and Danusia has gone to the seaside with our friends.

The climate varies in different parts of Australia. In Brisbane, the temperature often exceeds 35 degrees in the shade. It's extremely hot for two to three months of the year but they say that winter here is as mild as on the Riviera. Our flora and fauna are unique, and there is a profusion of fruit some of which I have never heard of.

I've written in great detail about what I've observed during our brief stay, and would be very happy to have news about you and Piszczac.'

---

* My Polish name.

*   *   *

My father never received a reply to this or any of his subsequent letters. The priest's silence, which puzzled my parents all their lives, was finally clarified during our reunion. Father Soszynski told me that the persecution of priests by the Communist government in Poland had made it dangerous to correspond with anyone in the West. But he had kept the letter in a drawer with other treasured possessions for almost fifty years.

My father had also kept a memento of Father Soszynski. After my parents died, my son Jonathan found a small framed picture of Christ among their belongings. On the back was a faded Polish dedication, dated 1944. Its origin remained a mystery until Father Soszynski explained that he had presented it to my father at a time when our life in Piszczac hung by a thread, because the villagers had threatened to denounce us to the Gestapo as Jews. The priest had given him the holy picture in the hope that Christ would watch over us, and my father had accepted it in the spirit of compassion with which it had been given.

As the priest's humanity had helped to save our lives in Poland, my parents hoped that his talisman would continue to bring us luck in Australia.

21

Beneath its picture postcard sky, Australia in 1948 sprawled in sluggish innocence, content to paddle in the sunlit shallows of life. Still appended to the British Empire, it awaited its own destiny while feeding on myths and deceptions. The land where the world's oldest living culture had existed for over 40,000 years was presented in history books as an empty space waiting to be filled by British colonists. Although Australians believed in giving everyone a fair go, beneath the veneer of egalitarianism lurked a deep-seated but unacknowledged racism. Aborigines on reserves had no vote and their children were being plucked from their mothers' arms to induce them to abandon their own heritage and embrace European culture. Asian migrants were excluded, Jewish immigrants were restricted, and foreigners were referred to as reffos, wogs and dagoes. Homogeneous, conservative and almost entirely Anglo-Saxon in origin, Australians were about to awake from their illusion of perfection.

But to us, the passengers of the *Derna*, whose countries and communities had for centuries been trampled, suppressed and enslaved, Australia offered a blessed haven. This seemed to be a land that had never experienced war or revolution, where the sun shone warmly and the plants grew tall and straight.

* * *

Rita was so excited when the *Derna* docked in Melbourne on 5 November 1948 that she hardly noticed the grey skies and drizzly rain. In the chaos of departure, she hadn't been able to find Philippe, her stowaway sweetheart, to wish him luck. She had given him her aunt's address and wondered if she'd ever hear from him again. Although she cried when she and Helle clung to each other as they said goodbye, she was certain it wouldn't be long before they saw each other again. After all, her aunt's farm in Kapaldo couldn't be very far from Sydney where Helle's family were going to settle. They would visit each other and exchange confidences just as they'd done every single day on the ship.

From the glowing letters Rita had received from her aunt, she could picture herself on the farm plucking sun-warmed fruit in the orchard, sun-baking on the beach, and saving lives in her nurse's cap and uniform. Nothing could dampen her high sprits: not the fact that it took most of the day to disembark and find their luggage, nor that they were tired and hungry and had no money. Once they reached Queensland all their troubles would be over. Even her mother had brightened up now that they had arrived. 'We're really lucky,' she said to her sister Lilija as they boarded the train. 'So many of the people on the ship have no one in Australia, but we have our family waiting for us.'

The locomotive chugged out of the city, grinding to a halt at desolate stations where few people alighted or boarded. The vastness of this empty land amazed them. Mile after mile of nothing, connected by occasional clusters of low houses with small windows and overhanging roofs shading small dark verandahs. Didn't people here like sunshine and light?

And the trees, so sparse and pale, with droopy leaves in that apologetic shade of grey-green, so different from the dense, dark woods of Latvia. Thinking about Latvia evoked memories of oak trees whose shadows made lacy patterns on the soft loam, and cool rivers flowing past fields of wheat. With an effort, Rita pulled herself out of her reverie in an attempt to find something pleasing in the spindly trees and dust-coated towns of her new country. Facing her, Aunt Lilija cradled her little son Arne and tried to hide her dismay at this inhospitable, arid landscape.

Announcements were made from time to time, but they could only look at each other, shake their heads and look hopefully at Jack, the older of the two boys, who had learned English in Munich. Pushing his fair hair out of his eyes, he sat forward and strained to make out what these flat, nasal voices were saying, but could only shake his head and shrug. These words didn't sound like the ones he'd heard in class.

Each time the train pulled up, they scanned the name on the platform and checked it with the one they had written down: Monto. Occasionally when the train made a longer stop, passengers would leave and return a few minutes later with a sandwich, some milk or a soft drink. They shook the bottles to mix the thick creamy collar under the silver foil top more evenly through the milk. Their white bread was so spongy that their fingers left dents in it, and the scent of yeast, corned beef and pickles filled the compartment. Rita tried not to look at the food which made her mouth water. It was horrible not to have enough money to buy even one sandwich for her little sister Sigride, who couldn't understand why there was nothing to eat.

An Australian couple in their compartment glanced their way occasionally, and from their expressions and lowered voices it was obvious that they were talking about them. At one point, they sat forward and asked something but no one understood what they said. At the next station, the couple left the train, but soon returned with a bag of rolls which they handed to Rita's mother. Tears welled in Rita's eyes. What a wonderful country this must be, to have such good people in it.

As they chugged northwards, the landscape changed. *Washed out, dried out and burned out,* she thought. Chasms gaped in the eroded earth as though split by a giant's axe. On their shadowy verandahs, lanky men in big floppy hats and women in faded dresses looked as dried out as the land. How could such a country sustain life?

Exhausted and hungry after their long journey, they could hardly wait to meet the family and see the farmhouse they had heard so much about. 'Your room is waiting for you,' her aunt had written in a letter they now knew off by heart. But when they got off the train at the tiny station, instead of their relatives, a stranger in a battered sweat-stained hat was standing there. After driving them to the farm in Kapaldo, he disappeared in a cloud of throat-biting dust and left them to survey their new home.

It was a tin shed, about as welcoming as a bus shelter. Lilija drew in her breath to stop herself from crying. She had visualised an inviting farmhouse like the ones in Latvia, with wooden beams, thick eiderdowns and lace curtains. There was no electricity, only a kerosene lamp, and no ceiling, just the corrugated iron roof over narrow camp beds. Exhausted by the journey and the heat, her grandmother slumped down and turned towards the wall. Rita couldn't bear to meet her mother's eyes. In the corner of the shack stood a piano, coated in dust. 'Look! A piano!' She tried to sound enthusiastic. 'I'll be able to play!'

Their aunt and uncle had not come to welcome them.

Later, Rita woke with a start, looked up and froze. Slithering on a beam just above her bed was a long snake with patterned skin. Her heart thudded and she opened her mouth to scream, but no sound came out. Too terrified to close her eyes and even more terrified of keeping them open, she lay awake for the rest of the night, imagining the grip of the slimy body as it fastened around her neck. Carpet snakes were to become frequent nocturnal visitors, but learning that they were harmless did nothing to dispel her terror.

Rita is reminiscing about her arrival in Queensland as we talk on the sunny patio of her home in Brisbane. She heard about my search for passengers while listening to the Latvian program on SBS radio several months ago and responded at once. 'There were eight of us travelling together on the *Derna*,' she told me over the phone and added with a laugh, 'I was a romantic twenty-one year old at the time and fell in love with a handsome French stowaway!' I found her open, friendly manner engaging, and several months later, travelled to Brisbane to meet her.

On the rare occasions when her aunt and uncle arrived at the farm to issue instructions about the chores Rita and her family were expected to carry out, there was no trace of the warmth they'd expressed in their letters. Only two other people ever set foot on the farm: the man who came on Thursdays to collect the cream and bring their bread and meat, and a Latvian neighbour who dropped in occasionally for a chat.

Rita's aunt had migrated from Latvia at the turn of the century because she had contracted tuberculosis and had been advised to move to a warm climate. Not long after she arrived, she had married the local Latvian pastor. By 1948, they had a tropical fruit orchard at Yeppoon and the dairy farm in Monto, amid the rich pastoral land of the Darling Downs. Although they had a milking machine on the farm, they instructed their relatives to milk the 150 cows by hand. 'Perhaps they didn't want to wear their machine out,' Rita says sarcastically. Because of the drought, the ground was parched and all the water holes had dried up, so Rita and her family had to chop down bottle trees so that the cows could suck moisture from the trunks.

'I hated living on the farm and loathed the work,' she shudders. 'I couldn't wait to start training as a nurse.'

But it soon became apparent that, despite their promises, her aunt and uncle had no intention of putting her through nursing school. 'We can't afford it,' her aunt said. 'Besides, we need you to help us on the farm. After all, we had to pay all that money to bring the eight of you out here.'

Her uncle never tired of reminding them that he had paid 600 pounds to the Red Cross for their passage. 'Do you know how hard we have to work to earn so much money, especially with the drought?' he would point out.

Rita is a motherly grey-haired woman with a gentle manner. As she talks, she takes my hand and looks into my face. 'I was so angry and disappointed,' she recalls. To think that she could have been in Germany, training to be a nurse, instead of living in a hovel at the end of the world, callusing her hands by milking those damned cows from dawn till dusk. If only she had taken up that offer to become a nurse in Munich! But when she had written that she wanted to stay in Germany and become a nurse, her aunt had replied that Monto had a hospital equal to any in the world and that she could train right here. *What a joke*, Rita thought bitterly, staring at her sore, roughened hands. While

she pulled the cow's long teats, the milk spurted into the bucket in time
to 'Buttons and Bows', the latest hit tune that kept blaring from the
radio. Most of the words of this American song about buckskin and
toting a gun were incomprehensible to her, but one line was painfully
apt: '*Don't bury me in this prairie* ...' She was buried there all right.

'We were lured to Monto to be slave labourers on the farm, to milk
cows, feed pigs and take care of calves,' she tells me in her lilting
accent. Their only payment was food, and from the miserly portions it
was obvious that their relatives begrudged even that. Furious at their
deception, she tried to stir her mother up to confront them, but the
argument always ended the same way.

'If they get angry and throw us out, where can we go? We don't have
any money and we can't speak the language. They've sponsored us.
Maybe we'll be in trouble with the government if we leave,' her mother
would reply.

It was the most miserable Christmas they had ever spent. In the
searing heat, surrounded by flies, they longed for a white Christmas
just like the one they recognised in Bing Crosby's hit song. They
yearned for snow-covered fields, frost-etched windows, a log fire, the
resinous scent of fir trees hung with shining baubles, and the traditional
casseroles and spiced cakes. Their hearts ached for the world they had
left behind. Their aunt and uncle stopped by to wish them a joyous
Christmas, and in a rare gesture of conviviality, Aunt sat down at the
piano, thumped the keys and belted out a raucous tune they had never
heard before. 'It's an Australian folk song,' she told them as she
proceeded to sing 'Waltzing Matilda'.

Being exploited by strangers is distressing, but being exploited by
relatives is unbearable. After two months, Rita could no longer stand
living at the farm. Embittered by forlorn hopes and false promises, she
was angry enough to explode. She hadn't escaped the Communists,
survived the bombing in Germany and the voyage on the *Derna* to live
like a feudal bond-servant, tied to her relatives without any hope for
the future. 'Even if I have to walk all the way back to Europe I'm not
staying here,' she told her mother one night, flopping onto her camp
bed, exhausted and covered in filth from another day of endless chores.

She found an unexpected ally in their Latvian neighbour. 'I know the matron of a small hospital in Brisbane,' the woman suggested one day. 'Maybe she'll give you a job.'

So Rita fulfilled her dream of working in a hospital, but instead of looking after sick people in a starched cap and snowy white apron, she spent her days scrubbing the tiled walls and waxing the floors of the Berwha Private Hospital in a faded dress that was falling apart. But even scrubbing floors was better than milking cows on the farm.

As there were no vacant beds in the nurses' dormitory, the matron set up a folding bed for Rita in a chilly room that contained a marble slab. Not many people could sleep soundly in a mortuary and Rita was no exception. It was sterile and cold with a penetrating chemical smell that sickened her. The thought of the blue corpses that had lain on that slab kept her awake as disturbing thoughts swirled in her head. Much as she needed the job, she couldn't stay in this gruesome room. Somehow she managed to communicate her distress to the matron who found her a more suitable room.

Rita had only been at the hospital for a few weeks when Matron called her in. 'You have to go to Kapaldo right away,' she said. Rita's throat tightened. Grandmother must have died. She knew how much her poor grandmother suffered in the Queensland heat. *You can't replant an old tree*, she thought sadly. But it wasn't her grandmother. When she arrived at the farm, a terrible silence greeted her.

Then her mother tottered towards her, ashen, tears streaming down her face as she fell into Rita's trembling arms. 'It's Jack,' she whispered. 'He's dead.'

'Not Jack!' Rita screamed. 'Not Jack!'

She repeats the words now, in a disbelieving whisper. Even now, after all these years, she still can't believe it. Jack was such a healthy chap and he was only twenty years old. Her beautiful, adored brother couldn't be dead. Couldn't be. In between her mother's sobs, Rita pieced together what had happened. While working at the dairy in Monto, Jack fell in love with an Australian girl who broke off her engagement to an Australian who worked at the local pharmacy. Jack was friendly and outgoing, a strikingly good-looking six-footer, but despite all the admiring glances that girls cast his way, he wasn't conceited or spoilt. On that tragic day, he had been on his way home when he collapsed in the street. Mrs Lindemanis answered the knock on the farm door a little later to see a policeman standing there. By the time she reached the hospital, Jack was already cold.

Rita's voice trembles and her eyes glisten with tears. Fifty-one years later, she still can't come to terms with this loss. For a few minutes we sit in a silence that is broken by the crystal call of butcher birds roosting in the trees around us, the cruel hooks of their beaks ready to tear into their prey.

Rita pulls herself to her feet, hobbles inside and returns a few moments later with a pile of old photographs, their edges curled with frequent handling. Looking through them, she picks out one of a gorgeous young man modestly holding a sheaf of flowers. 'This was taken in Germany on Jack's confirmation day,' she says in a low, hoarse voice that softens whenever she utters his name. 'Everybody loved him. It was so wrong. He shouldn't have died. I was the sickly one, not him. He'd never been sick a day in his life.'

Despite the strange circumstances of Jack's death, the doctor's certificate stated that he'd died of a twisted intestine, and the family was too stunned to question his diagnosis. It's still painful for Rita to talk about his funeral, even after fifty years. 'My mother was a broken woman, a total mess. We didn't have the money to pay for his funeral so some of the people from the local Lutheran church took up a collection for us.' She hangs her head and strokes the photograph. 'We had to depend on charity to bury him. Our aunt and uncle didn't contribute a single cent. They didn't even come to his funeral.'

Among the small group of mourners were some Latvian medical students who had been cutting sugar cane up north during the long summer holiday. When they saw the body, they commented on Jack's unusual colour and sudden death, and wondered whether he could have been poisoned. Suspicions and rumours circulated around the little town, but no investigation was ever held. Rita's family was too poor to engage a solicitor, and the police weren't interested in pursuing the matter on behalf of 'Nuts and Balts' who couldn't even speak English.

Within three months of arriving in Australia, their dreams of a happy future had been buried along with Jack. The land that had promised so much had brought only disappointment and death. It seemed to Rita that her life had been a succession of losses, each one more terrible than the last. She'd lost her beloved father, the ability to have children, the hope of becoming a nurse, and now the brother she adored. She was convinced she had even lost her chance of marrying her sweetheart. Eric had fled from Latvia to England and was waiting to follow her to Australia, but since she couldn't have children, she decided with a heavy heart that she should release him from the engagement so that he could marry someone else and have a family. Watching the vigour with which Rita scrubbed the floors, the matron admired the young woman's energy. She didn't know that pent-up anger and resentment were fuelling every stroke.

Sometimes while she spread the soap suds on the floor, Rita thought about Philippe. She knew that he had managed to stay in Melbourne because she had received one letter from him, but the voyage now seemed so far away. Too depressed to reply, she had never heard from him again. Often she daydreamed about the farmhouse in Latvia, and the smooth, sun-warmed rock in the river where she and Eric had sat with their arms around each other, making plans that could never come true. 'I hated Australia, despised Brisbane and wished I'd never come,' she says. In Monto they would talk about Brisbane as though it was some dazzling capital, but to her it was a backward, boring place. The town hall with its three pitiful storeys was the tallest building in town. With its funny houses on stilts, Brisbane was uglier and more provincial that any country town she'd ever seen in Europe. And more lifeless.

After Jack's death, her mother became so depressed that Rita knew she'd have to get her away from the farm and rent a house in Brisbane where the whole family could live together. 'The last straw was when my uncle told us he'd arranged for us to pick cotton in the fields nearby. He contracted us out like a gang of slaves to work together under his supervision,' she says in a voice crackling with anger. 'When my aunt and uncle found out that we were all leaving, they were furious. Uncle threatened to sue us. He said he'd paid the Red Cross for our passage and we owed him 600 pounds. He said he'd seen a solicitor and if we didn't pay him back, he'd take us to court.'

As Rita's wages at the hospital were too small to enable her to repay her uncle as well as support her family, she applied for a second job, as a dressmaker. 'Although I had no idea how to use a machine, my employer was a kind Jewish woman who also came from Latvia. She taught me how to sew.' Although she got on very well with her employer, Rita antagonised her Australian workmates by working fast. 'Take it easy, or you'll make it tough for the rest of us,' they would say in a warning tone. Occasionally one of the women would shout, 'Go back where you came from, you bloody Balt,' and then Rita would let fly with words she'd heard her uncle use on the farm, curses she didn't understand that shocked the bullies into silence.

'Even with the extra money I earned sewing, I still walked for miles to save a penny tram fare, and every morning I'd put a piece of thick cardboard inside my shoes to cover the hole,' she recalls. The best years of her life were slipping by and she felt worn out. On hot summer nights when the syrupy scent of frangipani wafted into her room and the sound of laughter rose from the street, she cried herself to sleep, but the following morning, she splashed cold water on her puffy eyes and told herself to snap out of it. There was no sense wallowing in self-pity.

One day, unable to hide her unhappiness, Rita poured out her heart to her Australian neighbour. 'I wish I could marry my sweetheart, but I won't be able to because I can't have children,' she sighed, and told her about the accident in Germany.

'Don't believe everything the doctors tell you, love,' her neighbour said. 'They told you you'd never walk again and you did. I'm going to take you to a specialist.'

After examining her, the gynaecologist uttered the most beautiful words she'd heard since arriving in Australia. 'There's nothing wrong with you, Miss Lindemanis. I can't see any reason why you couldn't have children.' That night, bursting with happiness, Rita wrote a long letter to Eric.

By then she was no longer the sole earner. Her mother was working as a cleaner in an insurance office and her aunt Lilija was working at the dress factory. When her uncle's job at the Tennyson power house ended, he went cane cutting with Rita's other brother Ted. After a year, Rita left her poorly paid hospital job and started waitressing. The little French restaurant in Wickham Terrace was popular with French woolbuyers who pinched her bottom but left generous tips.

When Rita's English had improved sufficiently, she visited the Red Cross office to resolve an issue that had puzzled her for a long time. The director seemed surprised by her question. 'We have no record of your uncle paying 600 pounds, or any amount at all,' she said, adding that the Australian Red Cross did not organise passages for immigrants. Rita had scrubbed miles of hospital floor on her hands and knees and sewn thousands of garments at break-neck speed to repay money that they had never owed.

As Rita and I reflect on the perfidy of people who exploit and deceive their own relatives, a commotion inside the house makes us start. A young butcher bird has flown into the kitchen through a chink in the screen door and cannot find its way out. Trapped inside, the bird is panic-stricken and hurls itself repeatedly against the glass window which refuses to yield under its sharp beak. Finally it knocks itself out and drops to the floor. Rita hobbles in, tenderly picks up the small limp body, coos to it and carries it outside. A few moments later the little bird stirs, makes a feeble attempt to flutter its wings and just makes it to the fence.

Resuming her story, Rita says that as soon as Eric received her letter with the wonderful news, he made preparations to leave London. Now that they would be reunited at last, she could hardly wait. When the other girls in the dress factory often chatted about the petticoats, scantee sets, nighties and negligees they were putting away in their glory boxes, Rita listened, wishing that she could spare a few pounds for her own trousseau.

In a tremulous voice, she says, 'Sometimes I would think it wasn't fair, but that's how it was. It was my duty to help my family. With my father and brother gone, my family relied on me.' Life became easier when Eric arrived in 1950, and in December that year Rita's dreams came true as she walked down the aisle to marry her childhood sweetheart. At first Eric worked as a builder's labourer, but before long he was working for himself.

To Rita's delight, the prediction of the doctor in Munich proved wrong and the children started coming. Three boys. 'I still dreamed of returning to Latvia but we didn't have the money,' she says. 'Anyway, I couldn't leave my mother behind. She became more depressed as the years went on, and spent more and more time staring at my father's photo. I think that in a corner of her heart, she was still hoping that one day she'd see him again.'

While we are talking, the phone rings. It's Rita's younger sister Sigride. 'She's a physiotherapist,' Rita tells me proudly and adds, without a trace of resentment, 'She got the education I never had.'

When we talk about the *Derna*, her face glows at the memory of her friendship with Helle. 'My beautiful Helle,' she says. 'You know, we poured our hearts out to each other and talked and talked all day every day, but after we said goodbye that day on the wharf in Melbourne we never saw each other again. Sydney was much further away than I thought and I never had enough money to get there. But I'd love to get in touch with her again.'

The sun is setting behind the jacaranda trees as the hospitable Eric, who spends his retirement conducting a Latvian choir and composing music, brings tea and chocolate cake onto the patio. Rita looks pensive. 'You know, I never put down roots in Australia,' she says. 'Whenever I'm dreaming, I'm always in Latvia, never in Australia. I've been back several times. The first time was during the Russian occupation, in 1986. I was sorry I went. Everything was run down and neglected. You couldn't go anywhere. Whatever we wanted to do, they'd say, "You can't go here, you can't go there. Don't take photos of this or that." Anyway, I went again with Sigride in 1992 after Latvia became independent. It was still shabby but it was beautiful. That's when we finally found out what had happened to our father.' She sighs. 'They said that he was deported to Siberia, interrogated five times on Christmas Eve in 1941 and shot, but when we wanted to recover the body, they said it was impossible because so many bodies had been buried together in the snow and ice.'

After so many years spent longing for Latvia, Rita would not return to live there now. 'I'm too ill to travel. I've just had open heart surgery. Besides, my children and grandchildren live here. But apart from that, the people have changed. After fifty years of Communism they've become dishonest. They've learned to lie and steal.'

Half a century after she and her mother opened the stable doors and let the animals loose, Rita's family has regained the family farm with its wheatlands and tracts of forest. They have cut away the rotting trunks, cleared the fallen trees and restored the family cemetery where headstones were stolen or smashed. But the farmhouse of her dreams is occupied by strangers and the neighbours are people she wouldn't want to know.

The fading light casts long shadows across the patio and the butcher birds have stopped singing. 'From the moment we left Latvia, we all thought we'd be back before long, that it was just a matter of time,' she says. *We'll be back*, we thought. *We'll be back*. But time went on and on. Mum thought she'd go back too. And in a way she did. We took her ashes back. Just like *Angela's Ashes*.' She takes out a photograph of a dark green river that flows beside the woods and points to a smooth-flanked boulder that pokes out of it. 'I feel so close to that spot,' she whispers. 'When I die, that's where I want my ashes to be scattered. That's the rock where Eric and I used to sit and dream about our future. Little did we know. Little did we know.'

22

Inside the flat-roofed, two-storey building in East Sydney that houses the *Estonian News,* a woman with a reserved manner ushers me into the large office upstairs. As we sit at her neat desk she tells me that she has been trying to retire from her editorial job for some time, but the publisher has been ill lately so she is busier than ever. It's Helle Nittim, Rita's confidante from the *Derna.* With her thick fair hair and tiny waist, she was one of the most attractive girls on the ship.

On the day that I placed a notice in the *Estonian News* to say I was searching for passengers, the phone rang. 'I hear you are looking for people who came out on the *Derna,*' a woman was saying in a low, even voice. 'I am the editor of this paper and I came out on that ship with my family.' Then she added, 'Lea, our Girl Friday, was also on the *Derna.*' I felt like a prospector striking gold with the first thrust of the spade.

At first Helle seems rather guarded, but as we begin reminiscing about the disasters that befell our ship, she becomes more animated. I'm thrilled that she still has the diary she kept throughout the voyage, especially when she offers to give me a copy in English. From the snippets she reads aloud, I can tell that she was an observant and perceptive girl. When I ask who she remembers from the ship, she says, 'There were Estonians, Latvians, Czechs and Jews — but of course officially there weren't any Jews, they were listed as Poles, Czechs and so on.' Although all the passengers were listed by nationality not religion, her tone suggests disapproval, and I wonder whether it is a sign of the antagonism that existed on board between some of the Baltic and Jewish passengers.

By now Lea has joined us, a vivacious brunette with a jolly laugh who was in Helle's cabin on the ship and now works for the same newspaper. Lea has brought along the journal in which her father, Arnold Ohtra, recorded statistical information and personal observations about the voyage. 'There were some nice Jewish boys on board,' she reminisces.

Helle nods. 'I liked the Czech one who played the guitar, but my father tried to keep me away from them. Not because they were Jewish,' she adds quickly, 'but because they were boys. Our fathers were very strict.'

When I ask Lea whether she fell in love during the voyage, she shakes her curly head, but Helle, who has been scanning her diary, looks up and laughs. 'Well, I've written here that you were making google eyes at somebody!'

Lea is squealing like a teenager. 'Tell me! Tell me!'

Lea, with her mother and father and little sister Tiia, disembarked in Fremantle because her godfather had migrated to Perth during the economic crisis in Estonia in 1927. 'All we knew about Australia was that there were poisonous snakes, spiders and queer-looking animals. My mother was so petrified, she sprayed anything that moved!'

When the Ohtra family arrived in Perth, the four of them lived in a closed-in verandah and cooked on a primus stove. They were considering moving to Sydney when Lea's godfather lent them 600 pounds to build a house. 'My father was a fitter and turner, not a builder, but with an instruction book in one hand and a hammer in the other, somehow he managed to build a ten-square house. What made it even harder for him was that we were used to the metric system, which was so simple, but here he had to work out inches, feet and yards. Twelve of this, three of that, and 144 of something else. And then there were pennies, halfpennies, shillings, pounds and guineas. It was all very confusing.'

Lea, who loved clothes, was intrigued by the way Perth women dressed. 'I arrived with one heavy overcoat with a little fur collar which I got from American aid in Germany, a green wool crepe dress and red shoes with rubber soles which I thought terribly posh! We thought it odd that women in their fifties wore floral hats, bright frocks and long gloves, and plastered rouge in bright circles on their cheeks. The food was different too,' she muses. 'The only restaurants we ever went to were Greek "caffs" where the menu was steak and eggs, chops and eggs and sausages and eggs.'

Suddenly she giggles. 'I must tell you about my first party. I was told to bring a plate. A young man picked me up in his father's car, a Ford Prefect which looked like a small box, but I felt very special being driven to the social in a car. When they asked us to go in for supper, I said, "I can't eat anything because I didn't bring my plate." To my amazement, my escort looked into my mouth and said, "I thought they were your own teeth!"' Helle and I are laughing as Lea continues the story of that disastrous evening. 'When he asked what I'd like to drink, I said in my most careful English, "I would like wine." Well, that didn't go down too well because no one drank wine in those days. Boys drank beer and girls drank lemon squash. Needless to say, I never saw him again!'

While Lea was settling down in Perth, Helle and her family travelled to Sydney by train. She stared at the unfamiliar gum trees, a name that made no sense when she looked it up in the dictionary. These trees did not exist in Estonia. 'So this is the beginning of a new life,' she wrote in her diary. 'End to DP stage, although we are still refugees, hoping to return to our homeland. Are we ever going to see that lovely little country again? Let's hope so!'

When the overnight train finally chugged into Sydney's Central station next morning, their sponsors, the Waabels, were there to meet them. At their brick home in Balgowlah, with its shady verandah and bay window, Helle and her little sister Maret shared one bedroom, their brother Rein slept in a tiny space among the brooms, brushes and ironing board, while their parents slept in a shed with latticed sides lined in tar-paper. 'So the wind won't blow you out of bed,' Helle used to joke.

She was feeling buoyant because among the mail awaiting them was a letter from her boyfriend Ilmar from whom she had parted heartbroken in Germany. After months of longing and dreaming, he had finally emerged out of her daydreams and returned to the real world. *How wonderful to be in touch again even though we're thousands of miles apart,* she thought as she danced around the house with her letter.

Another reason for her high spirits was that Mrs Waabel had given her some material. Painfully self-conscious about her short dress with the knees showing when everyone else was wearing skirts with longer hemlines, Helle quickly learned to use a sewing machine and made herself a green dress with a big collar and a full skirt that accentuated her small waist.

Before long, however, tensions arose because Mrs Waabel was keen for Helle to become a waitress in her restaurant. The Waabels, who had arrived in Australia in the 1920s, owned a high-class restaurant in Pitt Street frequented mostly by businessmen. But waitressing was one of three jobs Helle was determined she would never do. 'I told my father I would never be a waitress, nurse or shopgirl. I was too shy. I'd rather scrub floors. I feel the same way today,' she says in her down-to-earth way.

Even after she had found a job with a dressmaker, however, their sponsor continued trying to persuade her to work in the restaurant. 'You're a good-looking girl, you'll get good tips,' she would say, but Helle stood her ground. When the new term started, she enrolled at evening college and persevered until she matriculated. 'I was the only girl among twenty-nine guys doing Maths I and II. They were all helpful, but I was too shy to talk to them because I was terrified of making mistakes. It took nearly two years before I felt confident enough to speak English.'

She soon discovered that she didn't like anything about Australia and found it difficult to make new friends. 'I felt especially miserable at

Christmastime and still do,' she says. 'That's the time I miss Estonia the most and feel quite homesick, even now. Nothing feels right here, even though every year I prepare our traditional roast pork and sauerkraut, and bake little star and heart-shaped gingerbread cookies called *piparkoogid* for the kids.

'It feels wrong to be having Christmas in the middle of summer. We all sit outside in the yard with the traditional food and salads, talking together, and yet I feel as if I'm floating on the edge of it, as if I'm not really there.'

Helle's father, a lawyer who had worked as a bank manager in Estonia, was unable to obtain even a clerical job because his English was so poor. 'His pronunciation was so bad that my brother Rein and I had to go with him everywhere to translate. We were always fighting over whose turn it was, because we were both too embarrassed to go,' she recalls. Fortunately her father liked carpentry and found work at Hallstrom's factory making Australia's first refrigerator, the Silent Knight. Later he worked for the Warringah Shire Council. As soon as they could scrape up enough money, they bought a block of land. 'Dad built a garage and we lived there at first. We thought it was marvellous, because it was ours and we were all together again, but Mum had to clean the Waabels' house, like a servant. Such a contrast to her life in Estonia.'

After a few years, Helle met an Estonian she liked at a dance held at the Estonian House which became the social centre of their community. Lembit had arrived on a two-year government contract and worked in Wollongong for a concreting company. 'I was doing book-keeping at the time. I just sort of picked it up,' Helle shrugs. Genuinely self-effacing, she tends to minimise her achievements to avoid any semblance of boasting. Asked how she came to be editor of the *Estonian News,* she says that she started off as the book-keeper, later typed a few articles and then just 'fell into it'.

When Helle and Lembit married in 1952, they talked about migrating to Canada, but the quota was full. Two years later, when they could have migrated, Tonis, the first of their five children was born, and Helle began to feel more settled. Several years later, her mother fell ill. In an impassioned voice, she says, 'You know, people talk about God, but where is the justice of things? In Estonia Dad completed his studies, got married and had an important job. But when the Russians came in, my parents had to leave everything behind and start over in a new country. And after Dad finally paid off the house and life started being easier here, Mum got MS and became a vegetable. He had to lead her around.

'After Mum died, Dad was very independent and never wanted to bother us. He let me do his white shirts, that was all. He grew orchids. He must have felt his life was ending the day he phoned my sister to come and photograph his orchids. For some reason I decided to go with her, which was very lucky because that was the last time I ever saw him. That night we got a call to say he had died.'

In 1975, Helle divorced her husband. 'Lembit was a typical Estonian male,' she says. 'He thought a woman's place was in the home. I had three children in three years but he didn't help me at all.' Throughout the years, Helle continued to correspond with her first boyfriend Ilmar who was living in England, and in 1980, when they were both divorced, she travelled to Europe to meet him. This reunion after almost thirty years sounds like the beginning of an autumnal second-time-round romance, but Helle hastens to assure me that no fires were rekindled. Quite the contrary. During their holiday she discovered that their personalities were incompatible. 'I'm active and curious about things, I like travelling and camping in the bush, but he wasn't interested in doing anything or going anywhere,' she says. 'He liked sitting around, and joining wine and gourmet societies.'

Helle has five children. Tonis, who has a concreting company in Canberra, married a girl whose parents were Estonian-born; Ilmar spent six years in the army, where he met his Australian wife; Raoul is a radiographer in charge of the CT machine at Gosford Hospital; Lembit is very bright but doesn't stick at things; while Linda Ann, who has two children, is now fulfilling her lifelong dream to become a nursing sister. 'I made a scrapbook from my journal and inserted photographs from the *Derna* so my grandchildren would know all about our voyage to Australia,' Helle says.

All her children speak Estonian but none of them has visited Estonia yet. She hopes that one day they'll all make the trip together. 'I kept thinking we'd return to Estonia but when my oldest son Tonis was about thirteen, the age at which I was torn away from my home, I knew I could never uproot him and take him away from his friends and the life he knew.'

Helle has been back five times since 1989. 'It's always a good experience,' she says. 'But whenever I hear Russian spoken, it makes me mad and sad. *You took our country, you made us leave, and now you're living here and we're not.* But out on the island of Kasary it's very tranquil and I feel at home with my relatives. The funny thing is, when I get together with school friends I haven't seen since we were thirteen, even though our lives and experiences have been so different, we still have the same outlook on life. But I wouldn't like to live there now, even though I could live like a millionaire. Sometimes I feel I don't belong anywhere. It makes me mad when I read about those illegal immigrants in the detention centres complaining and demanding to be provided with things. We got nothing from the government and didn't want anything. We thought it was our job to look after ourselves. We were grateful that Australia took us in.

'I'm a very loyal Australian and I feel cranky when people put Australia down, but I'm sitting on the edge of two chairs called Estonia and Australia. When athletes from both countries were competing in the Olympics, I barracked for the Estonians. I'm loyal to both, but Estonia is closer to my heart. It upsets me that the children and grandchildren of Estonians don't speak Estonian. What future is there for Estonian culture if they don't speak the language? I've passed on the language and traditions to my children, but when I'm gone, I think that feeling will also be gone. I know it isn't as important to my brother or sister as it is to me.'

Her brother, Dr Rein Nittim, studied civil engineering in Sydney. In his laconic way, he compresses his brilliant academic career into one unadorned sentence. 'I worked for the Department of Public Works, got interested in water engineering, did my masters degree and then got a doctorate in water engineering.' Now semi-retired, he works part-time at the water research laboratory at the University of New South Wales. And Estonia? 'I never went back,' he replies.

Like Rein, Helle's younger sister Maret Vesk also became an academic with a doctorate. After graduating in science at the University of Sydney with honours in botany, she chose the highly specialised field of electromicroscopy. An honorary research associate, she teaches postgraduate students at the university, although officially she has retired. 'I married an Estonian but I'm not involved in the Estonian community,' she says. 'I feel more Australian than Estonian.'

After fifty-two years, Helle has recently resumed contact with her shipboard confidante Rita, whose address I passed on to her. They have exchanged a few letters, sent each other family photographs, and have spoken on the phone several times.

'We can't figure out why we lost touch for so long after being so close,' Helle muses, 'but now that we've got in touch again, we want to meet before long, either here or in Brisbane.'

One Sunday afternoon, a few months after our last conversation, Helle calls me, but this time she is not her usual calm, unemotional self. In fact she can hardly contain her anger. 'Have you read that article in the *Sun-Herald* today about that fellow who said he threw an Estonian overboard during the voyage? I've spoken to some of the Estonians on our ship and they've never heard anything about it. If an Estonian was missing, one of us would have known. Maybe it was a Jew pretending to be an Estonian. It's outrageous for that man to make out that Estonians are anti-Semitic!'

23

The man who upset Helle with his claim that he had thrown an Estonian overboard was Sam Fiszman. When Sam arrived in Sydney, the anger that had been bubbling inside him throughout the stressful voyage and had culminated in that fateful fight was still simmering. He was indignant that after accusing him of being a Communist agitator, the authorities refused to let him go ashore in Fremantle. Fortunately, Archbishop Rafalsky had written a letter vouching for his character, and the Jewish community in Perth, together with Sydney Einfeld, the then President of the Jewish Welfare Society, assured the government that he would not abscond. Without their support, he would not have been allowed to set foot in Australia.

But things did not improve after his arrival in Sydney. One of Sam's reasons for migrating here was to join his mother's sister. Although she had arranged accommodation for them in an old cottage in Bondi and paid the first month's rent, she lacked his mother's loving personality. It wasn't financial assistance he longed for but warmth, and he felt more alienated than ever.

Everything about Sydney irritated him. In his unsettled state, it seemed a backward place. He missed Paris with its free-wheeling atmosphere, smoky bistros and pavement cafés with their strong coffee and intense conversations. Bread here tasted like cotton wool, coffee was tasteless, while wine was denigrated as 'plonk'.

'I can't stand it, I'm going back to Europe,' he kept threatening Esther. Every week he would go to Orbit Travel in George Street to book his passage back to Paris, and every week Esther would calm him down and persuade him to stay. 'But it was a long time before I unpacked my suitcase,' he chuckles, and adds with an affectionate glance towards his wife, 'She didn't have an easy time with me.'

It's Friday afternoon and the aroma of chicken soup wafts in from the kitchen where Esther has been preparing the Sabbath meal for their daughter Mia and her family. The man who used to argue about the existence of God on the *Derna* with Archbishop Rafalsky is still not religious, but keeping the Jewish traditions is important to Esther and Sam respects that.

I've known Sam and Esther ever since we arrived in Australia. My mother, who had helped Esther with the baby on the ship because she was ill, would sometimes run into her while shopping in Bondi Junction. After each meeting, she would regale us with an account of Esther's bubbly personality and angelic face. Everyone felt protective towards this eighteen year old and her baby. Dr and Mrs Frant, who had accompanied the Jewish orphans on the *Derna* and had become my parents' closest friends, occasionally mentioned the Fiszmans and the difficulties they were having starting a new life in Australia. Like my father, Dr Frant was forced to repeat his studies here, but when he began to practise again as an obstetrician and gynaecologist, many of the women from the *Derna*, including Esther, became his patients, so the shipboard links continued.

Eager to continue working as a journalist, Sam applied for a job at the *Mirror* newspaper but was unable to obtain the kind of position he wanted. He started working at Crown Crystal in South Dowling Street, but unable to stand the heat of the furnace left after ten days. Working in a milk bar to improve his English didn't last long either. When the owner tied an apron around him and told him to wash the dishes, he stomped out. And each week he returned to the travel agency to rebook his passage.

Unlike Sam, however, Esther took to Sydney from the first moment. 'I took one look at Bondi Beach and fell in love,' she beams. These days her hair is cropped short and sprinkled with grey but her large grey eyes still glow when she looks at Sam. 'Whenever I wheeled Mia in the pram down to the beach, I knew this was the best country in the world. Our cottage in Watson Street was small and decrepit, but the door was always open to our *Derna* friends. Yvonne and Magda stayed with us for a time. I owe my life to Magda. If not for her, I would never have survived in Auschwitz.'

Involuntarily I glance at the smudgy blue digits tattooed on her forearm. Following my gaze, Esther says in her forthright way, 'Magda and I had very different attitudes towards the past and our friendship cooled because of that. But that's all over now and I'm glad we're in touch again.'

Magda, the intellectual young woman in Dr Frant's group, fulfilled her academic ambitions. Soon after arriving in Melbourne she was awarded a university scholarship. After her Master of Science degree, she obtained her PhD in endocrinology, became a lecturer at Monash University and conducted research into the hormones of Australian native animals. Esther cites Magda's achievements with pride, but her own ambition was never for herself. All she ever wanted was to take care of her family, who in her eyes can do no wrong. The feeling is obviously reciprocated. 'Just look at the poem my grandson Tull wrote when I turned seventy,' she says, bursting with grandmotherly pride. Tull Price, one of Mia's two sons, has made news recently for inventing laceless jogging shoes.

Esther, who lost her whole family at Auschwitz when she was twelve, has become the matriarch of her close-knit family. Her youthful beauty has been replaced with the glow of contentment and strength, but the warmth, outspokenness and youthful enthusiasm haven't faded. Neither has her admiration for her husband, whose health is now uppermost in her mind. As we talk, she potters around her homely kitchen chopping vegetables and stirring the soup while their old black labrador, Gorbachev, pads into the kitchen with a white toy bunny in his mouth, hoping that one of us will play with him.

Sam, who has been discussing some controversy with one of his political colleagues, hangs up, still laughing about the conversation. Back on the verandah, we resume talking about the Fiszmans' first few months in Australia. 'That was the worst period of my life,' he says in a quiet but assertive voice, shaking his balding head. Behind the shiny glasses, there's a watchful toughness about him, and even though the years have taken away the anger and added a settled rotundity to his frame, he has retained some of the watchful intensity that reminds me of an elderly Michael Douglas.

It was Syd Einfeld's friendship that provided Sam with an emotional anchor, channelled his energy and helped to determine the course that his life was to take. Syd was the indefatigable friend of the immigrants, the poor and the disadvantaged; a lifelong champion of social justice, lighting the path for his son Marcus. 'Syd was a jolly giant who would do anything for you,' Sam says of his mentor. 'He was always ready to help those in need and never wanted anything for himself, like a good father.'

To make ends meet, Sam shifted sofas and tables at RM O'Keefe's store in Pitt Street, drove a cab at night and hawked bolts of material door-to-door. Seeing an opportunity to sell goods in country areas, he teamed up with a Dutch hawker and they drove hundreds of miles along dusty roads, stopping at small towns to sell rugs, mats, materials, whatever they could lay their hands on. 'That's when I got to know salt-of-the-earth Australians,' he recalls. 'Country people were the most genuine and the kindest human beings I'd ever met. No matter how far you drove, as soon as you got to a town, they welcomed you with open arms. They accepted you for what you were.' With all the travelling and taxi-driving, Esther and Mia hardly saw him, but by 1950 he'd managed to save the key money for a flat in Warners Avenue which they rented for seventeen shillings and sixpence a week.

Sam discovered his flair for politics when Syd Einfeld asked him to distribute leaflets for the forthcoming Waverley Council elections. After Labor lost the election, Sam pointed out that dropping leaflets wasn't effective because it was too impersonal. You had to go out there, knock on doors, visit hospitals and nursing homes, and meet the people. Syd was impressed with the young man's political acumen and promised him a bigger role in the next council election. In 1962, the incumbent mayor of Waverley was Ray O'Keefe, whose wild son Johnny electrified audiences at rock concerts. True to his promise, Syd Einfeld encouraged Sam to work behind the scenes on behalf of the Labor candidate Doug Morey. Sam hoots with laughter. 'He won! He scraped in with twelve votes!' The year 1962 marked a new beginning for Sam and Esther in other ways as well, with the birth of their son Robert.

Sam's political activities brought him into contact with Labor politicians he came to admire as quintessential Australians. Syd Einfeld introduced him to Pat Hills, the Lord Mayor of Sydney, and Harry Jensen, the mayor of Randwick. In an impassioned voice, Sam says, 'Those men didn't care what I had, how much I earned, what I did for a living, what I wore, or whether I spoke with an accent. They took me at my own value. Their egalitarian way of thinking was amazing. I'd never experienced anything like it before. I felt I'd come home.'

After selling rugs and materials door-to-door, Sam decided to go into business for himself and opened Univers Carpets in Bondi Junction. But building up a successful enterprise was only one of his interests. A keen soccer player, he played for Progress and Canterbury. After being one of the foundation members of the Hakoah Soccer Club, he became its president, as well as the chairman of Sydney City Soccer Club. The Polish migrant became chairman of the 'Bring out a Briton' committee which sponsored British migrants to Australia. On outings with his Australian mates, he discovered the thrill of horse racing, and to this day a visit to Randwick racecourse is a Saturday afternoon institution.

His most consuming passion, however, was Labor politics. 'Labor has never tolerated right-wing racists, which you can't say about the Liberal Party and some of their National Party associates,' he says. 'Many Labor politicians have an Irish background and know about persecution. Even though there's not much true socialism left these days, there's a brotherhood, a kinship, that I haven't found anywhere else.' Later that day, I recall his comment when I hear that the Queensland National Party has given its preferences to the One Nation Party in the forthcoming state elections.

* * *

Although Sam never became a member of the Labor Party, his dedication did not go unnoticed. When Syd Einfeld became Minister for Consumer Affairs, he encouraged Sam to sit on the Consumer Advisory Council. When the state elections were approaching, Sam worked tirelessly to raise funds for Neville Wran. Gesturing around the comfortable loungeroom where we are sitting, he says, 'We discussed the strategy right here.' After Wran became premier of New South Wales in 1976, Sam continued his fundraising efforts and over the years has raised millions of dollars for the Labor Party, but his own lifestyle remains simple and unpretentious.

When I follow him into his study in search of a book he has mentioned, I am amazed to see that the walls are covered in awards, certificates and citations for activities as diverse as sport, charity, consumer affairs and tourism. A closer look reveals that over the years Sam has been awarded the highest honours Australia has to offer. Pausing in front of a photograph, I recognise the tall man standing next to him as Sir Roden Cutler, the then governor of New South Wales, who had just presented him with the Order of Australia medal.

'I was awarded that in 1981 for my work as chairman of the National Consumer Advisory Council,' Sam says, and adds with considerable satisfaction, 'It wasn't political payback, because I got it from Malcolm Fraser's government. That was an incredible feeling, being rewarded for doing something that benefited my new country. That's when I was very glad I'd never bought that ticket to go back to Europe!'

The honours kept coming. Eleven years later, in 1992, he received the Australia Medal. 'That was mainly for my contribution to tourism,' he explains. Convinced of the tourist potential of New South Wales, he promoted it energetically. As chairman of the New South Wales Tourism Commission, he introduced the idea of having a different theme each year. 'I'm sure you won't be surprised to hear that I chaired the Year of Sport!' he laughs. In the years that followed, he was appointed director of the Australian Tourist Commission and until recently served on the board of the Darling Harbour Authority.

As we talk, he rifles through his papers until he finds the letter he received recently to confirm the extension of his tenure as chairman of Tourism New South Wales until the year 2003. 'The usual retirement age is sixty-five, but a motion was moved in parliament, which I'm proud to say was seconded by the Opposition spokesman for tourism, to extend the age limit for my benefit, because I am seventy-four!'

An even greater honour was still to come. In the Queen's Birthday Honours of the year 2000, Sam Fiszman became an Officer of the Order of Australia for his services to the Australian tourism industry. After hearing his account of those initial unhappy years in Sydney, it seems amazing that the young hot-head who arrived with three pounds in his pocket and anger in his heart, who hated this place so much that he longed to go back to Europe, has received one of Australia's highest honours for promoting it as a tourist destination.

Several months later, on a warm November evening, over 600 formally attired guests, many of them luminaries of both the state and federal Labor Party, gathered at the Sydney Convention Centre. As they entered the cavernous Tumbalong Ballroom, Sam's photograph loomed from a huge video screen above the sign 'ALP dinner in honour of Sam Fiszman'. While Bob Hawke hugged him, Kim Beazley pumped his hand and Neville Wran whispered a joke in his ear, Sam looked dazed. 'This sort of thing doesn't usually happen until you're dead!' he said.

Esther, however, wasn't fazed. 'He deserves it,' she commented.

The aim of the dinner was to raise money for St Vincent's Hospital Blood and Cancer Research, the Victor Chang Cardiac Research Institute and Jewish Care — all causes close to Sam's heart. As the evening progressed, a succession of past and present leaders of the ALP stepped onto the dais. One by one they expressed their political gratitude and personal affection for the man to whom Bob Hawke said, 'more than most Australians, you embody the Australian tradition of mateship. I'll never forget the comfort and friendship you gave me. I respect your remarkable courage. I salute you and I love you and extend that to your wife and family, who have been a rock of support in your work.'

Michael Knight, the then Minister of Sport and Tourism, recalled the day he asked Premier Bob Carr for money to transform Darling Harbour into an Olympic venue. As his request had already been turned down several times, he wasn't very optimistic, but this time he brought Sam, as director of the Darling Harbour Authority, for moral support. To his astonishment, the Premier approved his request immediately. Recalling the occasion, Bob Carr later explained, 'As soon as I saw you come in with Sam Fiszman, I gave up!'

Neville Wran said that there were no halfway measures with Sam, no ifs or buts. 'His glass is never half empty, always half full,' he said. After paying tribute to his dedication as a fundraiser, he praised Sam's intuitive understanding of what ordinary people think and want. 'And he's never frightened to tell you,' he rasped in the voice damaged during surgery some years before. 'In fact, once he starts, it's impossible to shut him up! Sam, I'm privileged to call you my mate.'

Kim Beazley, who called it an evening of thanksgiving, expressed better than anyone else what Sam was feeling on this extraordinary occasion. After describing him with a smile as 'a one-man walking charitable institution with a very persuasive manner', he became more sombre. 'Sam is a man of politics because he understands the consequences of not being so,' he said. 'Through his own experiences during the Holocaust, he knows the consequences of intolerance and the evil in politics of lies given bayonets. He resisted it in his youth when he fought in the Warsaw Ghetto and later joined the Russian army to fight the Germans, and he has tried to resist it here.'

Finally it was Sam's turn to speak. He had been desperately ill in the past few months, having undergone four by-passes only two weeks earlier, but looking at him up on the podium that night, ruddy and glowing with happiness, you'd never have suspected it. 'I won't rest until Kim Beazley is installed as PM of Australia!' he announced. When the thunderous applause died down, he continued. 'I've received more from the Labor Party than I have given them. I've seen the wrong side of politics. I joined the Russian army to take revenge for my family and kill the Nazis, but discovered that the extreme left was no good, just as the extreme right was no good. You need a buffer, and that buffer is the Labor Party. So you could say that for me it's been a labour of love!'

Then he said something that plunged the entire ballroom into stunned silence. 'Some of you have been asking me for years about that incident on the *Derna*. I can tell you now that it's true.' And he proceeded to give an account of the circumstances in which he fought with an anti-Semitic passenger whom he described as Estonian, and threw him overboard.

Although Sam had previously told me about this incident, I was astonished that what had been a private revelation had now become a public confession. In the weeks that followed, several newspapers reported it, provoking outrage, amazement and incredulity. According to Helle, some of her countrymen were furious because they felt that by identifying his opponent as an anti-Semitic Estonian, Sam had slandered their entire nation. As speculation continued, others questioned various aspects of the incident. They wondered whether a passenger could vanish without a trace, how it was that no one seemed to know the missing man, and why the disappearance of a passenger had not been recorded or reported to the authorities.

Without seeing the ship's log, it's impossible to know whether the incident was ever recorded or not, but all efforts to locate that log have failed. The *Derna* was an unseaworthy, overcrowded vessel which did not adhere to the standards set by international shipping regulators, and one can only surmise that keeping accurate records, especially about events that cast a poor light on its procedures, was not one of its priorities. Major Weale, the Aliens Registration Officer who boarded the *Derna* in Fremantle, reported that Sam Fiszman had been involved in some disturbances during the voyage, but did not mention that he had thrown anyone overboard.

It's not often that the guest of honour at an official function confesses to manslaughter, and many of the guests wondered what had induced Sam to drop his bombshell that night. Was he proud that he had vanquished a bully, or did he have a guilty conscience and want to unburden himself? Some even suggested that Sam was a Walter Mitty character who had exaggerated or fantasised about an event that had occurred only in his imagination.

While the controversy continued to rage, I questioned Sam again about the incident, but he repeated the account he had given earlier. 'When that bully smeared the marmalade in the Jewish passenger's face and made anti-Semitic comments, I got mad. It was a fair fight, man to man, but I was fighting the war all over again. I saw SS men coming at me, like the ones who had shot my mother and sister. We threw a few punches, and then I was on my back with my feet on his stomach, and threw him with my legs. He went over the rail but whether he fell overboard or onto the deck below, I couldn't tell. All I know is, I never saw him again.'

Sam himself cannot explain why he made this confession at the dinner given in his honour, in front of 600 people. 'I was very emotional that night, partly because of all the tributes, and partly because I'd just come out of hospital after having by-pass surgery. I got carried away and said it on the spur of the moment.'

It's not surprising that he was overwhelmed by the occasion. He had just seen his whole life scroll in front of him, from the moment he arrived in Australia and was prohibited from landing, until that moment, fifty-two years later, when he was being honoured by the ALP.

His life story had come full circle. His confession made the *Derna* the subject of speculation, gossip and controversy just as it had been fifty-two years ago when we arrived, and once again Sam was at the centre of the storm.

24

Verner Puurand would have been appalled to know that the man he had denounced as a Communist agitator in 1948 was being regaled as a hero by the Australian Labor Party five decades later. Although he didn't live long enough to witness this event, with the help of the Estonian Club in Brisbane, I located his son Hans.

As I wait for him in a hotel foyer, I expect to see an austere man with military bearing, so when the man in a check shirt and jeans comes towards me with a shy smile and introduces himself as Hans Puurand, he takes me by surprise. His voice is quiet, his manner unassuming and his long greying hair is tied back in a ponytail, hippy-style. It hadn't occurred to me that he could turn out to be the antithesis of his father, the forceful submarine commander.

At sixty-eight, Hans has a retiring nature, much like the self-conscious boy he was when he arrived in Australia at the age of sixteen. 'It was humiliating to be put back to primary school at that age, but the headmaster said I had to stay in sixth class until I could speak English,' he says. 'I'd learnt English at high school in Germany but they spoke with a different accent here. But I did understand when the other boys called me a bloody Balt!'

When they arrived, Hans, his parents and younger brother Mart lived with their sponsors, the Kondrashoffs, in the working class suburb of Woolloongabba, in a wooden house on stilts which they thought very peculiar. The Kondrashoffs were Mrs Puurand's relatives who had migrated to Australia before the war. As Hans remembers it, there was only one source of discord between the two families. 'The Kondrashoffs' son George was a bit pink in those days, so he and my dad were always arguing about politics,' he recalls.

The Puurands found it difficult to adjust to life in this somnolent city where people lived at a much slower, quieter pace than in Europe. On Sundays life seemed to stop altogether. 'You could have shot a cannon up Queen Street and not hit a soul!' Hans smiles. What made it worse was that Christmas was approaching, but instead of snow there was sultry heat, beach picnics and the perfumed smell of tropical flowers. Like most of the Christian migrants, they missed the festive atmosphere and spiritual feeling that used to make December special.

Unhappy memories leave far deeper imprints than happy ones, and when Hans thinks back to that first Christmas, he recalls the day his mother gave him some money to buy presents for the family. Clutching the pound note, he rushed to Woolworths. As soon as he walked into the store, a display of sweets in shiny wrappers caught his eye. He decided to buy some for his grandmother who felt even more dislocated than the rest of the family because she spoke no English and couldn't listen to the radio or read the newspapers. When he handed over the money, the salesgirl rang it up on the big brass register and handed him the change, but when he counted it out, he was shocked to find that she had only given him change from ten shillings. But no matter how hard he tried, he couldn't seem to make her understand. He trudged home with the bag of sweets, wondering how he was going to explain the loss of so much money.

Hans's parents had troubles of their own. His mother was unhappy working in a clothing factory where she felt slighted by the owner, while his father was disappointed because his chief mate's certificate was not recognised here. At forty-four, Verner Puurand swallowed his pride and started working as an ordinary seaman on river vessels.

For most of 1949, he worked on the SS *Alagna*. Although the owners appreciated his expertise and dilgence, his workmates disliked him because of his dogmatic nature and hatred of Communism. On one occasion, when the crew decided to strike over their conditions, Puurand did not endear himself by telling them that they didn't know how well off they were. Whenever they criticised the newly elected Menzies government and praised the Soviet Union, he would harangue them about the evils of Communism.

'At one stage they got so fed up with him, they threatened to throw him overboard,' Hans recalls, and adds with a short laugh, 'Dad could come over very strong. He was used to giving orders. At home when he said "Jump!" you didn't ask why, you said, "How high?"'

When the waitress arrives to take our order, Hans orders tonic water. 'That's the strongest drink I have these days,' he says. 'I joined AA thirty years ago and haven't had a drink since. I don't have a problem saying that I'm an alcoholic. I'm not proud of it, but I'm not ashamed either. I'm very shy and drinking made me feel more confident. A few drinks and I could talk or dance with anyone, but nowadays it takes a lot to open me up. Dad disowned me when I was drinking, but eventually he understood that alcoholism is a disease.'

When he returns to the story, Hans says something that makes me sit forward. 'Dad told me that not long after we arrived, Australian Intelligence wanted him to work for them.' The idea that Verner Puurand had been sought out by ASIO was intriguing. Why did they approach him? What did they want? Hans looks troubled. 'I've gone through my father's papers but there are some things I can't figure out. Sometimes I wonder if I'm putting the correct interpretation on what he told me.'

Hoping that there would be a file on Verner Puurand, I applied for it under the federal government's Freedom of Information legislation. Several weeks later, a package arrived from the National Archives in Canberra, and to my delight the dossier was as thick as a telephone directory. As I pored over these documents, so excited that I could hardly sit still, I entered the arcane, secretive world of spies, moles, informers and double agents. Like a conspirator from a John le Carré novel, I read through memos, letters and reports thrillingly stamped SECRET, addressed to people whose identity was confined to initials, and signed by names that have been blacked-out to protect ASIO operatives. My heart raced as I came across one revelation after another about the man whose espionage activities could have furnished a writer of spy thrillers with a plot too convoluted to follow and too incredible to believe.

From the earliest memo, which was dated 1950, I could see that it was actually Verner Puurand himself who had taken the initiative and offered his services to naval intelligence while he was working on a vessel called the *Cementco*. Because of his offer, he became the subject of an investigation by Australia's newly formed security intelligence organisation, which came to be known by its acronym ASIO.

Puurand's offer created a dilemma, because he was living with a Russian whom they suspected of being a Communist. Although they were never able to produce a shred of evidence against Kondrashoff, the suspicion clung to him and, by association, to Puurand himself. It's ironic that a man who probably loathed Communism more than anyone in ASIO was suspected of being a Communist, but a nation's secret service acts out the fears and fantasies of its government, and the hunt for Communists was their top priority.

ASIO's obsession with Communists can be understood in the context of the world situation and the anti-Communist paranoia prevalent at the time. The Soviet Union, which only five years earlier had been regarded as the saviour of Western democracy, was now viewed as its greatest enemy. Since the end of World War II, the Russians had most of eastern Europe in their grip, and bellicose anti-Western rhetoric issued daily from the Kremlin. The Prime Minister, Mr Menzies, who regarded Communists as part of an insidious international conspiracy organised by Moscow to destroy democracy, attempted to have the Communist Party banned in Australia.

There was widespread pessimism about the future. Communist North Korea invaded the south in 1949, causing the Korean War. Many regarded this as the flashpoint for another global conflict, this time between the Soviet Union and the Western nations. The following year, Russia plunged the West into gloom by testing its first nuclear device, and when Menzies returned from Britain and the United States in September 1950, he warned Australians to be prepared for the possibility of World War III.

In this climate of suspicion and hostility, memos about Puurand and his supposedly Communist sponsor bounced back and forth between ASIO and the Immigration Department, who couldn't decide whether to use his services or deport him. After vacillating for eighteen months, the director-general of ASIO decided that it was time to interview Puurand and clarify the situation.

In April 1951, an ASIO field officer called Andersen knocked on the door of the small weatherboard cottage which the Puurands had bought from their sponsor in a quiet street in Woolloongabba. Verner Puurand opened a desk drawer to show Andersen fifteen neatly-stacked manilla folders, which he claimed contained information of interest to Australian intelligence. Giving a chronological account of his career, he mentioned that he had been sent to England for submarine training in 1935, appointed to command the *Kalev* submarine in 1939, and that he had continued this command during the Russian occupation of Estonia. He omitted any mention of his activities between 1941 and 1945.

Although the shifting allegiances and desperate struggles of tiny European states caught between the sickle and the swastika were confusing for most Australians, the regional director detected enough discrepancies in Verner Puurand's story to arouse his suspicions and to recommend an overseas check. When at the end of 1951, Puurand applied for permanent residence, ASIO refused to clear him until these checks were completed.

The report from Germany was startling. Its author, Captain Keith Turbayne, an ASIO security officer attached to the Australian Military Mission in Cologne, had actually written it two years earlier. He had hoped to alert Australian authorities to Verner Puurand's wartime and post-war activities before they approved his application to migrate, but by the time ASIO obtained the letter, he had already been living here for three years.

Captain Turbayne's report contained information he had obtained from US army files. Some of it had been given by a trusted informant, while the rest was based on interviews conducted with Puurand himself in the American zone in Germany in 1946 and 1947. After telling his American interviewer that back in 1938 he had changed his surname from the German-sounding Puurman to the Estonian-sounding Puurand, he told a story of espionage, deception and changing loyalties.

Verner Puurand explained that in 1940, while he commanded the *Kalev*, Russia seized Estonian naval bases and ordered him to teach Soviet crews to operate submarines. He was approached by a Russian naval officer, Lt Commander Donat Ferdinandovich Bock, who questioned him in detail about the technical and strategic capabilities of the British navy which had trained him. Several months later, he was approached by a Russian secret police commissar from the NKVD (National Commissariat for Internal Affairs) who wanted a list of his naval associates in England. After more questioning, he suggested that Captain Puurand should work for them, implying that refusal would not be wise. When signing an agreement to act as an NKVD agent, Puurand had chosen the code name JAVIN, which is an abbreviation of a Russian phrase meaning *I am guilty*. He agreed to collect information about the British navy but denied ever passing any information to the Russians.

One can imagine the shock of the ASIO operatives as they read that the man whose services they had considered using had once been in the employ of the NKVD, and possibly still was for all they knew. But Captain Turbayne's report contained other damning information. After the German occupation of Estonia, Puurand had been arrested, sent to a POW camp in Viljandi and threatened with execution because of his connection with the NKVD. He explained that to save his life, he had agreed to give the Germans information about coastal mine fields and Estonian naval operations. From August until December 1941, he advised German staff about matters relating to naval operations on the Estonian coast, which was then in Soviet hands.

And there were more revelations to come. While serving as an adviser to the German staff in the fall of 1941, he had apparently been persuaded to work for the Abwehr, the German military intelligence, whose director was Admiral Canaris. Puurand's task was to establish an espionage centre in Estonia to train wireless technicians and operators. In March 1942 he rented a forty-five hectare farm in Leetze, where he prepared false documents for German agents who were dropped behind Russian lines across the Finnish border.

Mulling over these disclosures, I recalled that Hans had told me about his father's espionage activities for the Nazis. 'Once he wore an army uniform, another time a navy uniform, but mostly he wore plainclothes,' he had said. 'I think he worked undercover and had carte blanche to wear whatever he needed. And he was armed. He kept a pistol in his coat pocket.'

Verner Puurand's activities did not end with the war. In his capacity as the Baltic Liaison Officer to the US army in Germany immediately after the war, he supplied the Americans with Baltic guards who had served in SS units of the German army. He issued them with certificates stating that they had been coerced into German service and advised them to surgically remove their SS blood group tattoos, to conceal their past from the Americans and from immigration authorities.

After reading Captain Turbayne's report, the director-general of ASIO, Colonel Spry, noted in a terse memo: 'Had I known about Puurand's espionage activities for the NKVD and the Abwehr, and about his deception of the Americans after the war, I would not have allowed him to enter Australia.'

Turbayne has now retired from the service. When I spoke to him in Canberra recently, I asked how it happened that an Australian selection officer had approved Verner Puurand's application. 'If the selection officer had known about the US army file, he wouldn't have accepted him,' he said. 'No one who had worked for the Abwehr, let alone NKVD, would have been accepted. But the officer probably knew nothing about this file and the machinery wasn't yet properly in place to investigate these people.'

Yet as we now know, largely as a result of the investigative work of Sydney author Mark Aarons, former Nazis were admitted to Australia in this period, sometimes with the knowledge of the government. Early in 1948, shortly before the formation of ASIO, the Commonwealth Intelligence Service protested at being unable to run security checks on 127 German scientists who were recruited by the Australian government. As the release of those documents has recently revealed, the protests were ignored. Information about the Nazi affiliation of the scientists, thirty-one of whom had been members of the Nazi party, while twelve had belonged to the SS and SA, was concealed because the government was eager to take advantage of their expertise.

Oblivious to all the departmental time and paper that had been devoted to assessing his career and espionage potential, in 1952 Verner Puurand offered his services to ASIO once again. By then, however, they had read Captain Turbayne's report and had decided that he was a 'power-seeking opportunist who couldn't be trusted... a person who has no national loyalty and who would work for or against the USSR or Australia as convenience dictated'. They were still considering deporting him, and might have done so if not for the probability that if sent back to Estonia, he would have been executed by the Communist government for his collaboration with the Nazis.

Although they stopped short of deporting him, they decided to withhold his application for permanent residence but to reconsider it in two years time. As Colonel Spry put it, 'I am of the opinion that Puurand's loyalty has not been established beyond a reasonable doubt and whilst not, at present, constituting a security risk, he is of security interest.'

The following year, while working on the SS *Moorah* in South Brisbane, Verner Puurand applied for a commercial wireless operator's certificate. Hans remembers testing his father while he was studying to gain this qualification. 'He studied so hard that I couldn't understand why he didn't get it,' he tells me. 'Whenever I went over the Morse code with him, he seemed to know it pretty well.' What neither Hans nor his father knew, however, was that the director-general of ASIO had intervened. Since Puurand's permanent residency had been deferred, he recommended that a wireless operator's licence should not be issued.

As Hans and I talk about the past in the Brisbane hotel, I reflect how unpredictable life is. If our parents had passed each other on board the *Derna*, my mother might have muttered something about Estonians collaborating with the Nazis, and his father might have said something about Jews siding with the Bolsheviks. And here we are, fifty-two years later, chatting amicably in a hotel in Brisbane, both Australians now, our parents no longer alive, our origins no longer relevant: just two people reminiscing about the past and a shared journey.

'Estonians didn't fight *with* the Germans,' Hans is saying. 'They were fighting the Russians in German uniforms.' He is not the first Estonian who has given me this interpretation of events. I can understand that being the enemy of their enemy, the Germans became their logical allies, but knowing how enthusiastically the Baltic nations welcomed the Germans, how eagerly many young men joined the brutal police militia and the SS, and how savagely some of them fulfilled their duties, I feel that this explanation is an attempt to shift the goal posts of history and avoid responsibility. The memory of those brutal events has been stirred up during recent attempts by the Australian government to arrange the extradition of Konrad Kalejs, a member of the savage Arajs Death Squad, to face charges of committing war crimes in his native Latvia.

But that was then. Now, as I listen to Estonian and Latvian passengers telling their stories, instead of seeing them as Nazi collaborators and German allies, I try to see them as individuals caught up in a life and death struggle for national freedom.

It's confronting to hear them talk about their terror of the Russian advance, and their hope that the Germans would win, knowing that if they had got their wish, I would not be alive today. It's difficult for me to sympathise with their nationalistic aspirations when a Nazi victory would have meant the total annihilation of the Jewish race, including me. Yet I can see that for them, with their terror of Russian occupation, this alliance offered the only solution. And when the so-called 'liberators' channelled the residents' deep-seated anti-Semitism and terror of the Bolsheviks, they unleashed the slaughter that ensued.

Like many of their countrymen, especially those who had co-operated with the Germans, the Puurand family moved from Estonia to Germany in 1944 to avoid reprisals from the advancing Russians. Recalling their life in Germany, Hans says, 'The Jews who had been to concentration camps got better treatment in Germany after the war, so some of them had their arms tattooed to make it look as if they'd been in the camps.'

For a moment, I'm too shocked to speak. When I ask what gave him that idea, he gives a dismissive shrug. 'People said so.'

I had hoped that we had left the prejudices of the previous generation behind, but hearing Hans repeating the racist distortions of the past, it seems that we are doomed to carry the burden of history on our shoulders.

When we move on, Hans tells me that after obtaining his trade certificates and engineering diploma in Brisbane, he chose a career at sea. 'A chip off the old block you could say, but that's what I always wanted to do.' He rolls up his sleeve and shows me an anchor tattooed on his forearm. 'Dad had one exactly like it except that his was at the base of the thumb, and that's where I wanted mine. But the tattooist said it was safer to do it higher up.'

Like his father, Hans was drawn to the sea and became an engineer on passenger and cargo ships. For a painfully shy young man, life at sea was liberating. 'The women just threw themselves at me. It must have been the gold braid and buttons on the uniform,' he smiles.

By that time, his father had given up working on the ships and had become a salesman for Electrolux. In 1954, while the Petrov affair rocked Australia, Verner Puurand surprised ASIO by asking to be interviewed. In view of his former association with the NKVD, and the fact that a former ship-mate had alleged that he was being watched by the Australian Communist Party, he decided to make a clean breast of his past activities.

The Petrov affair pushed anti-Communist paranoia to greater heights. It began with the defection of Vladimir Petrov, who posed as a secretary at the Russian embassy but was actually a high-ranking officer in the KGB. Day after day, sensational stories of spies, counter-spies, scandals and international intrigues were splashed across the front pages of Australian daily newspapers, confirming fears that Communism was about to undermine the Australian way of life. Everyone was shocked by the photograph of Petrov's distraught wife Evdokia being dragged by grim-faced Russian minders along the tarmac and hustled aboard a BOAC plane. Everyone had an opinion about the motives of the protoganists whose shady characters and hedonistic lifestyle surpassed any spy stories concocted by novelists.

The Petrov affair caused me personal embarrassment in an unexpected way. The ASIO agent who had befriended Petrov and had allegedly acted as go-between in his defection was Michael Bialoguski, whose svengali-like face with its intense gaze and triangular black beard was often reproduced in the newspapers. As it happened, our surname, Boguslawski, was sufficiently similar to confuse most Australians at a time when Polish surnames were still comparatively rare. In my third year at Sydney Girls' High School, I grew increasingly exasperated as I kept explaining to neighbours, schoolfriends and everyone who asked the same question, that my father was not the notorious character embroiled with the Petrovs, but a scholarly grey-haired dentist with no taste for intrigue.

For Verner Puurand, however, the Petrov affair was a threat. He knew that if his NKVD past was exposed at such a sensitive time he could be deported, so to forestall any unwelcome revelations he decided to speak out. This time when the ASIO officer called at his home, he filled in details omitted in his earlier interview. He not only confirmed the contents of Captain Turbayne's report, but substantiated it with ministerial passes, temporary passports, names and dates. He assured his ASIO interviewer that, like the majority of Estonians, he had always held strong anti-Russian and anti-Communist views. 'That's why I felt no moral objection to working with Germans,' he explained. 'I felt I was serving my country by doing so.' He admitted that he had urged the Baltic POWs to remove their SS tattoos and had lied to the American authorities about his own past to avoid being indicted as a war criminal.

Taking into account his unblemished record in Australia, the authorities decided in June 1955 to approve Verner Puurand's application for naturalisation. But ASIO hadn't forgotten his offer to spy for them, and three years later they considered this possibility once again. From their point of view, his submarine training, expertise in radio reception and transmission during the war, training of agents and saboteurs for service behind Russian lines and his excellent Russian made him a potential counter-intelligence agent.

In July 1958, another ASIO field officer arrived to interview him. He asked whether Puurand was familiar with present-day wireless telegraphy, whether he had any reason to think that the Communist Party of Australia was still interested in his activities and whether Russian intelligence had made any attempt to contact him. Puurand replied that he had abandoned his effort to gain his wireless operator's licence, and that the Russians had not been in touch.

In the course of the interview, Puurand volunteered his views about Communism. 'Communism will eventually engulf the world and there is nothing that the Western powers can do to prevent it,' he predicted. 'You will probably see it in your day, but I will never see it again. I have seen it in action once and that is enough for me. I have a rope and a tree selected, and I will never see Communism take over this country.'

By this time, Puurand had started building houses. 'That's what he'd always wanted to do,' Hans tells me, 'but he wasn't very successful. He was a good builder, but not a good manager.' When I ask about his mother, he falls silent. Like many women married to dominating husbands, Friida Puurand left a much fainter imprint on her son than the father whose voice resounds so powerfully in his life even now. 'Mother worked very hard,' he says. After a pause he adds, 'She was quiet.'

Hans's own seagoing career ended in 1963. After leaving the merchant marine, he studied draughting and design and became a design project engineer, specialising in control circuits for mine smelters. When his marriage to an Australian ended, he married an Estonian woman. 'People should marry within their own cultures,' he says. 'You understand each other better.' Hans and Kulla live with her father who is ninety years old. 'We've built a house with a granny flat so that her dad can live with us. If anything happens to Kulla, I'll look after him. It's not like that in Australian families, but that's the way it should be.' He's sad that the divorce has affected his relationship with his daughter, who works for the police force. 'We used to be very close, but the divorce hit her very hard. She didn't come to my wedding.'

Several months after our conversation, Hans returns from his first trip to Estonia. 'The whole place is dilapidated,' he tells me over the phone. 'The Russians ruined it. Their buildings are shoddy. Food costs about the same but they earn much less. The weather was good: it only rained once.'

When I ask how it felt to be back in Estonia, he says, 'To tell you the truth, I didn't feel I'd come home. The house we lived in was run down, like everything else. Drab. I managed to find where Dad's farm had been at Tamsalu but there was no house any more. It stood empty for years and just rotted away. The land is still in Dad's name so my brother Mart and I could claim it, but what for? Mart is ill with emphysema, he can't travel. Anyway, it's a small block without a house on it, so we couldn't sell it and we wouldn't want it for ourselves.'

While in Tallinn, Hans went to see the *Lempit,* one of the two submarines built in Britain for Estonia before the war. 'It was identical to my father's submarine, the *Kalev,* which sank during World War II after it ran into a Finnish mine. It's lying at the bottom of the Baltic Sea,' he explains. 'The *Lempit* looked exactly as it used to, except that the table and curtains were gone. When the caretaker asked me what colour they were, I still remembered. They were maroon. It was quite interesting to see our old home. Not overly exciting,' he hastens to add. 'I have no desire to go back to Estonia in a hurry. I didn't have much of a feeling for it. You could say I was quite detached.'

Wherever he went in Estonia, Hans searched for the traditional Estonian food that his mother and grandmother used to cook. 'We asked everyone, but nobody knew which restaurants served it. People there think we're all millionaires, so they kept sending us to posh hotels which served Western meals. Then on our last day someone mentioned a place called the Estonian House. They had the lot! Genuine food, reasonable prices and friendly people. That food brought back so many memories, just the taste of it. It took me back to my childhood. I cried all through that meal.'

25

The night sky hadn't begun to lighten over the canyon of city office blocks when Guta's footsteps echoed on Collins Street at four o'clock in the morning. She liked this metropolis of Victorian buildings and tree-lined streets where trams rattled past and the cheery conductors waved the passengers aboard. Melbourne's department stores amazed her with all their floors of merchandise. Myer, with its large windows and brightly lit showrooms was the modern one, while the dimly lit Buckley & Nunn's was popular with older matrons in flowered hats and wrist-length gloves.

Squinting at the address on her scrap of paper, Guta peered at the name of each cross street, until with a sigh of relief she turned into Little Collins Street. There it was: Henty House, one of the most important-looking buildings in the block. Taking a deep breath, she swung open the heavy doors of the Civil Aviation Department. The young woman who had been accused by Verner Puurand of being a Communist because she had spent her time on board talking to two sailors was about to start work.

This job, like everything since their arrival, had been arranged by Tosia Goleb. Although Guta's husband Dick had only met Tosia once shortly before she left Poland for Australia, she had met them at the wharf and taken them home. A survivor of the Warsaw Ghetto, Tosia had arrived in Melbourne two years earlier, and included Guta and Dick in the warm extended family that she had created for herself here.

With Tosia to organise and motivate them, they didn't go through the mental paralysis that afflicted many migrants who had no friends or family to guide them. She anticipated their difficulties and, with her boundless energy, smoothed the path for them. 'Guta, there's a science course at the university that would suit you, but you'll need a part-time job to keep you going,' she would say. A moment later she was making inquiries and phone calls and passing on names and addresses. 'Dick, you'll have to do electrical engineering again. They won't recognise your Polish diploma so you'll probably have to go to RMIT...' The two orphans had found a surrogate mother.

They had been staying with her in her small St Kilda flat for several weeks, wondering whether they would ever find a place of their own, when she rushed in bursting with news one afternoon. 'I've found you a house! But don't expect luxury,' she warned. Accommodation was scarce in Melbourne after the war, and even flats were hard to find. The house in Wordsworth Street, St Kilda was a tumbledown weatherboard cottage with dry rot, an outdoor toilet, leaning fences with broken palings and grass that straggled waist-high in the neglected yard. But they had a house and, what was even more astonishing, the rent was affordable. As Dick was an electrical engineer, the resourceful Tosia arranged that he would do the landlord's electrical repairs in return for a low rental.

It seemed miraculous to live so close to St Kilda Beach with its promenade and inviting curve of yellow sand. St Kilda was a dynamic enclave of European immigrants, especially Jews. On weekends they strolled along the windy beachfront, the men in jackets draped across their shoulders, the women in ankle-strap shoes and upswept hair. They congregated in cafés like the Scheherazade where Polish, Russian and Hungarian émigrés cooked dishes like their mothers used to make, and the smell of poppyseed cakes, cheese blintzes and walnut tortes was impossible to resist. The men banged their fists on the small tables as they argued about the political situation in Europe, their cigarette smoke swirling around them. More concerned about everyday problems, their wives discussed the clothing factories where most of them spent the weekdays bent over sewing machines, and exchanged information about children's schools and butcher shops that sold good veal. In Acland Street, refugees always found familiar faces to ask about mutual friends, a room going cheap or a factory looking for workers.

To the lively Europeans, Melbourne was a prim English city and Australians were disconcertingly Anglo-Saxon and inscrutable. They uttered stock phrases with a cheerful but flat monotone that seemed to use a grudging fraction of their vocal range, and one never knew what they were thinking. To the women, Australian men seemed stiff, sexless and lacking in gallantry. Instead of shaking hands, Australians said, 'How are you?' but never expected an answer.

That's the phrase Guta expected to hear from her new workmates when she entered Henty House. Inside the building, the five charwomen who confronted her gave her the once-over. Their narrowed eyes swept up and down her cotton print dress and came to an insolent stop on her nose with its flattened bridge. Guta didn't need to speak much English to understand the body language of arms folded across pinafores and eyes cold with disapproval.

Guta felt her throat drying up beneath their gaze. In fractured English she tried to explain that she was working so that she could study, when one of them muttered, 'Who sent her? We don't need no bloody students!' Guta tried again. Perhaps the woman hadn't understood. Surely being a student couldn't pose a problem. But she had no doubt about the sentiment behind the next comment. 'We don't want no bloody reffos here!'

Ever since Arthur Calwell, the minister for immigration, had introduced a policy to increase Australia's population through immigration as a bulwark against possible invasion, the scaremongers had whipped up fears that Australians' jobs, houses and their whole way of life were under threat. Even though the unemployment rate was less than two percent, articles and cartoons in newspapers depicted cunning foreigners taking jobs away from fair dinkum Aussies, undercutting their wages and grabbing homes that should have gone to diggers. With the right-wing press thundering about potential racial and religious disharmony, and the unions howling about unfair competition and the erosion of hard-won conditions, many workers resented the newcomers, hated to hear them speaking their foreign lingo and wished they'd go back to where they'd bloody well come from.

Guta was dismayed by the antagonism of her workmates. It wasn't as though she was taking their jobs or asking for special privileges, yet they seemed to regard her as an enemy. But she couldn't articulate any of that and suspected that they wouldn't listen even if she could. At nineteen, she was no match for these hard-faced harridans with their dried-out hearts and wrinkled faces. Guta gritted her teeth. She had survived the Nazis and she'd cope with these narrow-minded witches. There was no choice — she needed the work. If she had to spend each morning working in hostile silence, that's what she would do.

The Civil Aviation Department occupied six floors. On the first five floors, all the women had to do was empty ashtrays, whisk a feather duster around the tables and filing cabinets and mop the wooden floors. The most time-consuming was the sixth floor where the draughtsmen's rooms were located. Under large windows, tilted drawing boards were covered with blueprints of aeroplanes, all of which had to be carefully moved so that the surfaces could be dusted, and then replaced in exactly the same order. The grimy lino floor had to be scrubbed and polished every day until it sparkled. This was a thankless task because during the war, along with colourful Yankee navy jargon, the draughtsmen had also picked up the American habit of spitting pipe tobacco and grinding it into the floor.

It was the sixth floor that the charwomen unanimously allocated to Guta.

They had to be out of the building by the time the civil servants started work at 8.15. Guta couldn't help smiling when she saw them arrive. With their crew cuts, pipes stuck in their mouths and epaulettes on their jackets, they looked like extras for a musical about Yankee sailors. If they'd suddenly broken into a Fred Astaire tap-dancing routine, she wouldn't have been at all surprised.

But she didn't have time to loiter. As soon as she replaced the broom, duster and polisher, she patted down her springy ash blonde hair, ran through the double doors of the building and sprinted to the University of Melbourne to save the threepenny tram fare. If she made good time and reached the campus in twenty-five minutes, she had time for a quick shower at Union House before her lectures on anatomy, physiology and organic chemistry. Although Guta had dreamed of studying medicine, she couldn't afford to study for five years full-time, so she had enrolled in science instead. As she sat forward to catch what the lecturer was saying, she wondered whether she would ever learn the intricacies of this impossible language. Charlie's lessons on the *Derna* had not equipped her for the terminology the science course required. Apart from language problems, she had no grounding in science subjects and had little time to study. After lectures, she hurried back to Collins Street where she worked in the evenings as a receptionist for a doctor whose predominantly Polish patients needed someone who could speak their language.

At weekends, Guta washed cars. She charged ten shillings and sixpence for a wash and polish, which paid their rent. The cars belonged to the pre-war migrants whom the new arrivals called 'the allrightniks'. To those who had nothing, the people who had climbed one rung higher on the immigrant ladder seemed like millionaires.

Among Tosia's vast network of friends and acquaintances was Ray Campbell, a big-hearted elderly Australian woman who gave Guta lessons in spoken English. It was through Ray that she received an invitation to visit the Reads in the Riverina. From the moment they met, Guta was enchanted by this family and their property. Located in a lush pastoral area surrounded by magnificent countryside of limitless horizons and huge skies, it became a spiritual and emotional haven where she breathed freely for the first time in many years.

She felt as though she had known the Reads all her life and staying with them during the Christmas holidays became the highlight of her year. 'They were the first family I ever met who had no war scars,' she tells me. 'It amazed me that people could plan ten years ahead, and decide which schools their children would go to. And here was I, still not able to plan a day ahead.'

Migrants Say They Had Misery Trip Here On Panama Ship

Four migrants who walked off the 5000-ton Panamanian steamer Derna in Fremantle, stating they were disgusted with the ship's filth and the bad food, arrived in Melbourne today on the Adelaide express.

The Derna, an all-migrant ship, berthed at Fremantle early this week and is now bringing 600 Greeks, Italians, Poles, Germans, Czechs and other Southern Europeans, to Eastern States. About 20 people left the ship at Perth and continued their journey by plane and train.

Mr Philip Georgiades, 26, who flew with the RAF as a navigator during the war, and his pretty wife, Germaine, said in Melbourne today that the trip was a "misery one."

"From our savings we paid over £300 to travel immigrant class from Egypt to Australia," said Mrs Georgiades. "They said it was equal to third class —it was worse than tenth class. We were thankful we had enough left to come here by train.

"We were supposed to sleep in big dormitories. To dodge the bed-bugs I slept for 45 nights on a chair on deck.

"Every meal we left the table hungry. In the tropics the table boys told us the meat was rotten and advised us not to eat it. Afterwards it was thrown overboard and passengers took photos of it in the water.

HEALTH THREAT

"We were allowed to use the water for only three hours a day—black water at that," she said. "A day out of Fremantle we were given clear water for the first time, even some hot water, and the whole ship was disinfected.

"Passengers complained bitterly to the captain. He told us he couldn't do anything about it."

Mr Georgiades said that in Colombo, the Health Department threatened to seize the ship if it was not cleaned up. The dormitories were put in order, but were just as bad after a few days at sea.

While the dispute was on he and his wife stayed at a hotel.

"As well as the bugs, there were flies, mosquitoes and lice—in the middle of the ocean. Where else could you get that?" he said.

Asked about reports that Communists were among the migrants, Mr Georgiades said that others told them there were many Communists among the Poles and Czechs.

The Derna left Port Said on September 10. The trip to Fremantle took nearly seven weeks. The normal time is just over two weeks.

Picture—Page 1.

MIGRANT SHIP BROUGHT 15 NATIONALITIES

Fifteen nationalities were represented in the 500 European migrants who arrived in the Derna from (Genoa) yesterday.

The 500th passenger was a baby born three days out of Melbourne and named Derna.

Passengers' fares were paid by relatives already living in Australia or by the International Refugee Organisation.

Complaints about their quarters and conditions were made by some.

The master of the Derna (Capt. Pappalas) told reporters that he had tried to keep the ship as clean as possible. Cabins were inspected daily by the ship's doctor.

Miss Dorothy Ritter, a 26-year-old German migrant, said that the ship was cleaned up considerably after leaving Fremantle.

Captain Pappalas denied knowledge of Communist propagandists operating among the passengers.

Another migrant, Miss Gilda Brouen said that it was impossible to sleep in cabins when the ship was in the tropics. "It was even too awful to eat in the lower decks," she said.

THEY QUIT THE SHIP

MR AND MRS PHILIP GEORGIADES, passengers in the migrant ship Derna, who said they were so disgusted that they left the vessel in Fremantle, photographed at Spencer Street Station today. (Story, Page 2).

---

this page and overleaf: Extracts from articles published 5 and 6 November 1948 in *The Age*, *Argus*, *Melbourne Herald* and *Melbourne Sun*.

RED PROPAGANDA IN DERNA DENIED

CANBERRA, Wednesday. — Reports that migrants aboard the Derna included a number of Communists were inspired by a migrant escort officer, Lt.-Col. Hershaw, the Minister for Immigration (Mr Calwell) told the House of Representatives today.

The reports were not justified, he said.

Mr Calwell was replying to Mr Gullett (Lib., Vic.), who said that, according to a press report, the migrants included a woman lecturer, from the University of Riga, who had complained that during the voyage two young Jews had organised lectures in Communist theory and practice broadcast over the ship's public address system.

Mr Calwell said he had heard that Lieut.-Colonel Hershaw and one or two others in the Derna had made charges that some migrants were spreading Communist propaganda.

"Hershaw is a man of pretty unsavory reputation and if he had done in Australia the things he is alleged to have done aboard the ship, he would have been gaoled," said Mr Calwell.

"He seems to be a Fascist type and there are far too many of that type about."

An Immigration Department official, Major Weale, had made an investigation, Mr Calwell said.

NO FOUNDATION

He had reported that some of the migrants had been singing Ukrainian songs during the voyage. People who wanted to might have mistaken them for Soviet songs.

Lieut.-Colonel Hershaw had tried to get the captain of the Derna to sign a report alleging Communist activity in the ship, but the captain refused because he knew of no such activity.

"Inquiries by this responsible officer show that there was not the slightest justification for any of the charges," said Mr Calwell.

MIGRANTS FROM EUROPE

STUDIES ABOARD THE *Derna* when the migrant ship reached South Wharf yesterday. Left: Ambulance men were waiting at the wharf to receive a baby born while the ship was travelling from Fremantle to Melbourne. Centre: Mrs Lucy Cilia, a migrant from Malta. Right: Bishop Rafalsky arrived to become Primate for Australia and New Zealand of the Greek Orthodox Church.

RED PROPAGANDA SPREAD ON SHIP, SAY PASSENGERS

STATEMENTS that some young Jews had spread Communist propaganda during a passage of nine weeks from Marseilles by the Panamanian steamer Derna were made by passengers when the ship arrived in Melbourne yesterday.

Federal Security police met the ship to investigate reports that had been reaching Australia ever since she left Colombo.

Passengers described the 5,700-ton steamer as a "slum ship."

She carries a crew of 50 Greeks, and her 550 European passengers were crammed into cabins holding 6 to 18.

Madame Lidija Maulics, a former lecturer in languages at Riga University, Latvia, said that she and her sculptor husband were among the few Christians aboard. She thought at least 75% of the passengers were of Jewish extraction. She said that meetings were organised during the voyage by young Jews. Soviet songs had been sung and phonograph records played, and systematic efforts made to instruct "disciples" to teach Communist doctrine in Australia.

SPONSORED MIGRANTS

Many of the migrants were sponsored by the International Refugee Organisation and the Hebrew Immigrant Association. The Jewish Welfare Guardian Society brought out 29 youths from displaced persons' camps in Germany for adoption by Jewish families, and 22 more Jewish children of both sexes will go to Jewish hostels.

Cars and special buses were waiting at the wharf for many of the passengers.

Captain Stavaros Papalas, master of the *Derna*, said that hundreds of pounds' worth of damage had been done by passengers, who had hurled crockery and cutlery into the sea.

Explaining photographs taken by passengers of meat thrown overboard, he said he had ordered this to be done for health reasons, because some stores had gone bad through overloading of the refrigerators.

He said he had had to restrict water supplies for the protection of his ship. Poor quality coal was the cause of the long voyage.

Passengers said they had paid £150 each from Egypt to Australia, but Captain Papalas said he had no idea what fares had been charged. Officials of the Melbourne Steamship Company, the ship's agents, also said yesterday that they had no knowledge of the fares to Australia.

top left: Rita Lindemanis as she was on the *Derna*.

top right: Rita in Sydney, 1999.

bottom: Jack Lindemanis on the day of his confirmation in Hamburg, shortly before the voyage.

top: Silva Rae with her father, Rudolf Espere, on the block of land in Revesby where they built their house.

bottom: Verner Puurand with sons Mart (*left*) and Hans (*right*), taken shortly before the voyage.

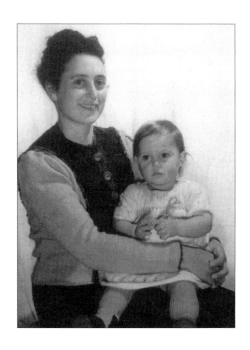

top: Irene Abrahamsohn with Eva, shortly before the voyage.

right: Elsie and Ignac Pataky on their wedding day, 1948.

top: The Fatseas family shortly after their arrival in Mackay: (*l-r*) Vassiliki (Vi), Petro, Betty, Peter, Mary, George.

right: Petro Fatseas in front of a poster of Kythera at his home in Paradise Waters.

top: The Matussevich family arrives in Auckland. Front row: *(l-r)* Red Cross officer holding Veronica, Olga *(mother)*, Anastasia, Alex, Nick. Centre row: Olga *(daughter)*, Nina. Back row: Basil *(third from left)*, Vasily, Red Cross officer holding Alice. (From a photograph taken by the *New Zealand Herald*.)

left: Clara Kraus with her sons Peter *(left)* and Paul *(right)*, taken in Sydney in 1958.

top: Sam and Esther Fiszman celebrating Sam's seventieth birthday in 1996.

right: The author's parents, Bronia and Henek Boguslawski, dancing at her and Michael's wedding in Sydney, 1959.

top: Mattie Veneris at her home in Albury, 2000.

left: Irene Abrahamsohn (Valentine) holding her cat Beatrice, with her daughter Eva at the retirement home in Auckland.

left: Dorothea Ritter, Sydney, 2001.

bottom: Cyla Ferszt in front of her paintings in her Melbourne flat, 1999.

top: Morris Shell's family on the occasion of his seventieth birthday in Sydney, 1993: (*l-r*) daughter-in-law Roma, son Allan, granddaughter Natalie, Morris. Front row: grandson Adam and Ruth.

bottom: Morris's daughter Rita Weinberg with her husband Yacov and sons Daniel and Richard.

top: Vala Seitz in Geelong on her eightieth birthday, 1999.

bottom: Bob Grunschlag with his daughters Simone (*left*) and Caron (*right*).

Fred Silberstein. Auckland, 2000.

Lars Meder in front of a photograph of his daughters. Auckland, 2000.

Nick Matussevich. Auckland, 2000.

Harold Kapp. Auckland, 2000.

(l-r) Harry Braun with his daughter Melinda, son Clifford and wife Brenda.

top: Bill and Emi Marr, Sydney.

bottom: Peter Rossler with his brother Henry Rossler (*far right*; *deceased 1991*) and their aunt and uncle at Peter's graduation, University of Sydney, c. 1956.

top: (*l-r*) Mietek Kalowski with daughter Jennifer Rosen, son Stefan Kalowski and Halina Kalowski at the Museum of Sydney, attending the author's talk in March 2000 about the voyage of the *Derna*.

bottom: (*l-r*) Dorothea Ritter, Bruno Tohver, Helle Nittim (Risti), Lea Ohtra (Holm).

At the Museum of Sydney, March 2000. Front row: Diane Armstrong, Silva Rae
(Palgi), Mietek Kalowski, Jennifer Rosen, Halina Kalowski, Alice Zalcberg
(Sternhell), Kitty Lebovics (Graf). Centre row: Stefan Kalowski, Anneke Twigg (Silva
Palgi's daughter), Bob Grunschlag, Harry Braun, Peter Rossler, Joe Neustatl, Vi
Comino, David Weiss. Back row: Bruno Tohver, Helle Nittim (Risti), Lea Ohtra
(Holm). **inset:** André Wayne.

Guta today is a handsome woman with a dignified presence. She is tall and slim, with crinkly grey hair pulled back from a strong face and an even gaze. The bewildered young girl who lacked the confidence to talk to the other passengers on the *Derna* has become a quietly assertive woman, but an air of vulnerability still lingers in her expression. Articulate and analytical, she speaks excellent English with a trace of a Polish accent. As we talk in the kitchen of her homely cottage in an old Melbourne suburb, her cat Pushkin paces up and down along the window seat and rubs against the glass until she opens the back door to let him out.

Guta's emotional recovery began with the Reads. Don had a wonderfully dry sense of humour, and kept a straight face while making comments that made her double up with laughter. 'When a newborn lamb kept us awake all night with its bleating, I asked Don why the mother wouldn't suckle it,' Guta recalls. 'He pointed at the massive ewe which resembled a shapeless bale of matted wool and said in a deadpan voice, "She doesn't want to ruin her figure!"'

Shocked to see that they threw out the curds from the milk, Guta suggested making cottage cheese, an idea that the Reads greeted with wrinkled noses and sounds of disgust. Undaunted, she asked for a bucket of curds and several days later presented them with natural yoghurt. Their stomachs turned. Refusing to give up, she let the curdled milk drip through a muslin bag to make cottage cheese, but that revolted them as well. 'Do you wait till your eggs go bad, and your tomatoes rot, before you eat them?' Don would joke, while the children shuddered and held their noses.

Although Guta and Don were on the same wavelength where humour was concerned, it was his wife Marjorie who became her confidante. Strolling beside the dark green creek that flowed through the property, sometimes they sat in the shade of the tall paperbarks whose skin flaked off like tissue paper. But no matter how much peeled away, there were always more layers underneath. Guta found it surprisingly easy to talk to Marjorie about everything, even about the traumatic experiences she had never been able to discuss with anyone else. Marjorie phrased her questions so sensitively and listened with such empathy that she evoked complete trust. And when words were inadequate, she would simply put her arm around Guta's shoulders and hug her. Dick, who was studying electrical engineering at RMIT at the time, was less sociable and never accompanied her on these holidays at the Reads'.

In between working and studying, Guta and Dick fixed up their house, mended the fence and planted a garden in what had been a wilderness, although they continued to sit on wooden crates because they couldn't afford any furniture. When one of their neighbours came over unexpectedly with a table and three chairs, Guta was speechless. 'How can we ever repay you?' she asked.

'There's no need,' the woman replied. 'Someone helped us when we arrived. When you're on your feet, help someone else and I'll be repaid.' Guta never forgot her words.

The neighbour on the other side was an old French woman who would stand on her verandah every day, watching out for the postman. 'Do you have any French letters for me?' she asked him every morning in her high-pitched voice. Reddening with embarrassment, he would mutter to Guta, 'Someone should tell that woman to stop saying that!'

But at the Civil Aviation office her workmates remained truculent. She thought them rude, crude and unattractive and did her best to ignore their taunts, although sometimes she was amused to hear them swearing non-stop for five minutes at a time without once repeating themselves — something not even Charlie the seaman with his scatological vocabulary was able to do. But despite her resentment, she gradually developed a grudging admiration for the solidarity that existed among these women. If one of them happened to be ill, the others would finish their own work and then converge on their workmate's floor to do hers as well. 'That's how we work here, so you'd better get used to it,' one of them told her in her brusque way. 'Anyone's sick or away, the rest of us pitch in so no one misses out on their dough.'

When Guta's English improved, she was able to follow their conversations. Occasionally they talked about the Depression, a time of soup kitchens, desperate mothers whose children fought over biscuit crumbs, and demoralised men who wandered around the countryside with swags on their backs in search of work and a crust of bread. Hunger and humiliation Guta understood only too well, but she never spoke about her own experiences.

In time, she came to appreciate their grasp of political issues. Although they were uneducated, they were shrewd enough to see through the pronouncements of politicians who tried to hoodwink the public. The only one they admired was the pipe-smoking prime minister, Ben Chifley. A country boy with little schooling who had started off cleaning railway offices before becoming an engine driver, he had entered politics and risen to the top. He was one of them. But when the Labor Party was defeated and the Liberals under Robert Menzies came to power in December 1949, they were livid. 'Bloody Menzies,' they would say. 'You can't trust him further than you can throw him. He's a real snake in the grass. Chifley was for the workers, not like these bloody mongrels,' they muttered.

During the coal strikes which caused chaos on the wharves, disrupted transport and resulted in power rationing and mass unemployment, the women were solidly behind the strikers, barracking for them to keep up the fight. When the government clamped down on the strikers, they reached new heights of vituperation about the rotten scabs and the stinkers in parliament who didn't care if decent workers starved. Most of their husbands were unionists who worked on the factory floor, and in their juicy language Guta heard a deep commitment to their cause.

The spokeswoman was Doris, whom Guta described to her friends as 'a cubical box of aggression with arms akimbo'. What Doris said went. One day when Guta stayed upstairs to scrub the floor during their tea and cigarette break, Doris marched up and rasped in her gravelly voice, 'You bloody well come down with the rest of us! No one works through the break!' Too intimidated to resist, Guta followed her and pretended to sip the nauseating milky fluid. In Poland only invalids and nursing mothers drank tea with milk.

Doris's mate Ruby usually arrived at work with shaking hands, a trembling voice and a small unlabelled bottle in the deep pocket of her coat. Periodically she would take it out, put it to her lips, close her eyes and swiftly glug down its contents. As if by magic, her hands soon steadied and her voice became firmer.

One day she came in with a black eye and a bruised cheek. As the women collected their keys that hung from hooks inside the lockers and pulled the polishers, wax and brooms out of the downstairs cupboard, Doris gave a long low whistle through her teeth. 'Strewth, Rube, did you get run over by a truck, love?'

'That stinker of a husband of mine threw a spud at me,' Ruby mumbled.

'Well I bloody well hope you threw it back at him!' Doris cackled.

Ruby drew herself up to her full height of about five feet and tilted her bruised chin. 'I wouldn't stoop that low because I'm a loidy!' she retorted. The others laughed and for once Guta joined in.

Suddenly Ruby swung around to face her. Her eyes narrowed and a look of sheer malice crossed her swollen face. 'What are you staring at? You bloody migrants come into this country and think you own the place, taking our jobs, grabbing the houses that our diggers should be getting. Why don't youse all go back where you bloody well came from?' While she continued her harangue, Guta stood there, not knowing what to do.

On and on Ruby went, her voice growing more strident all the time, while the others stood by in silence, their faces registering no emotion, until Doris suddenly yelled, 'E-nough! Everybody out!'

An hour later, Guta found Ruby slumped on the bench, head on her hands, not moving. *Now we'll have to do her work as well,* she thought. After finishing her own floor, she came downstairs, picked up the broom and started sweeping, churning with resentment.

Next morning, Ruby was at work as though nothing had happened and no one referred to the fracas of the previous day. After the other women had got out on their own floors, Ruby stayed in the lift with Guta as it creaked towards the sixth floor. Uneasy about the close proximity, Guta braced herself to rush out of the lift the moment the door opened. There was no knowing what this erratic woman might do. But before she could get away, Ruby grabbed her arm. 'Now listen here, love,' she wheezed, and Guta noticed that her bloodshot eyes were moist with emotion. 'I get carried away at times, see. I don't mean nothing by it. You don't want to take no notice of an old bugger like me, okay?' Guta nodded. This was obviously Ruby's way of saying sorry.

It didn't take long for the others to come round as well. Mollified by the way she had kept to their agreement to pitch in and help even after Ruby's onslaught, the cleaners began treating her like one of them. Instead of having five foes, Guta ended up with five mothers. 'Now look, love, don't go wasting your money in them shops. Just tell us what you need. My hubby works in the factory so I can get it much cheaper,' they'd tell her whenever she mentioned something she wanted to buy.

She knew she had been accepted the day a union official paid them an unexpected visit. 'You're not in the union, so you can't work here,' he announced. Guta explained that she'd tried to join but had been rejected because she was a member of the students' union.

'They told me I can't belong to two unions,' she protested.

'All I know is, you can't work here if you're not in the union,' he insisted. At this point Doris barged in, hands on hips and thunderbolts flashing from her eyes. 'Now you just listen to me,' she snapped. 'The kid just come here. She needs the money, see. She wants to work here and we want her to stay here, so why don't you bloody well get off her back? Shut your gob and push off!'

In her homely kitchen, Guta throws her head back and laughs triumphantly. 'That fellow never came back!' She has a gift for mimicry and imitates their speech with affectionate amusement but no resentment.

Gradually she regained her zest for life but she noticed that Dick was still finding things difficult even after he completed his degree. They hadn't known each other for long when they had decided to marry, two orphans who had survived the war and clung to each other from loneliness. Like her, he had also been withdrawn and depressed at the time, but now that their life was becoming easier, Guta was forced to face the fact that, for all his charm and wit, Dick was basically a loner with a depressive, introverted personality.

One of their major disputes was over having children. Although when they met neither of them had been keen on the idea, now that life was running more smoothly, Guta wanted to have a baby, but Dick wouldn't hear of it. Whenever her period was late, he panicked. 'You can't have a baby, because I won't be around to help you bring it up!' he would say. Dick had been two years old when his father died of a heart attack, and like many men whose fathers have died young, he was convinced that he would meet a similar fate.

Although Guta scoffed at his gloomy forebodings, he insisted that it wasn't pessimism but clairvoyance. When she came home after a pathology exam one day, he said, 'In the middle of that exam you blanked out for a few minutes and didn't know what to write.'

She stared at him. 'How did you know?'

He shrugged and gave a knowing smile. 'I'm clairvoyant, remember?'

By 1955, their relationship had deteriorated to such an extent that they could no longer live together, but they separated amicably. 'We never stopped caring about each other but we couldn't make each other happy. We functioned better as brother and sister than husband and wife,' Guta says. As she looks up, her cat Pushkin is standing on his hind legs, scratching his forepaws on the glass outside, spreadeagled against the window. 'Oh, you are so theatrical!' she exclaims and lets him in again. Now that she's up, she puts the kettle on and as we sip our mugs of tea, she continues reminiscing about the relationship. 'Dick would cry on my shoulder whenever he was depressed, and whenever I started to get close to someone, he would suggest us getting back together. We weren't compatible but the bond between us never died,' she says.

Nine years after their split, while Guta was working at the pathology department of the Alfred Hospital, Dick came in to the casualty department. He had broken a finger at work but because of the current anti-TB campaign, he was ordered to have a routine chest x-ray. They found a shadow on his lungs. A week later, the thoracic surgeon opened his chest, took one look and closed it up again. As soon as Dick came out of the anaesthetic, the surgeon told him, 'I'm afraid there's nothing we can do. You've got adenocarcinoma which is inoperable. I give you about three months.'

With perverse triumph, Dick told Guta, 'You see, I said I wouldn't live long.' Determined not to let him give up, Guta persuaded him to try radiotherapy. The treatment was still in its infancy and his sternum was badly burned in the process, but it gave him two additional years of normal life. In the last months of his illness, when he refused to go to hospital, she moved him into Tosia's flat.

The two women nursed him devotedly through the worst three months of his life, during which he suffered agonising pain and slow suffocation, and became so emaciated that his bones pushed through his skin. His torment ended in 1964, when he was thirty-seven. Not long afterwards, while cleaning out his flat Guta found a slip of paper wedged beneath the lino on the kitchen floor. He had left her a message in Polish. 'In spite of what you thought,' he had written, 'I loved you very much.'

Three years later, Guta fell in love with a teacher from Czechoslovakia.

'He was the love of my life. But eight years after we got married, he died of bowel cancer,' she sighs.

She continued working as a medical pathologist at the Alfred Hospital. 'It was just like detective work, chasing an invisible foe,' she muses. 'There were terrible moments when I saw a death sentence in the microscope, but there were great rewards too.' In 1975, after twenty-three years at the hospital, she started working for a privately owned laboratory. She had been working there for some time when a chance remark revealed that she and her boss had something in common apart from their passion for medical pathology. They had both arrived on the *Derna*.

It was Ella, the rebellious young woman with the strawberry blonde curls whose brother Anton had almost died of appendicitis during the voyage.

The turmoil in Ella's life that had begun during the war continued in Melbourne. As soon as she arrived, she was told that the guardian assigned to her had reneged on his agreement, so she would have to go to Sydney where another guardian had been appointed. The vehemence of her reaction startled them. Ella refused to go to Sydney. She hadn't travelled to the other side of the world to be separated from her brother, the only person she knew here, she told them. She was staying in Melbourne and that was that.

While Ella waited unhappily in the Frances Barkman Children's Home for accommodation to be arranged for her, Anton was having problems as well. His guardian, who had promised to send him to university, now wanted him to work on the family property in the country. Seeing how distraught Anton was at this prospect, Ella assured him that this would never happen. 'Even if I have to scrub floors, you'll study science,' she told him.

While Ella found a job at Kodak, testing paper emulsion, her brother found work as a bottle washer at a paint factory. It was so far away that he had to leave home at four in the morning and cycle across the city on his ricketty bicycle. But he did fulfil his dream of becoming a scientist and later worked for the CSIRO.

Ella's luck changed unexpectedly when she met a European couple who became so enchanted with her that they asked her to move in with them and treated her like their own daughter. In her foster-mother, Ella found exactly the kind of mother she had always wished for: uncritical, undemanding and warm. Their close relationship continued even after her own mother arrived in Australia several years later.

'I started blossoming in Australia,' she says when we talk in her bright modern home which is surrounded by bushland. The angry, sexy girl from the *Derna* has become a warm, grandmotherly woman who leads a hectic existence juggling the demands of business and family life. 'Over the years, I became a different person from the rebellious girl I was on the *Derna*. Two things healed me: one was marrying the kindest, most understanding and patient human being I've ever met; the other was becoming a social worker, which enabled me to do something useful for others.'

As Ella tells me about the harrowing events of her teenage years, she recalls standing on a platform about to be shot by German guards while her red-eyed father was restrained from rushing towards her. She describes her anguish after crawling to her mother's barracks in Auschwitz to find not a loving mother but an empty shell.

We sit in silence, surrounded by the ghosts of the past. Finally she says, 'For thirty years I avoided talking about these things. I decided that the past was finished, the Holocaust happened to somebody else in another century on another planet. But while I was studying family therapy, Elisabeth Kubler-Ross warned me that if I wanted to help patients who were afraid of death, I'd have to confront my own demons and let go of my own baggage. I wasn't afraid of dying because I'd already died more than once, but I didn't want to revisit the past.'

Several years ago, however, Ella was forced to do that. She was jolted when her son asked one evening, 'Who are you? You are a one-dimensional person. You have no past.' 'So I sat down with the whole family and talked all night about what had happened to me,' Ella recalls. 'I told them everything. They listened and cried with me. But next morning it was as though I hadn't said anything, and they have never alluded to it since then. They couldn't cope with it.'

As she shows me the photos from the *Derna*, she suddenly recalls an incident that happened recently while she was in Spain on a bus tour. 'One night over a bottle of red wine, some of our group started reminiscing about coming to Australia. When I said that I came out on a hellship, one of the guys from Melbourne said, "Well, it couldn't have been as bad as my hellship!" So we started competing to see whose ship was the worst. Then another woman joined in. "You haven't heard anything yet. On my ship, we had to throw all the meat overboard." That's when it dawned on the three of us that we all came out on the *Derna*!'

The other two were Morrie Frid and Anne Irons, both of whom were children during the voyage. Morrie travelled with his parents and sick baby brother. Anne, who was then called Haneczka Poczebucka, was the girl who dropped her new fez in Port Said harbour on her eighth birthday.

Ella is still laughing about that coincidence. 'Fancy having to go to Spain to find out that three people who live in the same city all came out on the same ship! But the same thing happened with Guta and me,' she says. 'We'd been working together for years before we discovered that we were ship-sisters!'

After Don and Marjorie Read passed away, Guta's network of friends expanded to include the younger members of the Read family. When Don died, his children asked her to give the eulogy in celebration of his life. 'They all laughed when I reminded them of the first time I made yoghurt and cottage cheese fifty years ago. Of course now they all eat it!' she laughs.

Like any proud aunt, she takes an album out of a drawer and shows me the family photographs. 'I've become an honorary aunt to the children and to their children too. For my seventieth birthday they gave me a party at a restaurant and brought out a huge cake. They asked me to invite whoever I wanted, and there we all were, my dearest friends in the whole world, Polish, Australian, Jewish and Christian, one big family.'

Now that she has retired from medical pathology after forty-four years, Guta spends her time trying to make the world a better place. 'Because of what happened to me during the war, I feel a kinship with the persecuted, the humiliated, the unjustly treated,' she says. She belongs to the Humanist Society and to the Jewish Democratic Society, a secular organisation that supports peace and Palestinian rights. A fervent activist and inveterate letter-writer, she pulls out folders bulging with brochures, letters and documents. The woman whose speech was once reduced to grunts and curses, who became so withdrawn that she could not talk to anyone, has become an impassioned fighter for the rights of others. 'I write letters, serve on committees and chair meetings on issues such as gun ownership and domestic violence. I'm for family planning, voluntary euthanasia, land rights and gay rights,' she says. 'I still have trouble managing time, but now I know that it is too precious to waste.'

26

While Guta was cleaning offices and washing cars, elsewhere in Melbourne another Polish couple from the *Derna*, Cyla and Max Ferszt, also struggled to support themselves. Max, who was a photographer, knew that he had little chance of practising his profession here. 'Melbourne isn't like Warsaw,' his sister had written. 'People here don't appreciate fine photography.' The problem of earning a living had preoccupied him during the voyage, but as soon as he stepped off the ship, he was offered a job. Among the throng milling around South Wharf when the *Derna* docked were representatives from General Motors Holden who had come to recruit labourers for the assembly line that was about to produce the 48-215 Holden, the forerunner of the FJ model which came out in 1953.

The launch of Australia's first locally manufactured car was a national milestone, marked by a special ceremony attended by Prime Minister Ben Chifley and 1200 luminaries including federal and state politicians, chiefs of the armed services, consular, trades hall and business representatives. The music played by the ten-piece orchestra was almost drowned out by the popping of champagne corks in the flower-decked hall. In a moment as dramatic as any Hollywood Oscar presentation, the silver lamé curtain was swept aside and a spotlight fell on an ivory sedan resting on black velvet. The prime minister's enthusiastic endorsement, 'She's a beauty!' was quoted in newspapers throughout the country.

The cost of the Holden, with its six-cylinder engine and 21.6 horsepower which could reach speeds of up to fifty miles per hour, compared favourably with its American and British competitors such as the Chevrolet, Pontiac, Chrysler, Morris Oxford and Austin A40. Australia's own car cost 675 pounds, about double the annual male basic wage. Cars were still a luxury but the advent of the Holden was to change that. I can still remember the excitement in my family the day in 1953 when my father called my mother and me to come outside, and watched our incredulous faces as he unlocked the door and sat behind the wheel of the first car he had ever owned: a 'Potomac blue' FJ Holden we always referred to as Oscar.

On his first Monday in Australia, Max Ferszt was already at work on the GMH assembly line at Fishermans Bend. In Siberia his artist's hands had been blistered by axes and chafed by frost; in Melbourne they were blackened by engine grease. Factory work was not what he had envisaged for his new life but at least it provided a steady income, which was essential with a wife and child to support.

Like so many children on the *Derna*, their three-year-old daughter Slawa had developed whooping cough. The child had been miserable throughout the voyage but now she was seriously ill. Every few minutes the paroxysm of coughing ended in a frightening croup-like rattle, after which she vomited up the little she had managed to eat.

It was actually Slawa who had put me in touch with Cyla. When she read in the *Sydney Morning Herald* that I was searching for passengers from the *Derna*, she immediately contacted her mother in Melbourne. Cyla wasted no time in writing to me, jotting down vivid vignettes of the voyage with finely observed details that whetted my interest. Even before we met, Cyla threw herself wholeheartedly into the search. Over the next few months, she sent descriptive letters containing her own recollections as well as the names of other Polish passengers in Melbourne with whom she was still in touch: Anna Szput Stern, Zosia Rogers, Hanka Pilichowski, Irka Falek and Leah Fein, all of whom by then had been widowed like her. Hardly a week passed without a cheery note from Cyla together with photos, reminiscences and more names and phone numbers of our ship-sisters.

'It was a difficult time when we arrived,' Cyla says slowly, in her lilting Polish–Russian accent. She has the placid sensuality of large women and even when she talks about bad times, she sounds philosophical. Although we have never met before, she wraps her arms around me and I feel as though I've known her for years. Everything about Cyla is warm and welcoming, from her big smile to the bright flowers she has painted all over the walls in her Elwood apartment. There are even sprigs of roses on the toilet walls and on the brick wall of her small balcony. This is a woman who opens her heart to embrace life instead of erecting walls to keep it out.

Over coffee and homemade cheesecake, she tells me about their early days in Melbourne. After meeting them at the wharf, her husband's sister drove them to a boarding house in Beaconsfield Parade, where she had rented them a room. As soon as the landlady heard Slawa coughing, she glared and Cyla felt her stomach churn whenever the child made those frightening whooping sounds. The room was cold, dark and damp and felt like a prison. The landlady continually watched to make sure that she didn't put the light on, and refused to let her use the kitchen, even to make tea. The whole house was saturated with the gamey smell of grilled chops and fatty sausages, which made her feel sick.

Depressed in the boarding house, Cyla started looking for a flat. She set her heart on a vacant bachelor flat in the same street, but when the landlord demanded 350 pounds key money, the situation seemed hopeless. Everyone urged her to be patient and wait until they were better off, but Cyla was adamant. 'I'm not staying in this boarding house. I didn't come to Australia to live like this. We're going to live in a flat on our own,' she insisted. By a stroke of luck, her aunt in Israel sent her a gift of 200 pounds and Max provided the rest by selling his Leica camera. After his attempts to stay in his profession resulted only in occasional weekend assignments to do snapshots at weddings, he finally abandoned all hope of working as a photographer.

After the bustle of European cities, with their sociable coffee houses, lively markets and crowded squares, Cyla found Melbourne lifeless. The centre of the city died every afternoon at five when shops and offices closed and the workers went home to their suburban streets of red-roofed houses. In that sprawling urban landscape, hardly anyone walked in the street or invited neighbours home. Australians guarded their privacy fiercely and seemed more comfortable looking out from behind drawn blinds than chatting with their neighbours.

Like many migrant women at the time, Cyla found work in the rag trade, which was concentrated around Flinders Lane. Until 1948, almost everything had been imported from Great Britain but in the post-war boom, manufacturing began to flourish. Many of the migrants from the *Derna*, including Abie Goldberg and Heniek Lipschutz, found their niche in this burgeoning industry. While making bras in a lingerie factory, Cyla enthralled her workmates with stories of life in Siberia. With her gift for storytelling, she described walking for miles across thick snow, chopping trees and sawing logs, and building huts with their bare hands. Listening to her was like watching a movie about exotic, far-off places.

While Cyla worked at the factory from early morning until three in the afternoon, Max worked the night shift at GMH from three o'clock until midnight. Distressed to see his fine white hands roughened and blackened from manual work, she sometimes pointed out that other immigrants borrowed money and started businesses which they gradually paid off. But Max had the soul of an artist, not a businessman, and the idea of borrowing terrified him. 'I wouldn't be able to sleep at nights if I owed money,' he told her. Although their alternating work shifts meant that they hardly saw each other, she tried not to complain.

'I was grateful that we had work and enough to eat, and didn't have to run away any more,' she says.

Max would take Slawa to kindergarten each morning, while Cyla collected her in the afternoon, and they communicated mainly through notes. Hers would read, 'The soup is on the stove, be careful not to burn the pot.' Late in the afternoon, she would sit by the window and gaze at the sea. In her melodious voice, she would tell Slawa fairy tales about princesses captured by dragons. But as the waves crashed outside and darkness fell, the stories often scared them both so much that she hurriedly invented happy endings. When the little girl finally fell asleep in her arms, Cyla put her to bed, and sat up alone listening to the radio playing 'Begin the Beguine' or 'Girls Were Made to Love and Kiss', which reminded her of the carefree pre-war days of their youth.

Late at night, she would finally hear the sounds she had been waiting for: the squeal of bus brakes followed by the creak of the iron gate as it swung open. Max was home. 'Why aren't you asleep yet, Cyleczka?' he would ask, using the affectionate form of her name.

'Because I wanted to wait up for you.' She'd smile up at him as he scrubbed his hands to try and remove the stains and smell of engine grease. Sometimes he would bring her a bunch of grapes, leaving them in the second-hand ice chest until they were cold and juicy. Many years later, recalling those early days with the nostalgia of hindsight, Cyla wrote, 'Since then, a lot of ice melted in our ice chest. The ice chest was exchanged for a modern fully automatic freezer but never again did the grapes have the balsamic taste of happiness like those from the second-hand ice chest.'

Cyla bought a sewing machine and supplemented their income by doing piecework at home. Every afternoon after work she would jump on the tram, clutching a big parcel of bras in one hand and Slawa in the other, to visit her closest friend from the ship, Fela Feigin. They are still in touch, although Fela has moved to New York. 'Fela was beautiful when we met and she still is, even though she is eighty-two,' Cyla says, pointing to the photograph of the pretty woman standing with a little boy in front of the *Derna* in Marseilles, just before they boarded.

Fela Feigin never wanted to come to Australia at all. She became a buyer in ladies clothes for the Myer department store but when she received a permit several years later from her sister in New York, she packed up and migrated to the United States with her husband and young son. 'She thought her dream had finally come true, but it didn't turn out that way,' Cyla comments.

According to her, Fela's son Danny couldn't settle down in America. Although he was a brilliant student, he was unhappy at school. During the Vietnam War, he became a protestor and carried a banner in a protest march. Then one day he took a room in a hotel in Philadelphia and hanged himself at the age of twenty. He was their only son. 'Fela always blamed herself for his death,' Cyla muses, then adds ruefully, 'We parents always blame ourselves, and when we're not blaming ourselves, our children are blaming us!'

Not long after Danny committed suicide, Fela's husband had a heart attack and died. 'So her dream of life in America turned into a nightmare,' Cyla sighs. 'But Fela keeps very active. She has a brain like a computer, never forgets anything. To this day she gets up at six every morning and takes the subway to Brooklyn where she works in a clothing store! She never thinks about dying, like I do. Whenever I say that time is running out, she tells me to stop talking nonsense.'

We return to Cyla's early years in Melbourne. Although she and Max alternated shifts during the week, at weekends all work stopped. Hospitable and energetic, Cyla always had a houseful of guests, many of them from the *Derna*. They sat around the small table eating her spicy borscht, herrings in sour cream, potato *latkes* and cheesecake while reminiscing about the voyage which, like many unpleasant experiences recalled in hindsight, provided an inexhaustible fund of amusing stories.

Eventually Cyla and Max saved enough money to buy a second-hand Renault, the smallest, cheapest car they could find, and went for drives on Sundays. Some nights they went dancing. Cyla sewed a dressy silver top for herself, bought Max a smart shirt, and looked admiringly into his dark eyes when they kicked up their heels on the dance floor.

As she cuts me another slice of her vanilla-scented cheesecake, Cyla becomes pensive. 'We had a pretty jazzy life when I come to think of it. We worked hard but we were trying to make up for everything we missed during the war. If I had my life in Australia over again, with all the difficulties, I wouldn't want to miss out on any part of it.'

As time went on, however, because of their separate work patterns, Cyla and Max began to lead increasingly separate lives, and their relationship suffered as a result. The war had deprived them of the best years of their life and now time was passing and so was their youth. She felt that unless they changed their lifestyle and spent more time together, they would continue to drift apart.

By 1958, ten years after arriving in Australia, they had saved enough money to put down a deposit on a business. Like many immigrants at the time, they bought a milk bar. It was in an excellent position in High Street, Armadale, and brought a good income, but Cyla came to hate the business. While their friends were free on weekends to go for drives and picnics, she and Max had to stand behind the counter in the milk bar serving customers. 'We lived on the premises and it was seven days a week, no Saturdays or Sundays off. In addition to that, I think Slawa felt embarrassed about living behind a milk bar.'

Three years later, they sold it for a profit, but after looking around for some other business ended up buying another milk bar. Everything else was either too expensive, too risky or too unfamiliar. With all its defects, at least this was a business they knew how to run profitably. It enabled them to send Slawa to McRobertson, one of the best schools in Melbourne. And now that they had a larger deposit, they were able to buy a more expensive milk bar in Toorak Road for $10,000. This was a high-class place which sold exclusive chocolates, confectionery and ice cream. Three years later, after Slawa had matriculated, they sold it and started looking for a new business once again.

This time they tried something different. The wine and spirit shop was located in a narrow lane opposite Flinders Street railway station, which was the nerve centre of Melbourne. Although the shop had been neglected, the position was excellent and the business seemed promising. Max was in his element. He revelled in buying French wines and learning the trade, and soon built up a clientele of connoisseurs who trusted his judgment and enjoyed chatting to him about wine. For the first time since coming to Australia, he loved his work.

Cyla's active mind was always looking for better ways of running the business. She wanted to expand by buying wine in bulk and turning the shop into a liquor supermarket, but Max resisted change. He liked the business as it was and was very particular about every detail. If she moved a bottle when he wasn't looking, he could tell, and would immediately put it back the way it was. But in spite of his conservative personality, the business flourished.

The wine shop coincided with the best period of their life. Slawa obtained a pharmacy degree and when in 1968 she married another pharmacist, her parents gave her the kind of wedding they had never imagined possible when they arrived. They had reached the stage when they could buy whatever they needed and didn't have to worry about the future. 'Even though we'd been married for so many years, Max would often tell me I looked lovely,' Cyla says with a nostalgic smile. 'He was a Warsaw gentleman to his fingertips and knew how to make me feel good.'

When Max became ill in 1979, the doctor told her he had leukaemia. Understanding her husband's nature, Cyla asked the doctor not to tell him. 'So we played this game,' she says. 'I pretended nothing was wrong and he pretended that I didn't know anything.' Three months later, Max died at seventy-four when Cyla was fifty-nine. When the lease on the wine shop ran out, she was unable to get a new one so she sold the stock and closed the business.

With her daughter Slawa and her husband and two children living in Sydney, Cyla's life became very lonely. As all newly single women discover, our society, like Noah's Ark, focuses on couples and invitations dwindle for the widowed or divorced. Seven months after Max died, a friend offered to introduce Cyla to a widower. When Cyla protested that she wasn't ready for a new relationship, her friend retorted, 'If you're going to wait until the time is right for you, maybe the right man won't be there!'

When Ralph called her, they talked for hours. They shared a zest for life and a love of music and theatre, but what was more important, they felt good together. 'That was twenty years ago and we've been together ever since!' she says. Just then the door opens and Ralph comes in, an elderly man with a neat moustache and a friendly smile who calls her 'Cyleczka' and brings a girlish flush to her cheeks.

The next time Cyla and I meet, a few months later, she looks pale and sad. Ralph, her beloved companion, has died. 'Even when he was dying, he didn't lose his sense of humour or love of life. It sounds foolish but somehow I never really imagined that one day he wouldn't be there,' she says, and we both wipe our eyes. 'It was a very different relationship from my marriage. When I was with Max, we were trying to establish ourselves and we worried about the future much of the time. But with Ralph it was all fun and pleasure. And now it's over, and at eighty I have to learn to live alone.'

27

Like Cyla, many other women from the *Derna* were to discover with the passing years that widowhood is a stony and uncharted terrain. That's how it was for Clara Kraus after her life partner died in 1977, and although she has come to terms with her single life, the vacuum that Jim has left can never be filled.

This is what she tells me in a Sydney restaurant one winter's day, in a strong voice that belies her age and grandmotherly appearance. Apple-cheeked with a creamy complexion and soft white hair, eighty-seven-year-old Clara is forthright and energetic, with a formidable memory and a gaze that doesn't miss a thing. I marvel that she had the energy to travel by train from Bowral this morning especially to meet me, but later when she describes her survival in a German forced labour camp, where she looked after one small child and gave birth to another in a bare hut in freezing conditions, I realise that for this determined woman no obstacle is too daunting.

Clara Kraus was relieved to see the last of the *Derna* when we docked in Melbourne in November 1948, but to her dismay the train to Sydney did not leave until the following day, leaving her and Jim stranded on the wharf in the rain with all their luggage and two little boys who couldn't stop coughing. When they were told that they could stay on board overnight with other passengers in the same predicament, Clara was adamant that she would not spend another night on that hellship. 'I'd rather sleep on a park bench in the rain,' she said.

The only alternative was to find a hotel, but wherever they went, hotel clerks shook their heads, astonished that anyone would expect to find a room in Melbourne during Cup week. Although the Melbourne Cup had been run three days before, the socialites, graziers and punters were still clinking glasses at the balls and cocktail parties that continued throughout this gala week.

The city was buzzing with stories about sixteen-year-old Ray Neville's spectacular 80 to 1 win on Rimfire, a six-year-old gelding that had recorded the fastest time ever run at Flemington. The grin that split the apprentice jockey's bony face was still plastered over the front pages of the dailies being sold by paper boys shouting 'Pie-pah! Get your pie-pah! Read all about it!' on every city corner. The bakers' strike, which meant that Melburnians literally had to eat cake that week, or at least pikelets and scones, occupied far less space in the dailies than the racing news. Premier McDonald's warning about the striking miners, 'We must fight the Reds on coal,' received less prominence than gossip about the horse race that had brought the whole country to a standstill for three minutes several days earlier.

After spending the night in a room with the charm of a broom cupboard, the Kraus family boarded the *Spirit of Progress* for Sydney the following day. They had just settled down for the night and the boys had finally gone to sleep when the train lurched and ground to a halt in Albury. They had to wake the children and trundle to another platform with all their belongings to change trains, because the railway gauge in New South Wales was different from that in Victoria.

Morning had broken over Sydney by the time the locomotive pulled into the fuggy gloom of Central station. Worn out from months of travelling, they struggled into a suburban train with their luggage and watched anxiously for Bankstown as they passed a dreary expanse of red-roofed houses surrounded by ricketty fences in a city that, like a boring story, didn't seem to know where to end.

Their sponsors owned a chicken farm in Canley Vale. The husband had been a chemist back in Czechoslovakia but as he couldn't practise his profession in Australia without studying again, he had decided to try poultry farming. 'I got the shock of my life when I saw that place,' Clara tells me, putting down her fork on her plate of goulash as a look of disgust crosses her smooth round face. 'It was filthy.'

We are having lunch at her favourite Hungarian restaurant in Centrepoint. Above the clatter of plates and hum of conversation all around us, she tells me about her son the doctor in Townsville. Peter, who as a six year old had watched tiny silver fish leap on deck during the voyage, became an obstetrician who now works at Townsville Hospital and lectures at the university there. It was thanks to Peter that I met Clara. Having read my memoir *Mosaic*, he contacted me to say that he and his family had also arrived on the *Derna*.

Leaning across the table towards me so she could be heard above the din at the next table, Clara shudders at the memory of the chicken farm. It was covered in dust and filth and the pungent smell of the chicken manure made her gag. Before stepping into the yard she would pray that the huge geese wouldn't see her because she was terrified of their snapping beaks and loud hissing, while Peter and Paul became hysterical whenever the geese chased them. The boys were still coughing and whenever she took them on the train to see the doctor, the other passengers would glare in their direction.

A few weeks later, Clara took Jim aside before he left for an appointment in the city. 'Tell me if the rest of Sydney is like this, because if it is, I'm not unpacking. I'm catching the next train out of here,' she told him. As soon as he returned, she pounced. 'Well, what is Sydney like?'

'It's a beautiful city,' he reassured her.

'Then let's start looking for a place of our own,' she said. 'I can't stand living here any more.'

But finding accommodation in 1948 was very difficult. As building had ceased during the war years, housing was scarce and landlords demanded large sums of key money. To aggravate the shortage, the government gave returned soldiers priority over civilians. While Clara was searching for a place to rent, aggrieved readers were bombarding the *Sydney Morning Herald* with letters blaming the migrants for the nation's housing problems.

'We read that 100,000 displaced persons will arrive in Australia in the next 18 months,' wrote one reader on 18 November 1948. 'Is there no way that the people of Australia can have some control over these sweeping invitations to displaced persons? Surely there is no room in Australia for hordes of foreigners until all Australians are housed? Like thousands of other Australian ex-servicemen and their wives, we are still unable to get a permanent flat or home.'

Mr Tasman Heyes, the secretary of the Department of Immigration, defended the government's policy. 'The arrival of migrants will not accentuate the housing shortage,' he wrote. 'On the contrary, newcomers may be expected to relieve it. In no case will a displaced person be allowed to accept accommodation to the detriment of an Australian... The suggestion that displaced persons and migrants "buy off" landlords is absurd. These people have lost their possessions and their homes and most reach this country penniless. They come to Australia to find new homes and a new life. It is the moral duty of every Australian to welcome these fine people and give them every assistance to start a new life.'

While arguments about migrants and housing bounced back and forth, Clara heard that a cottage in Chatswood was about to become vacant. 'I had no idea where Chatswood was or how to get there, but I couldn't get there fast enough,' she says. 'If I could have run all the way, I would have!'

On the way to Chatswood, the train rumbled across the Sydney Harbour Bridge whose inaugural ribbon had been cut only fifteen years before. This huge iron web flung across the harbour linked the divergent parts of the sprawling city. While the boys excitedly craned out of the window for a better view, Clara became pensive as she thought of all the bridges she had already crossed in her life.

Several weeks earlier, a plan had been announced to erect another monumental structure on the shores of Sydney Harbour. 'Only the prize-winning architectural design of an international competition, which I hope an Australian wins, will be worthy of such a site,' said Eugene Goossens, chief conductor of the Sydney Symphony Orchestra, quoted in the Sydney Morning Herald in October 1948. 'An opera house we can be proud of will focus the international spotlight of culture forever on Sydney. Without it, we will stagnate in outer darkness.' When his vision was finally realised, the Sydney Opera House became Sydney's icon but by then Goossens had been unjustly disgraced and was no longer living in Australia.

The two elderly women who owned the house in Chatswood were happy to let it to Clara, but advised her to arrive early on the day they vacated it in case a returned soldier happened to get there first. Determined not to lose the house, Clara rose at dawn, dressed the boys and packed a bottle of milk and some bread for the day.

The house in Chatswood was shabby outside and falling apart inside, but in time they painted the walls, mended the plaster, fixed the fence and brightened the rooms with Clara's embroidered cushions and colourful dolls. The next challenge was to find work. 'In Budapest I was a corsetière, but when I saw how slim Australian women were, I got worried because they didn't need corsets,' she recalls. As time went on, however, her clients recommended her to their friends and she gradually built up a clientele of mainly European women. In the evenings she enrolled at a sewing school in King Street run by a Polish émigré whose *haute couture* establishment was frequented by Sydney's society matrons. When Clara's sister-in-law arrived from Hungary the following year, the two women started up a dressmaking business together.

Clara's husband Jim, who had been a book-keeper in Hungary, was dejected at becoming a process worker for Berger Paints, while Paul, their younger son, was a sensitive child who suffered from the stigma of being different. One humiliating day he ran all the way home because he didn't know how to ask where the toilets were. The other children taunted him for not wearing the regulation Stamina brand shorts and carrying a different school bag. Miserable at school, he lagged behind scholastically, but outside the classroom he was an observant child who liked watching the trams glide along the street, the conductor changing the connector arm, and the baker leading his Clydesdale, Clarrie, along the lane to the blacksmith's to be shod.

Although Peter was outgoing and academically bright, the skinny bespectacled little boy felt the pressure of living in two worlds with two sets of values and expectations. 'The other boys teased me so much that once I played truant. They thought I was an oddity because I knew nothing about cricket and didn't have a clue what they meant when they told me to go to the outfield,' he recalls. 'They laughed because I couldn't tell the difference between words like *thick* and *sick*. I thought that St George was a street, and couldn't figure out how come the queen's page in *Alice in Wonderland* wasn't in a book. But there was one boy who hated bullying and prejudice. He was rather good on the piano too. His name was Roger Woodward!'

Jim worked long hours at Berger Paints for seven pounds a week, and came home covered in yellow dust that irritated his eyes, making them red and sore. Realising that with so much salt in the air, Australia was bound to have a huge rust problem, he obtained a Czech patent for a substance to rust-proof metal, rented a cottage in Artarmon and proceeded to experiment with anti-rust primers. Painstakingly he tested anti-corrosion paints until he developed Ferropro, which is on the market to this day. When the neighbours complained about the chemical smell, he moved to premises in Lane Cove. Although he was already over fifty years old by then, Jim spent twelve hours a day lifting drums and crates, loading and unloading chemicals, packing and unpacking boxes and travelling to sell them to stores and factories.

With the factory and Clara's dressmaking, life became easier. They bought a second-hand Austin 10 with a rear luggage rack from a retired doctor. In 1955 Clara took the boys on their first holiday in Australia. To Peter's delight, they caught the Central-West Express to Katoomba. Being a train buff, he used up most of the film in his Kodak box brownie taking shots of the locomotive.

Gradually Clara became contented with her new life, but the religious division within the family troubled her. While she and the children attended the nearby Anglican church on Sundays, after which the boys would go to Sunday school, Jim did not join them but continued to pray in synagogue on the major Jewish holy days. 'I became a follower of Christ during the war,' Clara tells me. Anxious to convey the profound soul-searching behind her conversion, she adds, 'That was the hardest decision I have ever made. During the war in

Yugoslavia, after the persecution of Jews had begun, I considered converting as a way of saving my son's life, but I was torn in two and felt very bad about it. When I discussed my conflict with the bishop of Subotica, he said something I've never forgotten. "You are not leaving your religion, you are taking it a step further," he said. That reassured me. Later, when I did change my religion, it was from conviction, not for convenience,' she says in her heartfelt manner.

Lonely and grief-stricken after her husband died, she described her wartime experiences and the circumstances of her conversion in her book *The Colours of War*. '*I will never deny my Jewish origin, but I was born into it and it was not my choice,*' she wrote. '*Christianity was and is my choice. I have an ardent wish which may sound naïve or utopian but I hope with all my heart that one day the barriers between Christianity and Judaism will completely fall down.*'

As the waitress brings our coffee, Clara discusses the division that arose within the family as a result of her conversion. 'When the boys would ask why didn't Daddy come to church with us, I found it hard to explain,' she says. 'Eventually Jim did join us, but we never concealed our Jewish origin from the boys. We were in a new country, starting a new life and I was determined that, with God's help, my children would never go through what I had suffered.'

Several months after our meeting, Clara's son Paul accompanied her to a talk I gave about the voyage of the *Derna* at the Museum of Sydney. A high school history teacher turned writer, Paul has described his traumatic childhood in *The Not So Fabulous Fifties*. His recent books have dealt with healing. It's a subject close to Paul's heart because since June 1997 he has suffered from the lung disease mesothelioma. 'But I've confounded the medical fraternity, including my brother, by surviving so long without any conventional treatment!' he says.

Clara lives alone in a retirement village in Bowral while her sons and grandchildren live in other parts of the country, but she works hard at leading an active, independent life. Jim's death has been one of the most difficult things she has ever had to deal with. These days, Paul's illness hangs over her, but she trusts in God and tries not to dwell on sorrow. 'Great happiness and tragedy cannot last forever,' she says philosophically. 'I'm lucky that I'm alert enough to look after my home and business affairs. I don't play bridge — that's a waste of time. I'd rather go to classes to learn something and spend time with people who think like me.' She goes to drawing classes, belongs to an embroidery guild, reads, walks her dog, tends the garden and cooks three-course meals. 'Thank God for my children and grandchildren who are a living rainbow, linking the generations and bringing hope for a new and better world,' she says.

28

Now that my mother was off the hated ship with its relentless rolling, the memory of which stopped her from stepping on board any vessel for the next forty years, she soon regained her energy and optimism. While my father weighed up the possibility of studying dentistry again, she became the matron of a hostel in Brisbane run by the Jewish Welfare Society where some of the orphans from the *Derna* were staying. She threw herself into looking after 'the boys', with whom she felt a special affinity. Her only brother had been murdered during the Holocaust, and whenever she came across a high-spirited boy with fair hair and jade-green eyes, she caught her breath.

Unlike 'the boys', whose only contacts were strangers who had offered to become their guardians and give them paternal advice, we had family in Brisbane. My mother's sister Mania, her only surviving relative, had migrated the previous year. The sisters hadn't seen each other since 1943, shortly before Mania and her husband Misko were caught by the Germans in Warsaw and deported to Bergen-Belsen concentration camp. They were among the tottering skeletons whom English soldiers liberated two years later in May 1945. After the war, Misko's cousin in Brisbane sent them a permit but just as the sun had started to shine on their faces again, Misko developed kidney failure and died. He had survived the war but not the peace, and my aunt was left alone at the other end of the world.

Their tragedy decided our fate. My parents had resolved to leave Poland with its bitter memories of the Holocaust and travel as far from Europe as possible. My aunt's plight solved the problem of where to go. From the moment we arrived, we were embraced by a warm-hearted extended family who treated us like close relatives even though we'd never met. Bronek Rappaport, a dentist like my father, had a charismatic personality and generous spirit that enriched everyone fortunate enough to cross his path. His wife's relatives, the Benjamins, also opened their hearts to us and included us in all their activities and festivities. My first Australian playmate was their daughter Maxine, whose merry giggle and uncomplicated personality helped me to start becoming an Australian child.

At the New Farm Primary School, frustrated at being unable to communicate, I felt as though I had become deaf and mute. At lunchtime, when we sat under the trees in the school yard, the other children would unpack dainty white triangles with lettuce and vegemite or Kraft spread, while I took out hunks of rye bread with tomato and egg which had become cemented into a hot paste inside my leather satchel. Whenever the children giggled, I thought they were laughing at me. It was like listening to a secret code without having the cypher to break it. When we all lined up in the school yard while the headmaster unfurled the Union Jack, I tried to copy what the others were saying. 'I honour my God, I serve my king, I salute my flag,' I parroted without having the faintest idea of what it meant.

As the button-making machine had been stolen on the ship, my father accepted that his fate was to remain a dentist, to the vast relief of my mother who had no faith in his commercial ability. He spent most of the day in the offices of the dental faculty at the University of Queensland, discussing the possibility of studying again. With his halting English and reserved personality, he found it difficult to go from one office to another, presenting the diplomas and degrees gained over the past twenty-five years in Poland and Germany and submitting proof of lectures he had given, clinics he had run and dental boards he had chaired.

Despite his qualifications and experience, the faculty insisted that he repeat the entire four-year course, but its counterpart in Sydney agreed to credit him with the first year. Since we had no money, every year saved was precious, but accepting the offer meant leaving our new relatives to travel to a city where we knew no one. Apart from having to decide where to study, would my father be able to understand lectures in a foreign language and cope with becoming a student again among people young enough to be his children? And how would my mother be able to support us when she had no trade or profession and no English?

Three years later, during my father's final year at the University of Sydney, his fellow student John Arnold, who has a dental practice in Perth, wrote about him in the annual year book: '*One of the older men in our year, Henry at first had difficulty with our language but has mastered it so quickly that now statements such as "I will borrow you my wax knife" are becoming rare with him. In fact he has been heard to use the expression, "It fits like a bomb". Henry has a very keen sense of humour and is able to appreciate a joke at his own expense. This, coupled with his ability and philosophical outlook, ensures him of a happy future in the dental profession.*'

At the end of that year, my father was asked to give his impressions of studying in Australia for the faculty newsletter. Always a diplomat, he explained that it was difficult to compare the content of the Sydney course with the one he had attended in Poland almost thirty years before, and concentrated instead on the differences in their teaching methods.

'*A point which impresses me very much and which I cannot stress enough, is that the lecturers here are teaching the students,*' he wrote. '*Yes, I know this will sound curious to you, and I shall try to explain what I mean. The lecturers in my previous studies were not interested very much in whether the students were following them or not ... Many lecturers with whom I was acquainted before coming here would rather give an incorrect answer than admit that they could not answer off hand. Here they say they will look it up or tell the student where to find the answer. The students are not misled by the lecturers here.*

'I might add that I have found it in Australian people generally, the property of being able to admit that they cannot remember perfectly every detail.

'The students have readily accepted me as one of themselves and I have found many good friends among them. Some of course have been indifferent, but that is to be expected anywhere and is only natural. There has not been a single case of unfriendliness towards me as a student from overseas and that speaks highly for the culture of the students themselves.' He concluded by saying, *'I consider it a high honour for a person to bear the degree of this faculty, and that the years I have spent as a student here have been all I could have wished them to be.'*

But in those first weeks in Brisbane, uncertain about our future and unable to speak English, my father kept making enquiries about the course, and my mother continued to look after the orphans at the hostel. They too were trying to adjust to their new life. After staying at the hostel for a few weeks, Peter and Henry Rossler's guardian sent some of the boys to pick strawberries at his brother's farm. Not used to Queensland's scorching heat some were sunburned, while others developed an allergy to the berries. Apart from the heat, the conditions at the farm demoralised them. David Kucharski, whose clowning and bugle-playing had made them laugh during the voyage, lost the urge to play and joke. It wasn't just the oppressive heat, the huge cockroaches and the mosquitoes. At mealtimes, the hungry boys would stare at their lettuce leaves, tomato and cucumber, slices of corned beef and white bread. It was like being back on the *Derna*, except that instead of spaghetti they were given salad every day. They pushed their plates away, muttering about rabbit food. Some nights when they were too hungry and too hot to sleep, they would raid the fridge and this led to reprimands in the morning. The manager was not sympathetic. 'This is the right food for a hot climate, so get used to it,' he said.

David Kucharski lived for Friday nights when the boys were invited to the rabbi's home for dinner after the service at the synagogue in Margaret Street. Realising how much they missed the food their mothers once cooked in the long-gone days when there were still homes, parents and grandparents, the rabbi's wife would prepare a feast for them. As they savoured the minced *gefillte* fish, chicken soup, chopped liver and apple cake, bitter-sweet memories came flooding back. 'I kept hoping they'd adopt us!' David tells me when I call him in Melbourne.

David's first job was making heels at a shoe factory in Stanley Street. When he collected his pay packet one Friday, he noticed that it contained only the basic wage, three pounds ten shillings; nothing for the overtime he had worked. When the same thing happened the following week, he mentioned it to his guardian. Harry Goldman was an influential man who owned a big clothing factory and employed 250 workers.

'That's not right,' Harry said and came to the factory on Monday morning to speak to David's boss. Shortly afterwards, David was sent upstairs to the book-keeper who counted out the money they owed him. Later that day he overheard the boss grumbling in Yiddish, 'These foreigners are only here five minutes and already they know the law!'

Before long, David enlisted his guardian's help again. When he rented a room with full board, his guardian advised him not to tell the landlady how much he was earning so that he would get to save a little. A couple of weeks later, when he came home from work, she met him at the door, yelling that he should pack his bags and get out or she would call the police. David was shaken and bewildered. He had no idea why she was so angry or where he should go. It turned out that the landlady had gone to his factory, marched into the book-keeper's office and demanded to know how much he was earning. When she discovered that he earned one pound more than he had told her, she was furious. 'If I'd had the money I would have gone straight back to Paris,' David recalls. 'I couldn't take the way I was treated in Brisbane at the beginning.'

With the end of the strawberry season, Peter Rossler returned to Brisbane. When he told his guardian he would like to study, he was sent to Brisbane Grammar, the best school in town. At eighteen, Peter was a good-looking boy, sensitive and intelligent, but his experiences in the Lodz Ghetto and in Auschwitz had left him shy and insecure. He felt physically and emotionally underdeveloped compared with the brawny, high-spirited and confident boys at school, and disliked the school's regimented routine. To assert his individuality he would occasionally wear brown shoes instead of black, or refuse to wear the school hat. He missed Prague and wrote homesick letters to his old school friends.

Two years after his arrival in Australia, Peter was awarded a Commonwealth scholarship to university. By this time his aunt and uncle had arrived from Czechoslovakia so he and his brother Henry moved to Sydney to join them. 'I wasn't as ambitious and focused as Henry,' Peter says about his older brother who became a successful architect, but died of cancer in 1991. 'I was no good at planning the future and took life as it came.'

Despite his laid-back nature, Peter graduated with a science degree in applied chemistry. After working for major pharmaceutical firms including Burroughs Wellcome, he worked at Unilever-Rexona for twenty-three years, developing aerosol fillers. 'It wasn't until I married Pauline and our daughter Carolyn was born that I started to feel I belonged here,' he says.

Before I leave his cottage near Sydney's Cooper Park, Peter threads an 8mm film through the spool of an antiquated little projector. As he turns the handle, blurred scenes of hawkers and rickshaw drivers flash past, followed by an image of the *Derna* moored in the harbour. This is the film he took in Colombo during our voyage.

While Peter and the other boys were picking strawberries, in another part of Brisbane, Elsie Pataky was about to give birth. Exhausted from the voyage and her advanced state of pregnancy, she let out the last pleat in her navy skirt and thanked God she had only one month to go, because the skirt was now stretched to the limit and so was she.

The Brisbane immigration officer who interviewed the young couple was charmed by the pregnant young Romanian woman who had a beguiling manner and spoke excellent English. When Elsie gave her aunt's address at Kangaroo Point, he called a taxi and wanted to pay their three shillings and sevenpence fare because he saw that they didn't have two pennies to rub together, but she was too proud to accept and took the bus instead.

A few weeks later, Elsie's cousin was shopping in the stocking department of David Jones. After she had given the saleswoman her address, a man standing nearby asked, 'Did you say 33 Kangaroo Point Road? Do you have a relative who has just arrived from Europe?' When the astonished girl nodded, he asked, 'Has she had the baby yet?' It was the immigration officer who had stamped Elsie's passport.

Their paths were to cross one more time. Eight years later, in 1956, when one of their friends in Budapest wanted to migrate, he told the Australian immigration officer that his sponsors were Elsie and Ignac Pataky. As soon as the officer heard the surname, he asked, 'Did they by any chance arrive in 1948 when she was pregnant?' It was the same man!

As she relates this story, Elsie's dark eyes sparkle with merriment. She's a lively, outgoing woman who connects easily with people. She's slightly hunched and walks with difficulty as the result of recent by-pass surgery and a mild stroke, both of which have taken their toll on her body but obviously not her spirit.

In St Lucia where Elsie and Ignac live, timber cottages are partly concealed by bushes and trees line the winding streets. Jacarandas are in bloom and their fallen petals cover the pavements like violet eiderdowns. Today this area includes a university campus and bustles with students, but when they moved here fifty years ago, it was mostly woodland and open space.

Their inviting bungalow, made out of native timber, was designed by their friend Roman Pawlyszyn, the Ukrainian architect they met on the *Derna* with whom they have remained close friends ever since. Elsie points proudly to the sideboard that her husband Ignac made, along with all the other furniture in their house. On the wall of Elsie's office hangs a framed photograph of the Queen in crowned regalia, and another one hangs in the bedroom. A staunch monarchist just like her English mother, Elsie is delighted that most Australians voted against becoming a republic in the referendum of the year 2000.

In the intricate chain of connections that has led me from one passenger to another during my search, I had heard about Elsie and Ignac from Kurt Herzog in Sydney.

'Have you spoken to a Romanian couple called Pataky?' he asked, and proceeded to describe Elsie's terror on the train from Innsbruck to Marseilles when the guard took away their passports. It was Kurt who had collected money for their hotel room in Innsbruck when they were so destitute that they picked up mouldy bread in the street, and Kurt who had shared his five pounds with them in Fremantle so that Elsie could buy herself a pair of shoes.

'Kurt is one in a million,' Elsie tells me, as she takes fine bone china cups out of the cupboard to make tea. 'One day I mentioned that I'd love to own some Rosenthal porcelain, and when our anniversary came round, he bought us a whole dinner set!'

Returning to their first year in Brisbane, Elsie says that it was a disappointment in many ways. The food was tasteless and the wooden houses on wooden poles with toilets in the back yard reminded her of backward Romanian villages. In comparison with Brisbane, her Romanian town of Braila had been a sophisticated metropolis.

But Elsie didn't have much time to dwell on the food or the architecture. Soon after they arrived, she had a check-up at the Brisbane maternity hospital. She was eight months pregnant and had never been examined by a doctor. When the obstetrician saw her swollen legs and took her blood pressure, he admitted her immediately. Her kidneys weren't working properly and both she and the baby were in such danger that for the next four weeks she wasn't allowed out of bed.

Their daughter Eve was born in December 1948 after being induced because Elsie's condition was so serious that the obstetrician couldn't risk waiting any longer. When I ask if it was traumatic having a baby in a strange country, she shakes her grey head vigorously. 'It was wonderful! The Queen of England couldn't have had better treatment! I arrived in hospital with nothing and left loaded up with clothes, a pram, a high chair and a cot. The sisters all knitted, crocheted and embroidered baby clothes for me! The chief obstetrician brought me a basket of red roses. Then the neighbours started coming over with things for me, for Ignac and for the baby. Don't laugh! To this day I love hospitals!'

Although the strangers were kind, the relatives were cool. Elsie missed her family and ached with loneliness. They had been sponsored by her aunt and uncle but their relationship was distant. Her aunt was so pernickety about her belongings that Elsie felt like an intruder, constantly under hostile scrutiny.

'From the moment Ignac started working, I started saving to return to Europe,' she says. On Fridays he received eight pounds and on Mondays she would deposit three pounds in the bank for their passage back. 'Everything here was so strange, even the way they set the table. Looking after a baby was strange too. I did my best but I'd never had anything to do with babies, and it didn't come naturally. Do you know, I never even saw a pregnant woman until I came to Australia! In Europe pregnancy was hidden, as though it was something to be ashamed of. In Romania only peasants walked around in the streets when they were visibly pregnant.'

When Eve was old enough to go to school, they sent her to Brisbane Grammar even though the fees took all of Elsie's earnings as a secretary: nine pounds a week. One day Eve told her mother with great pride that she was the only tradesman's daughter in her class. They lived in one room and cooked on a primus stove so that the most complicated meal Elsie could cook was a pot roast. 'But if I hadn't been so lonely none of that would have mattered,' she says.

As soon as she could, Elsie studied accountancy at Queensland University and later worked at Brett's in the city. 'I didn't like it,' she recalls. 'They were very tough in those days. If you spent one minute longer at tea break or went to the toilet, the boss would call you into his office and demand to know why.'

After working at the university for twenty-three years, Elsie retired in 1990. 'Since then I've become a bit depressed,' she says. 'I miss my work and have never been able to come to terms with retirement.'

Her daughter became a microbiologist. When I ask whether she is still working, there's a long pause. 'Eve is a very sick girl,' Elsie sighs. 'She's living on borrowed time. Five years ago they discovered a malignant tumour in her bile duct. The surgeon removed the tumour and reconstructed her bile duct with stents which have to be replaced every few years. She's only the fifth patient in Australia to survive this operation. But if you met her you wouldn't suspect anything was wrong because she's so full of life. Eve has a wonderful husband and three brilliant children and that's what keeps her going,' she says. 'Her daughter Tegan was awarded a $35,000 a year scholarship at Brisbane Grammar School and topped the school in Chinese and Science.'

Among Elsie and Ignac's friends from the *Derna* were the Hof sisters who had shared her cabin. For the first few years they were so close that when Elfriede and Ilse's parents arrived in Brisbane, they became Eve's surrogate grandparents, but over the years they drifted apart. 'We got together again when we organised a reunion in 1998 to celebrate the fiftieth anniversary of the *Derna*'s arrival in Australia,' Elsie says.

Inside Elfriede's spic and span cottage in a modest Brisbane suburb, the shelves have never seen dust. On the polished sideboard stands a framed photograph of Ilse's three granddaughters. 'I regard them as my grandchildren too,' says Elfriede who never married. She is a forthright no-nonsense woman with a hearty laugh and a strong voice in which I detect a German accent. With her jolly manner, lively interest in everything and her check shirt and sensible shoes, she reminds me of a hearty gym teacher. Her sister Ilse is quieter and less extroverted, but has a delightful sense of humour and a twinkle in her eye.

As we talk, Elfriede takes out her thick morocco-bound diary whose pages are filled with neat German writing and reads out the names of the other young women in her cabin: Elsie, Lusia, Gilda and Dorothea. She quotes from the witty poem that Gilda composed about the voyage, but when I ask whether I could borrow the diary, she shakes her springy grey hair. 'It's too personal!' she says, so while she is translating some of the entries, I can't help wondering what she's leaving out. In her systematic way, she has even recorded the menus. 'Mutton, mutton, mutton. Outlandish — strong smell. Got sick of it. If I ever land I'll never eat mutton again,' she reads, and then looks up with a laugh. 'And I never have!'

29

As the road sweeps down towards Sydney's Middle Harbour with its red and blue spinnakers billowing in the breeze, I feel a surge of joy at the light-hearted beauty of this city. I'm particularly elated on this fresh spring morning because I'm on my way to meet Dorothea, whom I never expected to find.

Elfriede had mentioned that Dorothea was in her cabin before moving in with the escort officer. Some of the male passengers, who had obviously eyed her with lustful thoughts, recalled her sunbaking on the deck outside Colonel Hershaw's cabin while the breeze lifted her skirt over her suntanned legs. Emanuel Darin and Uno Mardus ran into her in Sydney some years later, but no one remembered her surname until I spoke to Elsie Pataky's friend Kurt Herzog. 'Ritter,' he said with a reminiscent smile. 'Dorothea Ritter.'

Armed with the name of the girl who had inflamed the imaginations of so many men during the voyage, I scoured telephone directories in every capital city, but without success. Not that I was surprised. It wasn't likely that such an appealing young woman had remained single. Scanning the passenger lists yet again, I noticed something that my previous search had missed. Alongside her name was the name of the Sydney relative who had sponsored her.

Fortunately the sponsor's surname was unusual and there were only three listings in the Sydney telephone book, although my excitement was tempered by the thought that Fridl was probably no longer alive. The young man who answered the phone said he didn't know such a person, but a few moments later he exclaimed, 'Fridl! She was my grandmother, but she's been dead for years!' He knew nothing about the young woman whom Fridl had sponsored from Germany.

At the next number I dialled, the woman said, 'Fridl was my mother-in-law!' but went on to explain that since her divorce she had lost touch with the rest of the family. I was about to hang up when she added, 'Come to think of it, there was a young refugee who was related to my mother-in-law. Give me a minute and I'll try to remember her married name.' I crossed my fingers hoping that she had a good memory. She did.

As I dialled Dorothea's number with trembling fingers, I wondered how to tackle this interview with the young woman who had been so notorious on the *Derna*. I would obviously need to be tactful and not frighten her off by asking indiscreet questions about her private life. Perhaps the opportunity to discuss this delicate matter would arise during our conversation.

The woman who picked up the phone had a faint German accent and a youthful voice.

'The *Derna*!' she exclaimed, clearly astonished that I had tracked her down. 'I can tell you an interesting story about that voyage,' she said without any prompting on my part. 'Have you heard about the escort officer from the IRO, our famous Colonel Hershaw? I was his secretary on the voyage! I can show you a photo we had taken in Port Said!'

Dorothea's house stands on the edge of a leafy escarpment surrounded by tall eucalypts, some of which have been blackened by recent bushfires. The moment she opens the door, I feel that the air around her is charged with vivacity and enthusiasm. Still pretty in her seventies, she has large blue eyes brimming with fun, a youthful face with a creamy European complexion and a neat figure. Her manner is disarmingly frank with that no-nonsense German directness which makes her an interviewer's dream.

'All I knew of Australia was that there were lots of sheep,' she laughs. 'I had no concept of what it was like and I didn't really care. I just wanted to be free of memories of Germany and start a new life.'

When Dorothea arrived in Sydney by train, her cousin Fridl, who had sponsored her, was waiting at the station with her daughter. They recognised each other straightaway, even though it was ten years since they'd last met. That had been in 1938, just after Kristallnacht, and their parting had not been cordial. 'Fridl had come to visit my parents in Berlin but when she walked into my room she practically froze on the spot,' Dorothea recalls. 'Pasted on the wall was a picture of Hitler. I don't really know why I had it there, because I'd already been expelled from school and from the youth group for having Jewish blood, so I certainly had no reason to like Hitler. Probably I got caught up in all the hysteria. I don't know why my father didn't make me take it down either, but when Fridl saw that picture she walked out of the house and never spoke to my parents again. Shortly after that she left for Australia.'

Fridl didn't hold that incident against Dorothea and when she heard that her cousin wanted to migrate, she sent her a permit. 'I was very lucky to have a warm family here when I arrived,' Dorothea says. 'Fridl was much older than me and treated me like a daughter. I think she was surprised that the quiet withdrawn little girl she had known in Berlin had grown into a lively, confident young woman. I certainly started feeling a lot more confident when my suitcases turned up with all my clothes,' she recalls. 'They came on the next ship, just as The Honourable had said.' She says Hershaw's title with a sarcastic inflection and a mischievous smile, arousing my interest in her story.

The true nature of her relationship with the man she facetiously refers to as The Honourable intrigues me, because sharing a cabin with a strange man in 1948 flouted the standards of acceptable behaviour of the time. Unfazed by my comment, Dorothea looks at me with that wide-eyed innocent expression of hers. 'When he suggested I should move in, I thought, *Why not? It's better than sleeping in a crowded cabin in the hold.* Anyway, I knew I could look after myself. Don't forget, I'd been through a lot in Berlin with the Russians. I was almost raped twice but I got away, so I wasn't frightened of Ogden Hershaw. He struck me as being honourable and trustworthy and anyway, he was old enough to be my father, so I saw no harm in it. Besides, he told me he'd notified the captain of our arrangement, so it was all above board. I know that people used to gossip but that didn't worry me because I knew I wasn't doing anything wrong. Everyone thought I was sleeping with him,' she says cheerfully.

'Were you?' I ask.

'No!' she exclaims at once. 'No! Maybe I would have if he'd been younger and I had been attracted to him, but I wasn't! Once he tried to kiss me, but when I made it clear I wasn't interested, he left me alone.'

She shows me the photograph they had taken in Port Said. Ogden Hershaw is sprawled in his chair, leaning towards her, a long cigarette holder in his mouth, a fez on his head and one hand in his pocket.

'See his pose? That shows you what he was like. Full of himself. After I heard what he did with that young Italian girl, I moved out and didn't have anything more to do with him. I didn't even say goodbye when we got to Melbourne.' She still sounds angry with him after all these years.

Finding suitable men to go out with in Sydney proved unexpectedly difficult. 'I was often invited out, but the ones I met weren't my type,' she says. 'They were too materialistic for my taste, too focused on their future, and I didn't have much in common with them. I wondered if I'd ever meet my soulmate.' Her unsettled state of mind must have shown on her face because when she sent her parents a photograph of herself from Sydney, they wrote back: 'You don't look happy. Sell your ring and come back to Germany.'

One evening Dorothea was mulling over an invitation to attend a musical evening held at a private home in Strathfield. 'Do come with us,' Fridl urged. 'You might meet someone new.' Dorothea agreed to go although she didn't expect much from this soirée which usually attracted much older people. Around fifty music-lovers, mostly German refugees, had already gathered when she arrived at the home of Harold and Ellen Brent, who happened to be the guardians of one of the orphans from the *Derna*.

It was during that musical evening, somewhere between the Mozart and the Beethoven, that Dorothea met a lanky Australian with a craggy nose and an understated Anglo-Saxon sense of humour that made her laugh. She thought that he might be a Russian Jew, but in fact Don and his brother were the only non-Jewish visitors there that night. By a strange coincidence, this was the first time that Don had attended one of the Brents' musical evenings, and he too had gone under duress, dragged along by his brother. To make conversation, Dorothea asked where he came from but when he said Kensington, she had no idea where that was. As the evening progressed, however, she found him interesting, attractive and refreshingly different from the other men she had met in Sydney.

Her relatives had a European sense of propriety, didn't want their young ward to be touched by scandal and did not approve of Don coming to visit her while they were out. Decent young women did not receive male visitors when they were alone at night, Fridl lectured her. When Fridl had finished, Dorothea smiled demurely. 'Don came to propose,' she said. 'We're going to get married.'

They married at St John's Church in Darlinghurst in 1950, followed by a reception at Cahill's in Elizabeth Street, an elegant Australian restaurant which served toasted sandwiches, roast lamb with mint sauce, and blackberry flummery on silver platters and fine china. About ninety people came to the wedding, from both sides of the family. The only shipboard friend Dorothea invited was her German friend Gilda, but she was living in Melbourne and didn't come.

Looking fondly at her husband who has joined us for tea, Dorothea says, 'We've been married for fifty years and I've never regretted marrying him for one single moment.' Don's hair has turned white but he is still lanky and has a dry sense of humour. When I ask what appealed to him about Dorothea, he doesn't miss a beat.

'She was the right shape,' he laughs.

'Oh, come on!' Dorothea protests.

'It's true!' he insists. 'She was a bit plump, but everything was in the right place. She reminded me of my favourite film star, Madeleine Carroll. She was a great talker, got on with everyone, knew everyone's name and everyone liked her.'

'And we had lots of mutual interests,' Dorothea adds. 'I even got on well with his mother, though at first the idea of her son marrying a German girl horrified her.' Don's mother was fascinated to hear about Dorothea's experiences in Germany on the rare occasions she talked about those dark times. 'I tried to put the past behind me to such an extent that I ripped up my German work permit, which I should have kept because it was a historical document,' she says.

Having worked as a dental nurse in Berlin, she obtained a job with an orthodontist in Macquarie Street. Outfitted in her white shoes and starched white uniform, she liked chatting with the patients, but making appointments over the phone was difficult. She couldn't understand the Australian accent and to make things worse her employer would rebuke her in front of the patients, which mortified her. When she came home in tears one evening, Fridl was indignant. 'He can't treat you like that! You're not going back there,' she said.

'But I've left my shoes there,' Dorothea lamented.

'Doesn't matter,' Fridl insisted. 'I'll pick up your shoes and the money he owes you, and we'll find you another job.'

She was much luckier with her next employer. Jack Mantheim was a dentist from Frankfurt with whom Dorothea had such a good rapport that a few years later when her father, also a dentist, came out from Germany the two men became close friends. When her father celebrated his ninetieth birthday in Sydney, it was Jack who proposed the toast.

Dorothea was very close to her father. In 1952 when the *Australian Women's Weekly* ran an essay contest to celebrate the coronation of Queen Elizabeth II, the topic was 'The Happiest Day in my Life'. Tapping on her old Triumph typewriter, Dorothea described that miraculous day in Berlin in 1944 when she heard a knock on the door and there stood her father with a blanket over his arm and a piece of bread in his hand.

In 1952, the year she wrote that essay, tragedy struck Dorothea. Her first baby was born prematurely and died three days later. 'I wasn't so young any more and I wanted a baby so much. She only weighed one and a half pounds. They put her in a humidicrib in the Crown Street

Women's Hospital and kept telling me not to worry, that she would be all right. I just had to drink lots of water so I'd have plenty of milk for her. Then on the third day a nurse told me the baby was dead. They whisked her away and buried her in the hospital grounds. I don't even know where. Do you know, I only saw her once, a few seconds after she was born when they held up this tiny doll who was crying. I never even held her. When I think of it now, it makes me so angry, but we didn't know any better in those days. We just did what we were told and didn't question it.'

Two years later, when Dorothea became pregnant again, she was very careful to make sure she didn't go into labour prematurely. Evelyn grew into a quiet, shy child. Although she became a teacher, her sensitive nature found it difficult to cope with the impudent children who tugged her long plaits and answered back. She gave up teaching, married, had three children and has now launched into a new career: remedial massage, Dorothea says proudly.

As we talk, it strikes me that a number of children from the *Derna* have suffered from depression, drugs, eating disorders and alcoholism. Perhaps the traumas and uncertainties of the migrants have affected the next generation who acted out the grief and displacement that their parents suppressed in their drive to get established. Were these children deprived of empathy by parents who focused on making a living? Or did they rebel against the high expectations to achieve the academic success of which their parents had been deprived? Did the past create a chasm between them, or did it become a burden?

Dorothea says she started to put down roots in Australia after she got married. 'I really blossomed in Australia,' she says. 'In Germany I was made to feel inferior because my father was born a Jew, but here I was accepted and for the first time in my life I felt valued for who I was. When I started dreaming in English, I knew I had made it!' she laughs. 'But I didn't feel Australian until I went back to Berlin in 1956 with Evelyn. I didn't have any problem with the young Germans but felt very suspicious of the older ones, especially when they told me that they had helped Jews and didn't know anything about concentration camps.'

While Don studied for his PhD in Australian history after retiring as an engineer, Dorothea typed his thesis on the same Triumph typewriter that she had used to type newsletters and correspondence for Ogden Hershaw. She uses it to this day. Its black leather case is worn now, but the machine is still in perfect working order, she assures me, as she points to the pound and dollar keys she had put in before she sailed on the *Derna*. These days Don lectures at the University of the Third Age, a voluntary educational organisation for retirees. He is the past president of the Sydney branch while Dorothy runs discussion groups in German, learns French and takes courses in drama and music.

Several weeks after our meeting, Dorothea calls me. 'You'll never believe what I just found! I was going through an old drawer and found the letter that I typed about Ogden Hershaw, the one Dr Frant sent to the IRO!' While we're on the subject of the *Derna*, the conversation turns to her friend Gilda who had flown with her on the American transport plane from Berlin. 'I haven't seen her since the day we arrived in Australia,' she says. 'I invited her to our wedding but she didn't come.'

On a crisp winter's morning a few months later, a sprightly old lady with hair as white as the daisies sprinkled all over the lawn is waiting for me at the Roseville Retirement Village in the Melbourne suburb of Doncaster. Gilda tells me in her chirpy manner that she has lived here ever since being widowed in 1996, and leads me to her neat cottage.

It turns out that her real name is Gisa, but she called herself Gilda during the voyage because it sounded more artistic, more consistent with the image of the diva she hoped to become. When I mention her poem, 'The Ballad of the *Derna*', Gisa frowns and shakes her head. She can't remember writing it. 'Don't forget, I'm eighty-five now and my memory isn't so good any more,' she laughs. As we talk about the past, however, the memories come flooding back, and she recalls Fred Silberstein who flew out of Berlin with her and Dorothea on the American transport plane.

'A very handsome fellow he was, blond and quite Aryan-looking, with a wonderful sense of humour. I wonder what happened to him. And the two German sisters in my cabin, Elfriede and Ilse, we had such fun together, we played card games and sang. The three of us sang the aria from *The Magic Flute* together,' she reminisces and proceeds to hum it in a voice that quavers but is still melodious.

Gisa's dreams of becoming a singer were destroyed by the Nazis because her grandparents were Jewish, but after the war she sang for the Allied soldiers in Berlin. 'After one concert, an American colonel drove me home in his jeep and as we bumped through the ruined streets, he looked almost upset,' she recalls.

Although Gisa hoped to continue her musical career in Australia, it didn't take her long to realise that this was an impossible dream. 'I gave a few concerts for the ABC when I arrived, but there was no possibility of making a living as a singer here,' she says. She shows me a photograph of herself at the time, her brown hair swept back into wings on either side of a parting, pulled back behind her ears and rolled on the nape of her neck. 'I gave up my dreams of singing and became a radiographer instead,' she says.

It was through her new profession that she met her husband. 'I was almost forty when I married Austin Jedick who was also from Berlin. My relatives had introduced us while I was studying radiography, but nothing came of it until a few years later, when I ran into him at the hospital where I was working. We were very happy together,' she says. She's animated and down-to-earth, and I can see that she accepts whatever life deals out and moves forward. At the moment she's writing a book about Berlin.

Inevitably we return to the *Derna* and Colonel Hershaw. 'He was an unpleasant character and tried to seduce all the young girls. He propositioned me as well,' she recalls. 'Very blunt he was too. Just came out with it and asked me to sleep with him. And then there was that business with the Italian girl. It was terrible, she was so young and sweet. Everyone knew about it. I used to speak Italian with her. She was terribly upset, poor thing, so ashamed and worried about becoming pregnant. And she wasn't the last one he seduced either. Not long after we arrived I was very pleased to read in the *Argus* that he had been dismissed from his post and would never be employed as an escort officer again.'

And Dorothea?

'Oh, she was attractive, vibrant and had a good figure, but she was flighty and flirtatious,' Gisa smiles. 'We were very different. A short time after we arrived she wrote to tell me that she had met THE man in her life.' When I say that Dorothea is married, Gisa blurts out in an incredulous voice, 'To the same man?'

Now that I've stirred up the past, she would love to contact her old friend again, and on my return to Sydney, I give Dorothea her address.

The way they describe it, their first meeting after fifty-two years was pleasant but not emotional. They had both changed, their lives had moved along different paths and too much time had elapsed for any real connection to be re-established, apart from superficial reminiscences of a journey shared long ago. But although neither of them thought they would continue the contact, the reunion brought them a sense of completion.

30

When I called him from Australia, Fred Silberstein's reaction was so ebullient that I almost expected him to burst into my study through the telephone receiver. 'Oh my godfathers! How did you find me? How did you know I was in Auckland?' The popular young man who flew out of Berlin with Dorothea and Gisa was so friendly and eager to help that I felt I'd known him all my life. And when he gave me a brief outline of his extraordinary life story, and told me that he had photographs from the *Derna*, I could hardly wait to get there.

Several weeks later I fly to Auckland. Fred comes to the hotel to welcome me as soon as I arrive. I'm delighted to find that he is a great talker who remembers details and needs very little prompting. In his cosy timber home in Blockhouse Bay, where he lives with his wife Billie, we sit on a small patio overlooking the garden. When I ask the name of a shrub I've never seen before, he shakes his head. 'Don't ask me about plants,' he says and there's a shudder in his voice. 'After my experience at Gross Am Wannsee, I lost my taste for gardening.' As it turns out, gardening is the only topic he refuses to discuss in the eight hours we spend talking about his excessively eventful life.

Although Fred's fair hair has turned silver, and his slim figure has thickened around the middle, his eyes are still the startling shade of blue that prompted an SS officer to suggest he should try to save his life by joining the Hitler Youth movement. In his understated way, Fred does not flinch from describing the medical experiments they performed on his unanaesthetised body at Auschwitz, the cannibalism he witnessed at Nordhausen, or the agony of staggering on the Death March with nothing to eat but snow.

His voice sounds flatly matter-of-fact but there's a wounded look in his eyes. This is a macabre dance we are engaged in. He is trying to distance himself from the pain while I pursue him so that I can smell the blood. I know that no matter what I ask and what he replies, he can never recreate and I can never recapture the terror and agony that he suffered when he was fifteen. At times I lack the words, or perhaps the courage, to ask the questions that his descriptions provoke. As he was able to live through it, the least I can do is listen, but listening is harrowing. So is talking, and occasionally Fred utters a sound somewhere between a cough and a sob, falls silent, and then says in a hoarse voice that it's time for a break.

Two years after the war ended, he found out that his sister Hansi, whom he had not seen since the day the Gestapo abducted him in 1942, was still alive. 'Our reunion wasn't as emotional as you might expect,' he says. 'I think by then she felt closer to the friends she'd made in the camps who had shared the same experiences. It probably sounds odd to you, but we didn't hug and kiss or cry.' I imagine that their experiences distanced them like a hundred years of unbridgeable sorrows. 'I don't get emotional with people even now,' he adds, and I wonder whether this lack of emotion is the façade that has protected him from his deepest feelings and prevented him from grieving, breaking down and, what he probably dreads most of all, losing control.

When Hansi told him that she was migrating to Auckland, where they had relatives, he decided to follow her. 'I didn't think ahead or plan in those days,' he says. 'I knew nothing about New Zealand, but somehow I felt it would all work out. I was quite content on the ship, I had enough to eat, a place to sleep, lovely girls like Magda to dance with, and no enemy wanting to kill me.'

It was a sunny summer's day in 1948 when the plane touched down at the small airport in West Auckland and the captain, in the immaculate uniform of the New Zealand Air Force, said, 'Welcome to New Zealand.' Hansi was waiting to meet him with their aunt and uncle, but when Fred kissed his uncle on each cheek, European style, he drew away in embarrassment.

'Men don't do that here,' he said.

On his first Friday in Auckland, Fred went to the synagogue service, something he had not done for many years. As a boy he had resented the religious observances imposed by his father, and after the war, he felt too disillusioned to pray. Knowing that millions had been butchered on account of their faith did not engender gratitude towards the Almighty. But now, some emotion he could not explain urged him to return to his roots and pray. At the start of a new chapter in his life, ancestral spirits were stirring in his soul and he felt a yearning to reconnect with his parents and his past, to cheat Hitler of victory.

Soon after his arrival, Fred felt overwhelmed when his relatives organised a party in honour of his twenty-first birthday. Everyone else took this celebration for granted, but it was a long time since he had celebrated a birthday and to him it seemed miraculous. Wherever he went, the kindness of people in Auckland astonished him. Complete strangers would greet him in the street and ask how he was getting on. Sometimes they even brought him gifts, a comb or a handkerchief.

Although his aunt and uncle wanted to help him financially, Fred was determined to be independent as soon as possible. Ten days after arriving, he started work at a hosiery factory. Until then, New Zealand had imported women's stockings and socks from England, but had now begun manufacturing them. When Fred mentioned that he sometimes lost his way home because he had to change trams, every night his workmates would take turns to accompany him on the pretext that they were going that way themselves. He didn't find out until much later that they had gone out of their way to escort him.

Although Christmas was approaching and the radio stations continually played Bing Crosby's hit song 'I'm Dreaming of a White Christmas', the sun was shining and the beaches were crowded. Towards the end of December when Fred's boss handed him an envelope with a bonus for the Christmas holidays, he couldn't get over it. What a marvellous country this was, where you were paid not to work!

Whenever Fred told his aunt and uncle that he wanted to become a chef, they would shake their heads. Not a suitable job for a Jewish boy, they said. Eventually his uncle persuaded him to go into a carpet-cleaning business with a local businessman, but after persevering for five years, he quit and started an apprenticeship with a cabinet-maker.

As often as he could manage it, sometimes five nights a week, he went dancing. Ballroom dancing was sensual and sociable, and combined his love of music and meeting girls. At his favourite night club, the Wintergarten on the corner of Queen and Wellesley Streets, the jazzy décor with its glass floor transported him to a sophisticated world where all that mattered was elegance and grace. He appreciated the decorum that banned jitterbugging as too wild and insisted on formal dress. Men were required to wear suits while women wore formal gowns or cocktail dresses and gloves on the hands that rested lightly on his shoulder. Here he was no longer an impoverished refugee with too much past and not enough future, but a sought-after dance partner who spun his partner around the dance floor while the band wove ribbons of golden sound.

With his handsome looks, fastidious appearance and impeccable manners, Fred was popular with the girls, but their parents were less impressed. As many of the Jewish orphans were to discover, they were not regarded as good husband material. Fred found out that as far as the parents were concerned, a big question mark hung over every aspect of his life. He had appeared out of the ruins of Europe with no money, profession or prospects. Some people said he was irresponsible for spending too much on girls and dancing and advised him to start saving money, but Fred had no intention of settling down. For the first time in his life he was carefree and having fun.

'So it will take me five minutes longer to become a millionaire, but now I'm going to enjoy myself,' he would reply.

But beneath the calm exterior, Fred was not as tranquil as he appeared. Although he never talked about the past, it festered in the depths of his mind. At night, often his own screams would wake him. Covered in sweat, he would tremble, shaking off the invisible hands that held him down while white-coated Nazi doctors sliced open his flesh.

Things came to a head in 1959 when he had surgery on his leg. 'As I was coming out of the anaesthetic I became hysterical,' he recalls. 'I thought I was in the gas chamber and they were trying to kill me. I screamed for my mother and grappled with the doctors and nurses until I fell out of bed and crashed to the floor. They thought I'd gone berserk, they had no idea what was wrong with me.'

So when he needed another operation several years later, he alerted the surgeon beforehand. 'Be prepared in case I put on a floorshow,' he said, explaining what had happened the previous time. The doctor told him not to worry. He had arranged for a nurse to stay with him until he regained consciousness in case he had a similar episode. 'I had never come across such kind people before,' he says.

Through all the years, Fred had never abandoned his dream of becoming a chef. While working as a cabinet-maker by day, he attended catering classes at night and worked as a head waiter in various restaurants. One of them was a nightclub called Hey Diddle Griddle, then managed by Harry Miller who later became an entrepreneur and celebrity agent in Australia. In 1962 Fred fulfilled his lifelong dream. The terrified fourteen year old who had prepared doughnuts at a New Year's Eve party for the Nazi elite at Gross Am Wannsee twenty years before, gained his catering diploma, bought a restaurant they called Barbecue in Dominion Road, Mt Eden, and finally became a chef. By then Fred was married and his wife Billie did front of house while he was in his element in the kitchen, frying schnitzel, braising beef and preparing apple strudl. Fred's Wiener schnitzel, friendly service and reasonable prices attracted a devoted clientele. Although the restaurant was always full, they closed down in 1985, after the government introduced the GST. 'I preferred to close down than have to explain to the customers why we had to increase our prices,' he says.

From the concerned look on Billie's face while he talks, I can see how supportive and caring she is in her understated way. Billie isn't Jewish, nor are their daughters. 'That doesn't matter to me at all,' he says. 'It's not important. I am what I am, she is what she is, and we respect each other's differences.'

While Fred and I continue to talk, Billie calls out to say that she's leaving to visit their older daughter Dallas, who is about to have a biopsy for a tumour. 'Medical experiments!' Fred comments with a wry expression. In view of his past experiences, it's a chilling phrase, but he is trying to make light of it. I'm amazed that at such a stressful time, he is willing to spend all day talking to me about the past, but perhaps it distracts him from his anxiety. Looking at me with that stoic expression of his, he says, 'It will be all right, she'll be okay,' as if to reassure me, and probably himself as well. That's what his parents in Berlin used to say to reassure him when life was falling apart all around them.

Returning to the story of their restaurant, he tells me that it became a great success, even though he wasn't a good businessman. 'When the bank manager told me I needed an overdraft, I didn't want to take it. Finally I agreed to take it for six months but I repaid it as soon as I could and refused to take another one. I hated the idea of borrowing. It was like taking something that didn't belong to me.'

Apart from his abhorrence of debt, Fred didn't want to owe money because he didn't expect to live very long. In 1945, when he was emaciated, injured and sick with typhus at the hospital in Nordhausen, the doctor had warned that his life expectancy was short, that he wouldn't last beyond forty. Like an Aboriginal tribesman having the bone pointed at him, he was so convinced the prediction would come true that he didn't bother taking out life insurance. 'I was very surprised to find that I was still here after I turned forty,' he chuckles. 'It wasn't until my fiftieth birthday that I finally realised that I was going to live! But I never dreamed I would celebrate my seventieth with my wife, sister, children and five grandchildren around me!'

Fred and his sister Hansi are much closer now than they were when he arrived, but it took almost forty years for them to start talking about the past. On New Year's Day in 1994, when he dropped in to wish her Happy New Year, she told him for the first time what had happened to her after she was deported to Auschwitz-Birkenau and then forced on the Death March to Bergen-Belsen, where she was interned at the same time as Anne Frank. Finally she answered the question that had bothered him ever since he discovered that she had survived. Why had she not returned to Berlin after the war? She explained that she could not bear to go back after their parents had been taken away. By then the rift was healed and the reason no longer mattered.

The following year Fred was invited to Germany for the opening of the Holocaust Memorial in Berlin. It was his first time back since 1948 and the four days he spent there were agonising. 'I couldn't cope with the formalities and ceremonies while graffiti on the walls in Frankfurt said "Jews Out". Plainclothes policemen accompanied us around town, to protect us, they said. That made me freeze. I wasn't ready for the polite speeches or profuse apologies. The visit stirred up such vivid memories that the nightmares came back. After that visit I decided to forgive the Germans. Hatred only begets more hatred. But forget? Never!'

The visit to Germany had an unexpected result: it launched him into a new role. Until then, Fred had avoided talking about the Holocaust. As he speaks, my eye falls on the faded number below the short sleeve of his blue and white check shirt: 106792.

'Whenever people asked me about the tattoo on my forearm, I would say it was my telephone number. I didn't want to talk about it and I didn't want anyone to feel sorry for me,' he says. But when he returned to Auckland in 1995, he was interviewed on the *Tonight* television program and soon afterwards he was invited to talk about his experiences to schoolchildren.

'I was petrified. I'd never done any public speaking before. I didn't know how to talk to children about such things or how to describe such personal experiences.'

The first time he stood on the dais of a school hall with a hundred curious young faces turned towards him, he trembled so much he wondered whether he'd be able to stay on his feet long enough to tell his story. What if they were bored or made fun of what he was saying? How would he find the words to tell these young people about the things that had happened to him when he was their age? What if they didn't believe him?

There are times when one has a sense of being involved in something so important that it seems as though one was born to do it, and no matter how difficult it is, the significance of the task transcends personal discomfort. We who survived feel that we have been spared and owe it to those who were not to bear witness about the past. It's a sacred duty to tell what we saw and experienced because we alone can speak for the millions whose voices were silenced forever. On these stressful occasions Fred suffered anguish by day and recurring nightmares by night, but he overcame his anxiety to tell his story.

Since then, he has often spoken to schoolchildren and students, but each time his hands shake and his stomach churns. The Holocaust denial industry has found a strong foothold in New Zealand and sometimes their adherents attend his talks to try and discredit him, arguing that what he lived through did not exist. Every time this happens, he is paralysed with anger and terrified of losing his composure.

'I get choked up when they try to bait me but I have to control it,' he says. 'Each time before I start, I remind myself why I'm doing this. My message is really about understanding and tolerance. I tell them that you don't have to love people but you have to respect them so we can all live together without discrimination. But that terror of being challenged, of not being believed, never leaves me.'

Whenever he speaks at schools, universities, churches and charity gatherings, he always begins by saying, 'I only speak for myself. I don't talk about politics or religion, or say one faith is better than another, I only tell my story. And please, don't look at me as if I'm a hero. I'm not a hero. I made it, that's all, but why, I have no idea. I wasn't clever or resourceful or prepared for anything that happened to me. I just lived from day to day. I didn't even believe in God then, but I do now.'

The man who reconnected with his faith in New Zealand became vice president of the synagogue and president of the Chevra Kadisha, the Jewish burial society. 'I feel guilty about resigning after sixteen years but I've had enough of burials, coping with grieving families and sitting up with the bereaved all night.' He still works part-time for an Auckland firm, Fletcher Challenge, purchasing stationery, organising personal cards for the executives and co-ordinating their monthly board meetings.

On the walls of his study hang plaques, certificates and awards. The chef's certificate he shows me with pride; the others I discover on my own. He is proud of the community service award from the City of Auckland for voluntary work counselling people at a citizens' advice bureau. 'I'm happy to put something back into the community that welcomed me so warmly fifty years ago when I arrived,' he says.

31

The woman who answered the phone sounded pleasantly detached but as soon as I explained my reason for calling, she became quite excited.

'The *Derna*?' she exclaimed. 'Was that the name of the ship I arrived on? I never knew. I was one year old at the time and I could never get my mother to talk about it.'

Like Fred Silberstein, Eva arrived in Auckland in 1948, with her mother Irene Abrahamsohn and grandmother Gretchen. I knew that Irene was the German doctor who had organised food for the babies on board, but finding this family proved difficult as they were not listed in the Auckland telephone directory.

Just as I was about to give up, one listing caught my eye. The name was slightly different but I decided to try it just in case they had anglicised the spelling. The man who answered the phone had a clipped New Zealand accent and a laconic manner. After a long pause, he said, 'Gretchen Abrahamsohn. That would have been my grandmother, but she died a long time ago. Her daughter would be my Aunty Irene, I suppose.' With a little prodding, he added, 'Irene is still alive but she's in a nursing home.' While I was visualising dementia, Alzheimers and the whole catastrophe, he elaborated, 'Irene's daughter Eva lives in Auckland but I'm not in touch with either of them.' After mentioning a family feud, he suggested I call his brother for Eva's phone number.

Although Eva is eager to help me, she is dubious about her mother's reaction.

'Mother is very sharp mentally but she's eighty-seven and has a very difficult personality. I never know from one day to the next what kind of mood she'll be in,' she says in her resonant youthful voice. 'Still, some days she's better than others. I'll tell her you'd like to meet her but how helpful she'll be, I don't know. She doesn't like talking about the past.'

On our way to the Onsdorp Retirement Village in Glendene the following afternoon, Eva confides that her mother is not enthusiastic about this meeting.

'So I don't know whether you'll be there for ten minutes, one hour, or whether Mother will talk to you at all. When I told her about you, her reaction was, "Why should I tell her my story? I want to write my own book about my life!" So I told her she wouldn't need to tell you anything if she didn't want to, because you'd tell her stories about the other passengers.' I can see that Eva has become skilful at dealing with her mother's moods.

A trained nurse who works part-time in a medical practice these days, Eva looks as young as she sounds. She is small and energetic with brown hair cropped into a fashionably wispy style, a snub nose and large eyes behind shiny glasses. As we walk into the retirement home she turns to me with another warning. 'You need to know that my mother is a bit of an intellectual snob.'

The sign on the door says 'Irene Valentine' so I assume she must have married in New Zealand. The woman who opens the door has cloud-white hair that curls around her face, alert dark eyes and a beautifully shaped tip-tilted nose, unusual in an old person. The walls are covered in paintings and sketches, photographs are stacked against the wall, the shelves display knick-knacks and memorabilia, and the books are by writers such as Goethe, Balzac and Elie Wiesel. As we exchange pleasantries, the sharp scrutiny in Irene's gaze softens when

Beatrice, her handsome tabby, pads in from the sunny courtyard and swishes her tail against our legs.

A moment later Irene swoops on a large black and white framed drawing and holds it up to show me. With a smile that reveals protruding front teeth, she asks, 'Do you know who drew this?' Across the table, Eva's amused expression denotes 'I told you so'. I feel like Calaf when confronted by the last riddle of Turandot. Having come this far, however, I'm anxious not to fail the final test. As I scan the drawing, eliminating artists one by one, at last the distinctive interlocking initials in the right-hand corner stir my memory. 'Albrecht Durer!' Irene Valentine is nodding restrained approval.

'So, do I pass?' I ask. We both know it's not a question.

Irene migrated to New Zealand in 1948 with one-year-old Eva and her mother Gretchen because her brother had settled here nine years earlier. He was a builder at a time when tradesmen were being recruited by the government and met their strict criteria for non-British immigrants, which enabled him to get out of Germany just in time. The family had lost touch with him during the war and Gretchen was convinced that her son had died, a perception that she wasn't able to dislodge from her mind even after he contacted them and sent them permits and money for their fares.

By then Gretchen Abrahamsohn had lived through fifteen years of persecution and hardship in Germany. Because she had married a Jew, she had to deal with the loss of their home, business and income throughout the Nazi era. They lived on starvation rations and if it hadn't been for the occasional secret charity of their neighbours, they would not have survived. Humiliated and depressed, her husband died of a heart attack in 1943, while Irene was barred from practising medicine. Mother and daughter lived through the terrifying bombing of Berlin when buildings shook and collapsed all around them. They had to scrounge among the ruins of the starving city for food and water during the occupation by Russian soldiers who looted and raped indiscriminately.

After the ten-week ordeal on the *Derna*, during which she had broken her leg, Gretchen finally limped onto the tarmac in New

Zealand to discover that her son, whom she hadn't seen for nine terrible years, had not come to the airport to meet them. To exacerbate her feeling of abandonment, she didn't have the money for their cab fare and had to ask her son to come out and pay the driver when they pulled up outside his home. Much later, Irene discovered that her brother had felt so overwhelmed by the responsibilities that this reunion entailed, that he had been unable to face them. He and his wife had three small children and were expecting their fourth, and he felt crushed by the prospect of having three more people under his crowded roof. But Gretchen never got over her anguish at being rejected by her son after travelling across the world to join him.

They hadn't been in New Zealand very long when Irene met her ship-mate Herta Birnbaum in Auckland, which they both considered provincial despite its pretty harbour setting. 'Let's drink a toast to our new life,' Irene suggested.

As they entered a pub, a row of men slouching at the bar swivelled around to stare. Nice girls wouldn't be seen dead in public bars, Irene was later told. She didn't know whether to laugh or cry at this strange place where bars closed at 6 pm and having a social drink was solely a male prerogative.

Life in New Zealand proved much tougher than Irene had imagined. It was obvious that they couldn't continue to stay at her brother's place, where they felt unwelcome. She had to earn a living as soon as possible, but to practise as a doctor she would have to study again. With no money, an increasingly distraught mother and a small daughter to support, she felt the problems were insurmountable. A hundred times a day she cursed the moment she had decided to leave Berlin.

'I was emotionally drained, physically exhausted and thoroughly miserable,' she says, stroking the tabby that has curled up in her lap. 'If I'd had the money for our fares, I would have gone straight back.' In her distress, the harsh conditions of post-war Berlin seemed preferable to the hardship she faced in New Zealand.

The medical faculty at the University of Otago in Dunedin accepted Irene as a student in 1949, but repeating her studies proved to be a relentless struggle. When she had studied in Germany during the 1930s, she was shunned by her fellow students because she was half-Jewish, but in Dunedin she was regarded with mistrust because she was German. In 1939, in line with public opinion in New Zealand which had been against enrolling refugees, the University of Otago had opposed admitting foreign doctors. Although they later repealed this decision, this conservative Scottish enclave in New Zealand's South Island was parochial and insular and its residents were not used to foreigners. Although Irene spoke English, most people regarded her as a German, unable to distinguish between the Germans who had supported the Nazi regime and those like her who had been victimised by it. For four long years, she felt like a sparrow trying to survive among a flock of ravens.

Eva sits forward while her mother speaks, straining to hear every word. Although Irene has forbidden me to use my tape recorder, occasionally I hear a muffled click from Eva's handbag and realise that she is recording stories that she has never heard before and may never hear again.

Studying again in a foreign country was only part of Irene's problem. To earn enough money to support the three of them, she had to take menial part-time jobs and found this degrading. When work was scarce, she rolled up her sleeves, baked German doughnuts and hawked them around on a bicycle. To me that sounds courageous, but to her it was demeaning. From her curt answers it's obvious that this was a period of her life she would prefer to forget.

'It takes all your energy and pride to keep going in a new country when you are regarded as an outsider. I should have returned to Germany instead of going through all that,' she repeats, clearly upset at the recollection of those years.

While Irene was studying, she realised that her mother had a severe psychiatric disorder. For years Gretchen had continued to cling to the delusion that her son had died, even after receiving his letters, and brooded incessantly over the fact that he hadn't come to meet them when they arrived. But as time went on, she became even more fixated and irrational. Whenever she saw a tall chimney, she became agitated, insisting that Jews were being incinerated inside. Finally Irene had no alternative but to place her in a psychiatric hospital. Gretchen Abrahamsohn died seven years after arriving in New Zealand, surrounded by nurses and patients with whom she was unable to communicate.

With her mother in hospital and unable to look after Eva, Irene was at her wits' end trying to study, work part-time and take care of her three year old. When she discussed her problem with one of the doctors at the university, he recommended a couple who were willing to look after a child. For the next six years, Eva lived with the Arnolds and became part of a loving family where she felt happy and secure.

Recalling the surname Valentine on the door, I wonder at what stage of her life she married, but Irene shakes her head. With her huge dark eyes and small features, Irene was a fetching young woman but she didn't trust men and never married. She changed her surname by deed poll but refuses to tell me why, although from her recollections I surmise that she wanted to cut loose from painful memories and alien connotations.

'I named myself after Valentin, an impoverished student in a Balzac story, because I could relate to him,' is her sole comment, along with the recommendation that I should read the book. After finishing her medical studies, she became a house surgeon in a geriatric hospital in Dunedin, and later worked as a GP in Waikato. 'I liked being a country doctor,' she says, 'but it was a twenty-four hour a day job and very poorly paid.'

Before I leave, Irene shows me a watercolour she has painted of a pretty country cottage at the end of a shimmering garden. It's the house outside Berlin where she once lived with her parents. Looking at it makes her reflective. 'In the end all you have left is the soil and the seasons. Whenever I go back to that village, I feel I've come home. It's hardly changed in all these years.' Given her distressing experiences in that house, I marvel at the way that nostalgia has brushed out the dark shadows and painted over them in brighter hues. As we say goodbye, Irene puts her arms around me. 'I want to give you a hug,' she says. 'I know I was meant to meet you.'

It's an irresistible autumn afternoon lacquered with a golden light and on the way back to the city, Eva makes a detour to show me St Heliers Bay. As we stroll along the wide promenade that skirts the water, she talks about her turbulent life. After living with her foster-parents for six happy years, she returned home from school one afternoon to find her foster-mother in bed. This was unheard of and she sensed at once that something was wrong. That night Eva was told to pack her things because her mother was coming to collect her in the morning.

'Just like that,' she says, shaking her head. 'No warning, no time to adjust. I was devastated. I'd become a real little Kiwi child living with my lovely, uncomplicated foster-parents, and suddenly I had to go and live with a woman I hardly knew, with her strange foreign ways and erratic personality.'

Musing about her adjustment to her new circumstances, she says, 'The only way I was able to cope was by keeping my distance and guarding my own space. I don't think the rift between us ever really healed. Too much time had elapsed and we were too different.

'My mother has been unhappy all her life. She has always been an outsider. I suppose it was hard being a single mother in New Zealand in the 1940s and 50s. She never affiliated with Jews, but she didn't mix with New Zealanders either. She didn't trust men in particular or people in general, and I grew up not trusting people either. I felt like an outsider too.'

As she drops in to the supermarket to buy something for her mother, she says, 'In some ways I've mothered her more than she's mothered me. When I was finishing high school, wondering what course to take, I had no one to discuss things with or get any encouragement from. I didn't even know I was capable of studying, so I did nursing. My mother was always working, always absorbed in herself. She didn't guide me.' An inveterate carer, by personality and profession, Eva takes good care of her mother. She visits almost every day, pays her bills, does her shopping and indulges her whims. 'Mother has become paranoid lately. Sometimes she thinks that people are after her, or that her phone is bugged. She won't talk on the phone any more.'

At the Mecca, one of the trendy little bistros that line the parade facing St Heliers Bay, we sip cappuccinos and discuss our lives. Eva met her Japanese husband Sam on a kibbutz in Israel. 'I went there to pick oranges. Not from any religious feeling because I had no Jewish or European orientation at all,' she says, 'I was brought up as a Kiwi child, remember? The funny thing is that I started seeing him because I was sure there was no future in our relationship, but we've been married for twenty-five years!' And we burst out laughing at the wonderful unpredictability of life.

As Eva and I share our life experiences, we tap a vein of common experiences.

'Do you feel you've made your own choices in life?' she suddenly asks. She has a refreshingly direct way of speaking about life that cuts through small talk and focuses on what really matters. Reflecting about herself, she says, 'I never made a fuss when I was growing up. I still don't make a fuss. I couldn't cope when my daughter Emma started acting out, but I suppose she was making up for me. I moved around so much from place to place and had so much uncertainty and anxiety in my life, I suppose I was hoping that by fitting in and being good I'd prevent more change.'

This seems a common pattern of behaviour for the children of the *Derna*. Like Eva I was also a child who made no fuss, hoping that by being docile and invisible, knitting in a corner and causing no trouble, I would protect myself from insecurity and my parents from any further distress.

As her mother never spoke about the voyage, Eva sits forward eagerly to hear what I have discovered. We talk about it all the way back to town and as we say goodbye, she asks, 'But how are you going to put all those stories together? That's what I'd like to know!'

32

'Oh my giddy aunt!' Nick Matussevich bursts out when I tell him why I'm calling. He was twelve when he came out on the *Derna* with his parents and seven siblings, and is so excited about my project that he immediately starts telling me stories about his family, firing my curiosity to fever pitch. As soon as I say that I intend to come to Auckland, true to traditional Russian hospitality, he invites me to stay at his home even though we've never met.

A number of passengers had mentioned the large Russian family on the ship. Elsie Pataky told me that there were eight children but by the time we reached Melbourne, the mother was pregnant again. Emil Kopel, one of the orphans in Dr Frant's group, reminisced about his shipboard romance with one of the daughters, the fetching Nina who wore her blonde hair braided on top of her head. Several months after our arrival, Emil was amazed to receive a telegram from Nina in New Zealand asking, with that flirtatious charm of hers, whether he was still interested or not. It sounded like a fascinating family but no one knew their surname.

Looking through the passenger list, I noticed a big family called Matussevich with first names that might have come straight out of a novel by Tolstoy. Since Emil had received the letter from New Zealand, I looked up the Auckland telephone directory and to my delight I found Nick.

When the Matussevich clan turned up at the flying boat base in Sydney on 6 November 1948, the booking clerk at Tasman Airways explained that there weren't enough vacant seats on the seaplane to accommodate them all. But when he suggested that they could travel to Auckland separately, Vasily Matussevich wouldn't hear of it. 'The family has stayed together all this time and we're not going to be split up now,' he declared. It was an ironic statement because within a short time his family would be broken up in a more tragic and irrevocable way than he could possibly have imagined.

When they all arrived together in Auckland one week later on 14 November 1948, they were met by representatives of the Red Cross and by a press photographer from the *New Zealand Herald*. The following day, when the readers opened the newspaper, they saw the whole Matussevich family. The striking mother, her smooth black hair parted in the centre above her straight eyebrows, wore short white socks and white sandshoes just like her daughters with their braided hair. In the front row stood Nick, a cheeky grin on his impish face. At the back, only his stern face showing, was their father, Vasily Matussevich.

All over the city, flags fluttered from mastheads and coloured bunting was draped over city shopfronts. 'After the reception we got at the airport, we thought that the flags were there to welcome us, but later we found out it was to celebrate the birth of Prince Charles!' Nick laughs.

I'm talking to him in his homely cottage at Beachhaven where every shelf, wall and surface is covered with souvenirs from past holidays, family photographs and assorted memorabilia. Nick has lost a few teeth over the years and his hair has turned white and receded from his high forehead, but when he laughs, his full mouth curls up in a disarming, puckish smile and I feel I'm looking at the lively tow-haired twelve year old he was on the *Derna*.

It rained the day they arrived in Auckland, and they spent the afternoon at the Civic Theatre in Queen Street to see the appropriately named movie, *Singin' in the Rain*. The three boys spent that night with their father at the YMCA in Wellesley Street, while the girls and their mother slept at the YWCA in Queen Street. The following day they caught the train to Tangawhahine to stay with their grandfather, whom the children had never met.

While they were still living at the DP camp in Austria, Olga Matussevich had discovered through the Red Cross that her father, Paul Gerabine, was living in New Zealand's North Island where he owned a farm. He had migrated there in the 1920s when the government enticed farmers with offers of 200 acres on a ninety-nine-year lease. With the assistance of the Red Cross, Olga's father brought his daughter and her family out to join him.

The Matusseviches were among the 5000 refugees accepted by New Zealand after the war. In 1945, a Dominion Population Committee had considered ways of increasing the country's population, which was then under two million. The government's policy was to restrict the number of displaced persons, while assisting British migrants, so that New Zealand would remain predominantly British.

The children had heard about their grandfather's farm and couldn't wait to ride the horses. Paul Gerabine was a resourceful man who wasn't afraid of getting his hands dirty. After fleeing from Russia, where he had been a diplomat in the time of the Romanovs, he opened an antique shop in London and later manufactured sweets. In New Zealand he cleared the property himself. It consisted mainly of low-lying land which turned into swamp when it rained, but the run-off from a hilly area enabled him to create a waterhole from which he obtained fresh water for the homestead he had built.

Nick gives a short laugh. 'I did get to ride a horse on Grandfather's property, but it was a draught horse, not the sleek thoroughbred I'd hoped for. We actually spent more time milking cows than riding horses. Grandfather ran a military-type operation and recorded everything meticulously in his notebook. What he bought, how much he paid, when a cow calved, which one was sold and for how much.'

Paul Gerabine was a big, broad-shouldered man with an erect bearing who didn't take any nonsense. Compared with him, Nick thought his strict parents seemed almost easy-going. 'But we weren't there very long, maybe only a week or two, because an argument blew up between my mother and him,' Nick recalls. 'She stormed off and said she didn't want to see him again as long as she lived. And she never did. When he died, she didn't go to his funeral.'

Many years passed before Nick found out why his mother had been mortally offended. When she was dying she told him that the argument had been about her own mother, who had stayed in Russia when her father left. By the time the Matussevich family arrived in New Zealand, Paul Gerabine had another family.

'When Mum asked him why he hadn't brought her mother out to New Zealand, he said she could have lived with him as his housekeeper. That's what made Mum so mad,' Nick explains. 'That created an argument with Dad, because he told her she should respect her father no matter what he said. Dad was very traditional in the way he treated women. Whenever they had friends over, he'd always insist on the men eating first and the women and children afterwards. I don't hold with that. My family all eat together,' he says and points to the photos of his four daughters on the wall. He's given them all Russian names: Maria Beryl, Helen Olga, Gail Galina and Tamara Dunya.

Shuffling over to the sideboard in his well-worn slippers, Nick brings me a photograph of a raven-haired young woman outside her parents' villa in St Petersburg before the Russian Revolution. Olga Matussevich's smooth hair is parted in the centre and pulled back severely from a striking face with arrow-straight black eyebrows, high cheekbones and a melancholy gaze. I can imagine her, haughty and remote, strolling around the estate with the borzoi hounds, or galloping over the steppes, her fur-trimmed cloak flying behind her. Hers is a haunting face that reminds me of Chekhov's wistful heroines, and I can understand why Vasily Matussevich couldn't get her out of his mind from the moment they met. Already at sixteen she had an air of lingering sadness, as if she had a presentiment of what life had in store.

Although she had resolved to have nothing more to do with her father, she told the children that he was their grandfather and that if he invited them, they should visit him. 'Sometimes I would bicycle over to the farm in the school holidays,' Nick recalls. 'I liked the old man but I don't recall ever seeing a smile on his face. After we moved to Dargaville, though, we lost touch.'

By the time Olga and Vasily's last child, Tanya, was born in July 1949, the family had moved north to Dargaville. To earn some money, their father went share-cropping and share-milking in Hikurangi, and later scrub-cutting at Kerakoponi. Unable to speak English, he was willing to tackle any physical work and knocked on farmhouse doors looking for fences to mend or scrub to clear. Nick often worked with his father, cutting down ti-tree to clear the land so the farmers could plant grass for pasture. It was pleasant working in the fresh air, and when they piled the wood and made big bonfires, the smell of eucalyptus in the air made them inhale deeply and close their eyes with pleasure. I can almost smell it myself as he describes it.

'We were scrub-cutting at Kerakopeni when it happened,' Nick says and the smile has gone from his cheerful face. 'It was a miserable wet Sunday morning when those two guys from the fish shop in town came to the farm. Ever since then, wet mornings have depressed me and still do to this day. "I'm sorry, Missus, but your son is no more," one of the men said. It was an odd way of putting it, but what's how it came out. They said something about a fishing accident.'

It took a long time for it to sink in that Olga's second son Alex, the mischievous one who made up for his short stature with high spirits, always skylarking and joking, the apple of her eye, was dead at fifteen. Distraught, she kept screaming those terrible words over and over again: 'Your son is no more! Your son is no more!'

'Dad was beside himself,' Nick recalls, 'but his English was so atrocious, he'd string a few German words together and think he was speaking English. He kept asking, "Wass is? Wass is?" and there was a terrible look in his eyes. When he finally understood, he lashed out at one of the men, and I'm telling you, he was ready to do them in. Then he jumped into the van, I jumped in the back, and he tore off to town so fast that I nearly flew over the top.'

Alex's death came at the end of a chain of events that had begun with Basil's accident, and that, according to Nick, had started with his own adolescent prank. 'I'd been watching through the window at my aunty getting dressed to go to a dance when my brother Basil caught me and clipped me across the ear for being a Peeping Tom. He was the serious one in the family. We started fighting but when Dad went after him, Basil climbed a tree so Dad wouldn't give him a hiding. While he was up there he fell and injured his back so badly that he had to go to hospital,' Nick says. 'So my prank backfired on me. If I hadn't been a Peeping Tom none of those terrible things would have happened, but I can't change the past. I have to live with it.'

Nick's prank was to have far-reaching repercussions. Basil had been working in the local fish shop, and after his accident he talked his brother Alex into replacing him until he was able to return to work. Alex was at high school at the time but was given permission to leave before the end of the school year because the family needed the income.

When the owners of the fish shop offered Alex one pound to go fishing with them in Whangarei Harbour one evening, he agreed. But the sea was rough that night and while the two men were below, either asleep or playing cards, Alex stayed up on deck alone. The coroner's verdict was accidental death: Alex had become sea-sick, had vomited and choked. There was some talk of an epileptic fit, but as he had never had one before, that did not seem probable.

White-faced and swaying on her feet, Olga Matussevich saw her beloved son's body laid out in the morgue, his clothes sodden with seawater.

'She never believed those two men and always suspected there was more to the story than they told her,' Nick says. 'She cursed them and put a hex on their families.'

The way things turned out, however, someone must have put a hex on the Matussevich family. Basil had initially been sent to the local hospital but when he developed bed sores requiring skin grafts, they transferred him to Auckland. He had just started walking gingerly on crutches, and spoke of becoming engaged to a nurse at the hospital, when he slipped and injured his back again. It was about this time that he found out what had happened to Alex.

The chain of events that linked Alex and Basil was to have an even more tragic outcome. Sensitive and withdrawn by nature, Basil blamed himself for his brother's death. If he hadn't asked Alex to stand in for him at the fish shop, Alex would still be alive. According to Nick, he was depressed by the prospect of more surgery on his back, brooded about the accident and felt he had let the family down. At the age of twenty Basil decided that living was too painful. He tied the sheets together and hanged himself.

'We survived the war and the bombing of Berlin, came to this peaceful country and within two months my parents had lost two sons and I'd lost both my brothers,' Nick sighs. 'Mother went crackers when she heard that Basil had hung himself in hospital. The eldest son is the kingpin in a Russian family. I don't think Mum and Dad ever recovered from the deaths of my brothers. They became bitter about New Zealand, blamed the country for the tragedies and wished they'd never come. Gradually the wounds healed, but the pain never went away. I wouldn't have been surprised if Mother had given up on life, withered and died.'

But Olga Matussevich was as resilient as the slender birch trees of her native land that bend in storms but do not break. Her face became more melancholy as she continued to devote herself to her family. Every year on Alex's birthday she would take down his toy plane from the top of a cupboard, wind up the motor and watch it circle around the room.

With the help of a Yugoslav friend who lent them the money for a deposit, the Matusseviches bought a tumbledown cottage in the quiet rural community at Awakino Point, three kilometres out of Dargaville, where they kept chickens. Vasily worked at Portland Cement Works through the week and on weekends he became the barman at the Northern Wairoa Hotel in Dargaville, where Nina worked at the telephone exchange. It was probably from there that she sent the telegram to her shipboard sweetheart Emil Kopel in Melbourne.

Olga, who began her privileged life in an aristocratic mansion with servants in St Petersburg and cantered around her parents' estate on an Arab pony given to her by the Shah of Persia, made the best of life in this sleepy country town at the other end of the world. She spent her time sewing and knitting clothes for her daughters and cooking the

Russian dishes they loved. She made her own butter because, like most Europeans, she preferred it unsalted and baked yeast cakes filled with cream cheese, raisins, poppyseed, honey and hazelnuts. The vision of their mother with flour all over her hands stayed with her children all their lives. At Christmas, she would bake the traditional Russian plaited bun with almonds and raisins, while their father bought them generous presents which, according to Nick, took him most of the year to pay off.

Although Nick did well at school and was awarded the school cup for English, he was always in trouble. 'Us boys were always skylarking,' he grins. 'There were lots of fights at school because when the other boys found out we were Russian, they started calling out "Bloody commies!" and I'd yell back, "Don't you dare call me a commie!" Sometimes I got the cane from the headmaster because I argued with my fists!'

As in Australia, there was widespread fear of Communists and 'pinkos' in New Zealand. Anti-Communist paranoia was fuelled by a growing number of strikes. Things came to a head in 1951 when there was violence on the wharves. The government declared a state of emergency from February to July and sent in the troops to load cargo. As Nick discovered, any mention of Russia or Russians provoked jeers and accusations.

Although he was always in the top half of the class, Nick didn't like school and left as soon as possible to become a share-milker's assistant. Occasionally he mended fences. As he grew older, conflict with his father increased. Always strict and watchful, Vasily Matussevich had become even more protective of Nick, who was now his only son.

'Dad was always checking on me: when I was coming home, what I was doing, who with and why. I had to answer to him all the time. If he didn't like what I said or did, he'd belt me.' As we sit in the cosy kitchen sipping scalding tea from our mugs, Nick is pensive. 'Dad was very strict, but looking back on it, I wouldn't have it any other way.'

His wife Beryl puts her head around the door, but disappears again, not wanting to disturb our conversation. When I ask how they met, he launches into the story with obvious enjoyment. 'One evening when I was going to the pictures, I "borrowed" a bike I saw in a garage, intending to return it. Next morning, I cleaned it up but just as I was putting it back the owner grabbed me. He called the constable who took me home and Dad gave me a hiding. Not long after that I met a girl at the skating rink in Auckland and we started going out. When she took me to meet her father, I nearly died of shock. It was the garage owner!' Nick shakes with laughter and Beryl, who has been standing in the hallway, laughs too.

'Dad was disappointed in me when I married Beryl in 1962 because he wanted me to marry a Russian girl,' Nick recalls. 'He said I'd let myself down. When we started having a family I got naturalised for the sake of the children, but he didn't like that either. He never got naturalised. "Oh, so you sold yourself!" he said. "How could I sell myself?" I said to him. "You brought me out here. I came with nothing and I've got nothing to sell!" He was also upset that I had four daughters and no sons, because that meant our name would die out. Dad never saw his native land from the time he left at sixteen, yet he stayed intensely Russian and Tsarist until the day he died. As it turned out, not one of us married a Russian.'

Nick tried a variety of jobs. 'Through my own stupidity I left school early and became a self-taught man, but I always liked doing things my own way,' he says. After two years in the processing plant of the Colonial Sugar Works, he worked as a storeman on the wharves. 'Jobs were so plentiful in those days you never had to worry, not like now,' he says. His next job was processing lead into sound-proofing at Dominion Lead Mills in Newmarket, where he melted lead ingots in heat that was over 700 degrees without a mask. Later they would pour the molten metal into huge moulds to make sheet lead for x-rays, sound-proofing, roofing and solder wire. 'It was worse than the engine room of the *Derna*!' he says. 'The red lead comes to the surface as fine dust and gets into your bloodstream.'

In time, Nick developed lead poisoning. 'I only found out about it when I went to donate blood at Auckland Hospital. "When was the last time you had a lead test done?" the nurse asked when I told her where I worked. I had no idea what she was talking about. I never knew I was supposed to have blood tests. Anyway it turned out I had over ten percent lead content in my blood instead of two percent. I felt lethargic, my bones ached like toothache and I was sleepy. They said if it rose to eleven percent I'd have to go into hospital. I had to drink a lot of water and stay away from work for three months. After that the level came down to four percent, but I had a family to support so they let me go back to work on condition that I kept a mask on and drank a pint of milk a day.'

After thirty years at the plant, Nick obtained a better job at an electronics firm but he didn't leave until he'd given proper notice. 'Be loyal to your company, don't take time off and don't abuse privileges — those are the principles my father drummed into me.' He gives a mischievous grin. 'But I have a spiteful streak. When the boss wouldn't come and have a drink with me at the farewell party after I'd spent thirty years working there, I took sandpaper and methylated spirits and removed all the markings I'd made on my machine, so the next guy wouldn't be able to use it!'

These days Nick still works as a storeman for the same electronics firm but at nights he cleans offices. 'It's hard to exist in New Zealand these days on one wage,' he says. 'My daughter Tammy moved to Sydney because she couldn't find work here.'

While Nick was processing lead, his father Vasily was working for Portland Cement, and later worked at a factory making salad oil. 'Language was Dad's problem,' Nick muses. 'He had the brains but never learned English properly. He was too dogmatic, drank like a fish and smoked like a chimney. When he had heart problems, the specialist gave him some medication but one day he just threw the tablets across the room and said he wasn't taking any more. Mum told him he was being foolish. That's when she started asserting herself. After all the years he'd been rough with her, she was getting her own back. Eventually Dad decided he would take the medicine, but it was too late by then. He died of emphysema in 1981, when he was seventy-nine. He had a hard life. For all his faults, I don't think I'd have liked Dad to be any other way.'

*   *   *

Five years later, the high-spirited Nina, who was everyone's favourite, died of leukaemia at the age of fifty-four. 'I've never seen such a transformation in a person from one week to the next,' Nick recalls. 'One Saturday I went to see her in hospital and she was talking and joking as usual, and the week after she was staring at the ceiling, no life in her at all, and a nurse was swabbing her mouth.' His voice becomes husky. 'I keep close to my sisters now.'

The following year, in 1987, his mother died of abdominal cancer at eighty-one. She had outlived three sons, but after Nina's death she seemed to lose the will to live. Her eldest daughter, Olga Brock, nursed her at home until the end.

Olga Brock still lives in the house that she and her late husband Bert built at Greenhithe forty-five years ago. It was sparsely populated then, with a few simple farmhouses, but today this is a thriving area of orchards and nurseries, increasingly sought-after by city dwellers who erect villas on the land.

Olga's lime-green cottage stands in a large garden of tall trees. When my taxi pulls up around the side of the house, she looks out of the back door, sees me getting out but goes quickly back inside and waits for me to go to the front door. Inside the house, birds chirp in a cage, posters of animals are stuck on the walls and memorabilia, papers and souvenirs are piled on couches and on the floor. Olga, in a neat print dress, has greying hair around a Slav face and a wary manner. Although she opens up while reminiscing about the voyage, as soon as I ask about her parents, she becomes tight-lipped. She can't understand why anyone would want to know about their lives and regards my questions as intrusive. From her reluctance to talk about her parents, I sense that she has inherited their mistrust of outsiders and the conviction that family matters should never be discussed outside the family circle. She seems fiercely loyal to her parents, determined to protect their privacy and guard their secrets.

With the inheritance he received after his parents died, Nick took his first overseas trip in 1988 and visited the Soviet Union. While in Leningrad, he discovered that his grandmother had died in 1941 during the Siege of Leningrad and was buried in one of the mass graves where thousands of dead bodies were found entwined after the frost had thawed. 'That visit made me realise that I belong to both countries,' he says. 'My roots are in the Soviet Union but my heart will always be in New Zealand.'

There are forty-nine members of the Matussevich clan today. 'When I look at my grandchildren today,' Nick reflects, 'I'd rather have what we had, than the way things are now. Values today are shot to pieces. We had more respect. If I had the chance of starting a family all over again, I don't know if I'd have a family.'

One windy spring morning in the year 2000, around the fifty-second anniversary of their arrival in New Zealand, Nick made a pilgrimage to Dargaville with his sisters Olga, Veronica and Anastasia. At Tangawhahine, their grandfather's homestead was still standing near the road leading to the railway line, which has been named Gerabine Road after him. Not far away, in the peaceful country cemetery where their grandfather and brothers lie buried, they pulled up the weeds and cleaned the tombstones while rabbits scampered around them and pheasants pecked the grass seeds. 'While tidying the graves, we talked to Basil and Alex and told them all about our lives,' Nick says. 'It felt as if they were very close to us.'

33

Harold Kapp hobbles out to the gate of his flat-roofed home in the Auckland suburb of Sandringham to greet me. 'I built this house myself in the fifties and made the garden,' he says in a strong Estonian accent. Beside the path are the rose beds which he has covered with wire meshing to stop the cat next door from digging them up.

Ushering me inside, Harold takes me on a tour of the house, pointing out the solid rimu archetraves, the mahogany table and chairs, and the sturdy sideboard he made with his own hands. There's a vase of fresh flowers in the bedroom. He has placed flowers beside his wife's bed every morning for the past five years, ever since she died. When he opens a drawer to show me the shirts and sweaters and singlets folded crisp-edged like exclusive merchandise in a designer boutique, I notice that two fingers on his right hand are missing. The result of an accident at work, he explains.

He's so pleased that I've come, he doesn't know what to do for me, and offers me a glass of wine although it's only ten o'clock in the morning. In the garden where rows of neatly planted flowers are soaking up the winter sunshine, he picks several feijoas and cuts one up for me, urging me to taste it. Its perfumed sweetness simultaneously attracts and repels me.

One year after his wife died, Harold had a knee replacement. He shows me his reconstructed knee, marvelling how the surgeon scraped away the bone and replaced it with a cap of nylon mesh and stainless steel. Ever since then he has kept to a very strict regime to avoid gaining weight.

'You must be very disciplined,' I comment.

'Oh yes!' he exclaims with a laugh. 'I have been in three military units! Estonian army for nine months, the Red army for one year and then in the Wehrmacht.'

Puffing because he is short of breath, he explains that he was wounded while fighting the Russians. 'I was sent to Narva with the Estonian division of the Wehrmacht, the Waffen SS. When the front retreated, I was wounded on 24 July 1944.' To illustrate, he pulls up his right trouser leg and shows me the holes in his calf. 'From shrapnel at Narva,' he says. They operated on him in the military hospital but he lost so much blood that they didn't expect him to survive and took him straight to the morgue, where he hovered between life and death for three days. 'But I didn't worry whether I'd survive or not,' he shrugs. 'It didn't matter at all. Whatever is coming, is coming. Like now. I'm an old man, eighty-two. If I die, I die. I have always been like that.'

When the war was over, Harold and some of his fellow soldiers tried to escape from the Russian zone. They travelled by night and hid by day so the Russians wouldn't see their Wehrmacht uniforms. Eventually he reached the American zone at Regensburg, where he found a job serving coffee to the American convoys.

After marrying Alide, an Estonian dressmaker, Harold realised that with his war record it would be dangerous to return to Estonia, so they decided to migrate to New Zealand where an old uncle of his had migrated during the 1920s. On board the *Derna* they befriended Elisabeth Meder and her son Lars, and the Maulics family, all of whom were going to New Zealand. Some years later, Harold Kapp and Lidija Maulics founded the Baltic Club in Auckland. Mrs Maulics, who had been a university lecturer in Latvia, was quoted in the *Argus* when the *Derna* docked in Melbourne, complaining about the number of Jews and Communists on board.

As we reminisce about the voyage, Harold leans forward. 'You know, there were a lot of young Jews on board — mostly Hungarian boys. They did make a lot of mess there.' He shakes his head in disapproval. 'They damaged the toilets, tore off the seats, broke the doors.' Knowing about the loose hinges, ill-fitting doors and shoddy plumbing in the washrooms when we left Marseilles, I'm wondering why he is blaming the orphans for their terrible state, when he adds in a conspiratorial tone, 'Those boys had concentration camp numbers on their arms but they were never in a concentration camp!'

With Fred Silberstein's tattooed arm still vivid in my mind, I find Harold's comment chilling. When I ask what makes him say that, he makes a dismissive motion with his maimed hand. 'People talked about it on the ship,' he replies with a finality that makes further discussion futile.

Ever since I began talking to the Baltic passengers, I had attempted to put aside my own preconceived ideas about their alliance with the Nazis. Gradually I had understood that as a result of their domination and repression by the Russians, they feared the Bolsheviks much as the Jews feared the Nazis. I could even accept that it was a marriage of convenience rather than a love match, and that they had slept with the Germans out of self-protection, not out of sympathy with their anti-Semitic policy.

But now, hearing someone who had fought with the Wehrmacht maligning the survivors of Nazi concentration camps stretches my tolerance almost to breaking point. I feel angry and choked up, and saddened too, because I realise that no matter what I say, I will not convince him. We hold onto the beliefs that support our perception of the world and our place in it, and facts are powerless against prejudice.

When Alide and Harold arrived in Auckland, it was an old-fashioned city of 280,000 people, most of whom lived in brick bungalows. What was called 'the city' consisted of a grid where few buildings rose higher than two storeys. Although the war had ended three years earlier, some foodstuffs as well as petrol were still rationed, and coupons were needed for meat and butter because much of New Zealand's butter and lamb was being sent to England, which created local shortages.

Harold felt reassured when his uncle pointed to a whole newspaper column of positions vacant for cabinet-makers. During his interview at Smith & Brown, Auckland's biggest furniture firm, his uncle did the talking.

'My nephew is a qualified furniture-maker, he has been trained to make an entire piece of furniture from the timber stack to the customer's home. He can work in assembly or in the machine shop, but he can't speak English yet,' he said.

The manager slapped his shoulder. 'That's perfect,' he said. 'Someone who can work and not talk!'

Harold started off earning nine pounds five shillings a week, which was a very good wage, but before long they were paying him well above award wages because they asked him to make prototypes. 'They worked very differently here,' he remarks. 'In Estonia a cabinet-maker had to do everything from assembly work to machine shop and French polishing, but here every aspect of the operation was kept separate.'

When an Estonian friend offered to lend him 1400 pounds, he jumped at the opportunity to buy a place of their own on Marlborough Road, much closer to the city. With his wages from the furniture factory, and the wedding and confirmation dresses that Alide made, they paid the house off in five years and borrowed again to buy a 1954 Hillman, which became their pride and joy.

By then Harold had teamed up with another Estonian and opened the Contemporary Furniture Factory at Mt Roskill. Thanks to Harold's expertise, they became so successful that before long they supplied shops all over New Zealand and had orders for several months ahead, but eventually the partnership broke up.

Seeing an opportunity to buy a quarter-acre lot, the Kapps borrowed 900 pounds from their friends and built the home in Sandringham where Harold lives to this day. By then they had been married for ten years, but were still childless. When tests showed that Harold had a low sperm count, they decided to adopt a baby. The first child they were offered died in hospital, the second they refused because he was dark-skinned while they were both fair, but the third time round they were delighted when a healthy white baby boy became available. Alide bought a baby bath, bassinet and pram, attended classes to learn how to take care of a baby, and two weeks later they brought little Arvo home.

At first everything went smoothly. Harold points to a photo on the shelf behind him of a smiling little boy with smoothly brushed hair, beside a photograph of his wife. 'When Arvo was two or three years old, he started having nightmares,' he recalls. 'He often walked in his sleep and sometimes I would wake up to see him standing beside our bed. He didn't make a sound but I always knew he was there. I would take him back to his cot, but he would come out again. Something was wrong with him.'

At school the boy couldn't keep up with his classmates and the teachers described him as lazy and absent-minded. Whatever the reason, his mind was always far away and he couldn't take things in. Whenever Alide cut sandwiches at the school tuck shop, she was upset when the other mothers talked about their children's homework, because Arvo always told her he didn't have any. When she took him for a professional assessment, the psychologist failed to diagnose the problem.

With his poor scholastic record, studying was out of the question, but Arvo refused to learn a trade and became the mail boy at Amalgamated Theatres instead. When he packed his bag one Friday night and said goodbye to his parents, they thought he was going on a tramping excursion with the scouts, but on Monday morning his boss rang to ask whether Arvo was sick because he hadn't turned up at work. Harold and Alide were shocked. They had no idea where he was.

He stayed away for fourteen months. 'He sent us one postcard from Wanganui to say he wasn't coming home any more,' Harold says in his quiet, even way. 'My wife was upset but she had been upset with him for a long time. They didn't get on. He did come back for a while, but later went away again. Once he came to see me when he knew she was away, but otherwise we hardly heard from him.

'When I went to the South Island for a holiday in 1981, I looked him up,' Harold says. 'I thought maybe being adopted was part of his problem so I asked if he'd like to find out who his parents were, perhaps he wanted to contact them. His reaction was, "They gave me away and didn't look for me all these years, so why should I look for them?" '

His adopted son came to see him once after his mother's death. 'He was very agitated that time. He used terrible language, swore at me, called me names and threw a cup of coffee across the room.'

Harold sighs. 'In spite of all the problems, I still regard him as my son and when I die I'll make sure he is provided for. For his last birthday I sent him a pair of shorts, a shirt and some underwear. He never writes, but last September he sent me a card in shaky handwriting, probably because of the medication he takes. That was the first Father's Day card he ever sent me.'

34

As the *Spirit of Progress* rattled along the rails from Melbourne to Sydney in November 1948, Lars Meder sat beside his mother, his freckled nose pressed against the window as he took in the parched countryside, so different from the summery greenness of Estonia. As soon as they walked out of Sydney's Central station, he smelled the sourish odour of hops in the air. Pointing to a sign on top of the building facing the station, he asked his mother what it meant. Although Elisabeth Meder spoke fluent English, 'Tooheys' was one word she had never come across, but for once consulting her dictionary didn't help. As Lars laughs about this word which no longer needs translating, I'm intrigued by the selectiveness of memory. After fifty years, this is what he remembers of his first glimpse of Sydney.

Along with other passengers destined for New Zealand, including Alide and Harold Kapp, Lars and his mother had come to Sydney to take the *Wanganella* ferry to Auckland. In view of Lars's later career, however, it was a stroke of luck that the ferry had recently run aground. With the *Wanganella* out of commission, the only way of making the trans-Tasman crossing was by flying boat. As the pontoon wobbled and swayed under their feet, Lars could hardly wait to climb into the aircraft. The doors slammed shut, the pilot clambered into the cockpit, adjusted his earphones and revved the motor to a deafening roar. The whole cabin shuddered so violently that Lars wondered whether the plane was going to fall apart. Then they were off, the water spraying up above the windows on both sides. Lars had never heard of a flying boat, and as it sped off in the water, skimming the waves, he wondered whether it would hurtle across the sea all the way to New Zealand. Suddenly there was a surge of power and the horizon tilted as they took flight. Lars wanted to whoop with joy as they rose above the city and into the clouds.

'That was my first taste of flying and it affected my whole life,' he smiles. 'Until then I wanted to become an engine driver, but from that moment I knew I'd become a pilot. Although I've retired, I'm still flying, but only part-time these days.'

We are talking at Lars's home at Takapuna, with his older brother Jens who migrated to New Zealand after the rest of the family. It's an easy walk to the beach and the sprawling shopping centres that have replaced the simple corner shops with their white bread, Amber Tips tea and Chesdale cheese where Elisabeth Meder shopped over fifty years ago. The modern townhouse is bright and inviting with vivid prints on the walls and stylish furniture that wouldn't look out of place in a home decorating magazine. From the large family photograph on the wall, I can see that his two dark-haired daughters take after their attractive mother. 'My wife is one-eighth Maori and English,' Lars says.

Lars has a friendly, laid-back manner that puts me immediately at ease. The reddish hair has thinned out now and his face has become rounder, but he still has the placid personality he had as a twelve year old on the *Derna*. As he talks, I realise that he is the first of the passengers I have met in New Zealand whose life seems to have unfolded smoothly, without stress or tragedy.

Our conversation is frequently interrupted by telephone calls for his wife and daughters, and in between answering the phone and relaying messages in his good-natured way, Lars reminisces about his arrival in Auckland. After seven exhilarating hours in the air, the flying boat taxied to the pontoon and as they peered through the water-streaked window, his mother suddenly pointed, 'Look! There's your father!'

All that Lars knew about New Zealand was from the postage stamps and parcels that his father sent them in Germany, but he didn't remember his father at all. After Captain Meder's ship had been torpedoed between Portugal and England at the beginning of the war, his mother had let everyone believe that he had died along with most of the crew, so the Russians wouldn't come looking for him. She never talked about him to Lars in case he let something slip, and it wasn't until after the war was over that he discovered his father was alive and working in the merchant marine in Canada, and that they would all meet again in New Zealand.

While Lars is taking another message for his daughter, Jens resumes the story. 'Our grandparents lost everything in World War I, and our parents lost everything in World War II, so Father had enough of Europe,' he says. Several years older than his brother, Jens combs his white hair straight back from his ruddy face and speaks in a booming voice with a strong Estonian accent.

Their father had chosen New Zealand because of its progressive social welfare legislation, which had been widely reported in Estonian newspapers before the war. During the 1930s, the Labor government had introduced visionary reforms that provided New Zealanders with pensions and allowances covering unemployment, sickness, poverty and old age. Families received benefits of one pound per week, school children were given dental care and free milk and there was a public housing program. A country with a government that protected its citizens from womb to tomb seemed the ideal place to live.

Unlike other children from the *Derna* who found it difficult to adjust to living with fathers they didn't know, Lars and his father were friends from the beginning. As New Zealand did not recognise his maritime qualifications, instead of studying again, Lars's father bought a thirty-two-foot launch, converted it into a fishing trawler and made a good living in waters that teemed with snapper and flounder. In the mid-1950s he capitalised on the demand for shark. 'The wealth was actually in the shark liver which was processed into pharmaceuticals, vitamins and cosmetics,' Lars recalls. 'Dad only had room for forty shark carcasses on board and when his two forty-four-gallon drums were full of shark liver, he had to jettison the carcasses.'

With the income from fishing, the Meders were able to buy a four-bedroom home in Herne Bay Road which Lars's practical mother helped to pay off by renting out two rooms for Bed & Breakfast. But the shark bonanza ended abruptly in the 1960s when traces of mercury were found in the shark meat.

There was no bigger treat for Lars than going out with his father on the boat. 'I always knew that we'd have an adventure, or meet some colourful characters who told better stories than I read in my books. My father had a gift for striking up friendships with hermits, prospectors and old sailors. I remember an old recluse in Coromandel who started off my collection of Maori artifacts with a Maori axe.'

Although most of his memories are pleasant, there was one terrifying night he cannot forget. 'We anchored in the usual place in the Coromandel Peninsula and everything seemed normal, but after a few hours we heard what sounded like thunder. It was water, rushing with a power I'd never seen before. For some reason, the tide had suddenly changed and the current was so strong that we drifted for miles until we finally ran aground. Usually a tide takes six hours to go out, but this time it only took forty minutes. Imagine the power! On the way we picked up a lot of flotsam and jetsam, and got dragged out to sea with a huge log stuck in our bow. Even by daybreak the tide hadn't returned to normal. When we got back we found out that there had been a massive earthquake in Chile and that's what had caused this freak tidal wave.'

While Lars answers the phone yet again, Jens, who owns a chain of bakeries, expounds on his own economic theory. 'I thought about it for a long time and discovered that it's not hard work, but saving and investing that creates wealth. If everyone was induced to save money and buy their own home, there would be no more Communism, because people with assets don't become Communists,' Jens says in his forceful way. He has retained his antipathy towards Communism even after the Soviet Union has disintegrated and the Communists have been overthrown.

Lars puts down the receiver and with a nostalgic smile recalls his school days, golden days that stretched through endless summers. As I listen to this affable man, I cannot help thinking that personality dictates destiny. It can't just be chance that has made his life so uncomplicated. At Bayview Primary School, the teachers and pupils were kind and the worst thing he remembers is that some of his school buddies who were assigned to teach him English taught him swear words instead, which aroused consternation among the teachers but hysterical giggling among the boys. Life was a wonderful adventure spent chasing each other along Herne Bay Beach, splashing in Cox's Creek, diving off Ponsonby Wharf and racing each other in the Shelly Beach swimming pool.

The longing to become a pilot, which began with that flight on the flying boat, persisted throughout his school days. While at Mt Albert Grammar School, Lars joined the air cadet corps, but to his disappointment they stopped flying lessons before he had time to learn. Undaunted, he resolved to pay for the lessons himself. He gave up his Sundays and rose early on Monday and Friday mornings before school and ran to the bakery where he rolled dough, cut out doughnuts, scrubbed the bowls and cleaned the benchtops, until he saved enough for Saturday's flying lesson.

'I joined the Auckland Aero Club, got my commercial pilot's licence in December 1960, and I've been flying ever since,' he beams. 'When I started off, the airline was called the National Airways Corporation, but it later became affiliated with Air New Zealand.' After being obliged to retire at fifty-five, he started flying for EVA Air, the Taiwanese airline. 'When I turned sixty, I had to retire from EVA Air as well, but I missed flying, so now I fly with Air Pacific as a co-pilot. The ego thing doesn't worry me. I don't have to be the captain, I just love flying,' he says. 'But when I turn sixty-three I'll definitely retire. I'll spend most of my time sailing and fishing.'

35

Stepping onto the small platform at North Geelong station, I wonder how I will recognise Pauline Seitz, but before I have time to look around, a tall, big-boned woman in loose-cut slacks with a string of large beads around her neck strides towards me with a big smile. Even before we've introduced ourselves she wraps her arms around me in a hug, and we walk along the street chatting like old friends.

Pauline contacted me several months before to say that she had also arrived on the *Derna* as a child. I assumed that she was calling in response to the notices I had placed in ethnic newspapers and on radio programs, but as it turned out, she knew nothing about my search for passengers. Her curiosity had been aroused by an article I had written about the fiftieth anniversary of the arrival of post-war migrant ships, and she had done some impressive detective work to track me down.

Thanks to her tenacity, the story I got to hear was a multicultural saga that included Germans and Russians and spanned the Caucasus, Iran and Germany. Like Lars Meder, Pauline had also crossed the seas with her mother to join a father she didn't know. Being of German origin, he had been deported from Teheran by the British as an enemy alien in 1941 and sent to an internment camp in Australia. Pauline was ten days old at the time, and neither she nor her mother had seen him from that day until they arrived in Australia seven years later.

Now, in Geelong, as we turn into a street of old-fashioned cottages surrounded by picket fences and step into her front garden, she says, 'Isn't it amazing to think that you and I must have seen each other on the *Derna*? Maybe we even played together. And here we are, meeting again after all these years!' Although we don't recall ever playing together, the idea surprises and intrigues me. I have been so focused on the other passengers that I have forgotten to include myself among them. Perhaps this is the underlying motive for my search. By probing into the past, am I attempting to recover the serious little girl with brown plaits who spent the voyage watching and knitting?

In Pauline's country garden we step over clumps of forget-me-nots, patches of lettuce and a lone artichoke plant and enter the sunny sitting room where her tabby Firouz is asleep on the couch. On the bookshelf stand two carved wooden elephants, one of which has lost a tusk. 'Remember Colombo?' Pauline exclaims. 'That's where Mother and I bought those carvings.'

A few minutes later her mother arrives and immediately the room becomes charged with energy. Vala, who also lives in Geelong, is a born storyteller and launches into a lively account of her convent days in Teheran. She embellishes the anecdotes with her flair for drama, pausing for effect at just the right moment and leaping to her feet to mimic the admonitions of the nuns and the swishing gait of the mother superior up the stairs. It's a virtuoso performance that has me hanging on every word. Even Pauline, who must have heard it a hundred times, listens with rapt attention.

'You can tell I always wanted to go on the stage!' Vala exclaims, and mother and daughter go into peals of laughter.

While Pauline pours us strong coffee and slices her freshly baked apple cake, Vala describes an incident in Ankara when the German politician von Ribbentrop arrived to visit the women being repatriated to Germany. She has an excellent command of English and speaks with the careful enunciation of those who have learned it as a foreign language.

'Von Ribbentrop asked to see the youngest child in our transport, you see, and that was Pauline, so he bent down and kissed her hand!'

Pauline is laughing so much that she has to put down the coffee jug. 'I'm not game to tell my Jewish friends about that!' she says.

Now Vala is reminiscing about the journey to Germany which dragged on for two months. Waving her smooth, soft hand towards Pauline, she says, 'When I was finally able to give her a bath, I didn't recognise my own child. I thought she had dark hair! Do you remember?'

Pauline rolls her eyes. 'How could I? I was one month old!'

As we chat about the voyage, Vala riffles in her handbag and takes out the yellowed telegram that she received in Germany from the Australian Immigration Department, informing her about their passage on the *Derna*. Taking out a compact to check her pink lipstick, she frowns at her reflection. 'I look as if I've just come off the *Derna*!' Now we're all laughing because her pretty face and creamy complexion belie her self-criticism.

The day she did come off the *Derna*, they flew to Brisbane to meet her husband. Viktor had moved there with his father after they were released from the internment camp at Tatura when the war ended. As the Australian National Airways plane taxied towards the airport building, Vala, who until that moment had been chattering non-stop, became very quiet. She was scanning the group on the tarmac.

Following her mother's gaze, Pauline craned forward. 'Which one is it?' she asked.

Vala's heart was thumping as she pointed to a solidly built man with dark hair. In a choked voice she said, 'That's him!'

Meetings after many years of separation are overloaded with exhilaration, tension and disappointment. So much hope and longing are concentrated on an event that often collapses under its emotional burden. The joy of regaining a husband and no longer having to struggle alone is soon counterbalanced by the loss of freedom and independence. The reunion is a gossamer-fine bridge across a chasm of unshared experiences.

You cannot cross the same river twice, nor meet the same person at the end of a long and difficult separation. Vala was no longer the dependent young wife she had been in Teheran in 1941. In the past seven years she had taken care of a tiny baby during their frightening journey to Ankara and during four years of exile in a foreign country. She had survived the privations of the war and the terror of Allied bombing, supported them after the war, and crossed the oceans, spurred on by the dream of being reunited with the man she loved.

But after having been deported to a country at the other end of the world, interned in a camp for aliens and regarded as an enemy, Viktor had also changed. The witty, sophisticated older man who had swept her off her feet and made her laugh when she was an impressionable young girl with no experience of life or knowledge of her own strength, was now a reserved man whose conversations were punctuated by silences.

But in one respect he had not altered, and that was his conviction that the man was head of the family. If Vala found it difficult to defer to Viktor again, Pauline, who had never known her father, found the adjustment even harder. For the first time in her life she did not have her mother's undivided attention, and had to take orders from someone else. A bright, strong-willed child, she found the situation intolerable and distanced herself from it emotionally.

'I saw it as an intrusion in my life and just shut down,' is the way she explains it now. 'To give you an example, I persisted in using the feminine form of adjectives even when I referred to my father, as though I didn't acknowledge his role in the family.'

After the exciting position Vala had held at UNRRA in Germany, where her work had been highly regarded, becoming a Brisbane housewife was a demotion. She disliked this tropical city where the pavements sizzled with such heat that it dried the breath out of her body. To make matters worse, she had no friends and missed the sophisticated people she had known in Munich. She became depressed and lost weight.

Pauline was unhappy too. She hated the house in the inner city suburb of West End where she slept in the narrow sleep-out, detested the gloomy furniture with the bowl of waxed fruit on the dining table, and often vomited after meals. Today a psychologist would say that she was disturbed by the major life changes she had experienced, but in 1948 there was no vocabulary to express emotional turmoil and no patience to delve into the reasons.

'I was terrified of my father,' she recalls as we sit around the oak table in her rustic dining room while she serves paprika chicken casserole from an earthenware dish. 'He seemed so large and so powerful. He was actually the first authority figure I'd ever experienced and he came between my mother and me. I suppose it must have been difficult for him too, because he had no idea how to win me over.'

Pauline was the only foreign child at her primary school, a uniqueness she enjoyed. 'All the foreigners were referred to as Balts, so the kids called you a Nut and Balt no matter where you came from. Sometimes they called me German Sausage or Citroen Front-wheel Drive. I had no idea what they were talking about but it didn't upset me. It was just something they chanted. I felt different, but in a positive way because I got a lot of attention. I was a pretty feisty kid and if someone teased me, I gave as good as I got. We used to barter sandwiches. I always wanted their lettuce and vegemite, but when my mother helped out at the tuck shop, everyone wanted her rich Russian pastries.'

A devoted teacher called Miss McBride made it her task to help Pauline learn English. 'Every playtime and lunchtime she would take me aside and drill me in grammatical English,' Pauline recalls. 'If she ever heard me saying "youse" in the yard, she'd haul me inside and correct me. I started imitating her and ended up with an English accent!'

While Pauline was adjusting to life in Brisbane, her father was demoralised because he couldn't find work as an engineer. He pottered in the shed at the back of the house making furniture, but couldn't see any future for himself. Halfway through 1949, he received a letter from a friend in Geelong urging him to move there because with two big local factories, Ford and International Harvesters, there were plenty of employment opportunities. Vala couldn't pack fast enough.

Geelong in 1948 was an insular town where people swivelled their heads in shock whenever they heard Vala and Viktor speaking Russian or German. Foreigners were still a novelty and the ABC Café was the local version of a restaurant. The Italian fruit shop was the only shop that stocked garlic, but the greengrocer kept it under the counter because only reffos ate it. Vala gives a deep-throated laugh. 'In those days Australia was divided into two groups of people: those who ate garlic and salami and those who didn't!'

Life was grim that first year in Geelong. Although Viktor obtained work in the Ford factory which was producing cars to compete with the popular new Holdens rolling off the assembly line at GMH in Melbourne, he was despondent. The war had interrupted his engineering career in Teheran and brought him to Australia to become a factory labourer. Vala, who spent her days typing invoices in the office of International Harvesters, was upset for her husband but tried to console herself that at least they were a family again and Pauline had a father.

While scanning the employment notices in the newspaper one day, Viktor saw that the Geelong Water Works and Sewerage Trust were looking for an engineer able to use a theodolite. He applied with some trepidation because he had no documents to prove his qualifications, but they employed him and in time he became the site engineer on the West Bowen dam. Having a well-paid, responsible position commensurate with his skills restored his self-respect.

Things improved for Vala too. When the girls high school advertised for a secretary, her engaging personality, along with the glowing references from UNRRA, helped her get the job. Some time later, when the headmistress decided to introduce French classes, Vala became the obvious choice because she had learned the language from the French nuns in Teheran.

In the meantime, Pauline and her father were beginning to understand each other. 'As it happened, we had similar personalities,' she says. 'We were both thinkers who worked things out logically in our heads.' Viktor's way of relating was to give her books and show her how to do practical things. How to eat a mango over the bath to avoid staining your clothes, how to solve mathematical problems. He was delighted when she asked for a small carpentry set for her birthday because it was something they could do together. 'I was a tomboy who could out-throw, out-run and out-hit everyone in my class. Even the boys were so impressed that they used to ask me to play in the footy team!' she laughs.

If she felt like an outsider at times, it was because, apart from her grandfather, she had no extended family, while the other children had grandparents, aunts, uncles, cousins and a shared past in Geelong.

'I adored Grandpa, he was exactly what a grandfather should be,' she says. 'His hobby was French polishing. I loved sitting under our grand piano while he was polishing with bags of shellac all around him. He polished everything, even apples, and whenever I went somewhere special, he would polish my shoes. I was devastated when he died.'

Throughout her school life, Pauline's parents insisted that education and knowledge were all that mattered. 'There was no pressure on me to get married, but relentless pressure to study,' she recalls.

Suddenly Vala chimes in proudly, 'Pauline was the first foreign girl to be head prefect at her high school. I was there when the headmistress announced it to the whole school!'

Although Vala's shipboard companion Nadezhda Alexandrovna Metschersky had settled in Sydney, the two women continued to correspond. The elderly Russian aristocrat, whom Vala still calls *Kniginia* or Princess, was living with her daughter Madame de Vignal and her family in Chatswood. Vala visited her on one occasion and still remembers the elegant furniture, palatial staircase and tastefully planted garden in Madame de Vignal's home. From the wide terrace that was draped with sweet-scented wisteria, they gazed over the whole city and talked about their lives. 'The *Kniginia* was very contented with life in Australia,' Vala says.

While in Sydney, Vala took the opportunity to attend a service conducted by Archbishop Rafalsky, who had recently been appointed archbishop of the Russian Orthodox diocese of Australia and New Zealand. The service was held at the new St Peter and Paul Cathedral in Strathfield, which was his achievement. Apart from his phenomenal knowledge of theology, philosophy and music, the archbishop also had a practical mind and a talent for enlisting people's help. Without any prior experience, he organised building the cathedral which was completed within one year. That same year, 1953, he was awarded the Queen's Coronation medal for helping Russian and Eastern European refugees settle in Australia.

While Pauline spoons apples and nectarines spiced with cardamom into our dessert dishes, Vala reminisces about the last time she saw the archbishop. 'He was such an exceptional human being, such a saintly man, that just being in his presence was enough to move me to tears,' she says. From my conversation with Archbishop Rafalsky's biographer, Father Michael Protopopoff, I know that the entire congregation felt the same way. Whenever he raised his arms to heaven in supplication, it seemed as though he was speaking directly to God. They almost expected the Creator to step through the ceiling and arrive in their midst on a shaft of light. Blowing her nose, Vala says, 'When the archbishop looked at you, he looked into your soul.'

Archbishop Rafalsky was fifty-nine when he told his tearful congregation that he felt strangely light, as though he was no longer of this world. After conducting his last service, he said, 'I will never come this way again,' and tears ran down his gaunt cheeks. He died two days later of coronary complications and was buried in the churchyard of the cathedral that remains his monument to this day.

When Vala goes to services at the Russian Orthodox church in Geelong, which she helped to found, she always brings her precious prayerbook with the archbishop's signature on the flyleaf. And Pauline still carries around the holy picture he gave her when she was a little girl on the *Derna*. It's frayed now, but she keeps it as a talisman. 'I'm not religious, but the picture is very special to me because it's a memento of him,' she says.

Vala has brightened up. 'When I went back to Teheran in 1967, I visited my old convent school and you wouldn't believe it, they still had the landscape of the Caspian Sea hanging on the wall of my old classroom! The same picture! When I went to see my old ballet teacher from St Petersburg, in the hall with big mirrors where I used to practise, she still wore the same wide bandeau on her forehead. She burst into tears when she recognised me. It was so moving.'

Teheran had changed enormously in the past twenty-six years, but one ancient street was just as they remembered it from their courting days. 'Viktor and I couldn't believe it. We walked along holding hands and not saying a single word. It was like stepping back in time. We didn't want to break the spell of all the memories around us.'

Vala didn't realise how attached she had become to Australia until they returned from that trip. 'Viktor was restless and found it hard to settle down again, but I knew I belonged here. When one of our Russian friends made a disparaging remark about this being an island of convicts — well, did I let him have it! I told him he knew nothing about it: that the first Australians were dumped here against their will, that they didn't want to be here away from their families, and they had to work so hard to build things and make things grow. I went into full dramatic flight and when I finally ran out of breath, they all applauded!'

It took an overseas trip to London in the 1960s for Pauline to realise that Australia was home as well. By then she had gained a BA degree from Monash University, majoring in French, Russian and politics. 'Studying politics seemed to be an extension of dinner table arguments at home,' Pauline smiles. 'After every news broadcast there was a family row, but I learned to stand my ground. Father and I argued fiercely, but we were similar in many ways and that's probably why we clashed so much. As I got older, we became drinking and debating buddies. Father was very much his own person, not sociable and sunny like Mother. I'm more like him: outwardly gregarious but reserved. I like my own company, whereas Mother makes friends everywhere.'

After Pauline graduated, she had no idea what work she would do. 'All I knew was that I was never going to teach.' This makes me smile, because that's exactly what I said when I finished my Arts degree, but when my husband Michael and I were living in London, I discovered the joy of teaching students and learning from them in turn, just as Pauline eventually did.

In 1971 she was appointed Director of Schools and Conferences at the Council of Adult Education. 'I didn't have a clue what the job involved, but I learned as I went along and enjoyed it. I was responsible for organising short-term activities, summer schools, seminars, conferences, study tours within Australia. That job was a major turning point in my life because I found my niche in adult education.'

Three years later she was sent to Edinburgh University to do a postgraduate diploma in adult education, but after her return, she felt restless as there didn't seem to be much scope for applying the exciting new ideas she had been studying. That's when she joined the Hawthorn State College, a teacher-training institute in the TAFE system, and found her passion in the very thing she had declared she would never do. 'Adult education was burgeoning at the time, there were new ideas in the air, new attitudes about teaching adults and giving people a second chance. It was exciting.'

Pauline distinguished herself by becoming the first female president of the Australian Association of Adult Education. 'It was just the right time to be in adult education. Whitlam was in power and reform was in the air. But it all petered out by the time I left. The classes were getting bigger, the staff was smaller, courses were collapsing and morale was plummeting. Maybe it always goes like this, in cycles, and perhaps this year's graduates will be saying the same in time. But after seventeen years, I was ready to retire.'

Not long after Viktor's death from lung cancer in 1979, Pauline made her first trip to Russia. Her tour included Tbilisi, where her father's family had lived before moving to Teheran. 'Dad used to describe the foothills of the Caucasus Mountains in spring, the colourful markets and the Georgian Military Highway that crossed the whole country, so it was familiar and unreal all at once, and very emotional. I liked the Georgians and felt happy that this place was part of my heritage, but my father and I had always planned to go there together and it was sad to be there without him.'

36

Albury is a sunny university town on the border of New South Wales and Victoria with well-kept gardens and an air of bustling energy. I've come here to talk to Mattie Veneris. Like Lars and Pauline, she sailed to Australia with her mother, her sister Katina and cousins John and Stan in 1948 to join her father who hadn't seen her since she was a baby.

Mattie's grey-haired husband George meets me at the little airport. As we drive along the sunlit streets lined with gum trees, he tells me that he and Mattie lived in neighbouring villages on the Greek island of Kythera and have known each other all their lives. He is the president of Albury's Greek community, which consists of about eighty families. They are currently raising money to build a house for a resident priest because at the moment he comes only once a month from Sydney.

'It's not just a matter of religion,' George says. 'It's to keep the community together and maintain our heritage and traditions for future generations. The young people are growing up in a more permissive environment, so it's harder to keep them involved.' It's a problem all minority groups face in a tolerant community.

Mattie is standing outside their little brick bungalow when we arrive and welcomes me with a beatific smile that lights up her face. She is as thin as a winter sparrow and just as unassuming, apologising for the smell of estapol in the house because their floors are being sanded and polished. As she leads me inside, she explains that her mother couldn't come because she didn't want to leave her sick ninety-year-old husband.

In their dining room, in pride of place on top of the sideboard, stands a photograph of a venerable Greek Orthodox priest with a long white beard and black vestments.

'That's Uncle Serafim who left home one day and wasn't heard of again until he became the abbot of an ancient monastery outside Jerusalem,' she says softly in the distinctively Greek accent with its elongated diphthongs. Byzantine icons with mournful faces hang on the walls, imbuing the home with an aura of spirituality.

A few moments later, Mattie whips out an album and points to an old photograph. 'This was our Greek group on the *Derna*,' she says. As I scan the faces, she points to a pretty little girl with a shy expression in the front row. 'That's me,' she says. 'And that girl on my right is the one I used to play with, but I can't remember her name. She was travelling with two sisters and an older brother.'

'Was it Vassiliki Fatseas?' I ask. Mattie claps her hands delightedly, amazed that I know her friend's name. By now I have discovered that this search is a jigsaw puzzle. The more pieces you find, the easier it becomes to slot in others.

When Mattie's father George Travasaros arrived in Australia in 1938, he went north to Queensland to work in his brother-in-law's café in Ravenshoe. After several years, George decided to strike out on his own. He made his way down the coast, looking for a place to settle until he came to Albury which had a small Greek community. By the time Mattie arrived with her mother and sister in 1948, he already owned the Hume Weir Café in the main street, where the ANZ bank stands today.

When Mattie arrived with her mother and sister, Australians still needed ration cards for tea and butter, and the local Ardmona cannery attracted female workers with tobacco and cigarette rations. The front pages of the Albury *Banner* advertised sales of Hereford and shorthorn cattle and romney and merino sheep at Dalgety's auctions, while the paper's women's columns offered household tips that suggested striking 'a gay and whimsical note in tiebacks for your curtains this summer'. The town chemist advertised Sterisol liquid antiseptic for two shillings, germicidal soap for one shilling and sevenpence, and Bisby indigestion powder and Blackies Little Liver Pills for one shilling. Mate's, the town emporium, advertised 'Milanese slip and scantee sets with matching pantettes'. The total assets of the National Bank of Australia came to 158,044,010 pounds.

Mattie, who has a gentle, giving nature, took her father to her heart from the moment she saw him, but her sister Katina, who was almost two years older, was more reticent. 'I was twelve when we arrived and after not having a father for ten years, I didn't know how to react,' she tells me when I call her in Canberra. 'I was expected to accept this stranger as the head of the family, but it didn't happen overnight.'

Although she was docile and loyal, Mattie felt suffocated by the restrictions imposed on her by her Greek parents. On Kythera, all the children had lived by the same rules, but in Albury she was the odd one out. 'I couldn't have friends, couldn't go out, couldn't wear modern clothes or make-up. I had to stay home and work and that was it,' she says. 'It was like living in the eighteenth century. I felt like someone from another planet. No pictures or dances, and no boys. My father wouldn't let me wear bathers, so I couldn't even go swimming with the other girls.'

The ban on wearing a swimsuit made such a deep impression on Mattie that she feels uncomfortable about it to this day. 'When x-rays showed I have osteoarthritis in my spine, my doctor recommended hydrotherapy twice a week at the hospital pool,' she says. 'So after all these years, I've finally started wearing bathers, but it feels wrong, as if I have broken some moral law!'

Her mother, who could not speak English, worked at the back of the café, while Mattie and Katina helped out after school and during the holidays. 'I had a very difficult time,' Mattie recalls. 'The other girls, they couldn't understand the way I was brought up. I didn't want to upset my parents but I wanted to go out so I hid things from them, the school excursions and the pictures.' She is such a stoic, uncomplaining woman that I can imagine how deeply she must have suffered as a girl.

'Even after George and I got engaged, whenever we went to the pictures, my mother had to come too!' she says. 'My father never smacked me, but when I was getting married, he said, "Just because I've never hit you, don't think I won't if you don't behave yourself!" I was nineteen, but he still felt he had the right to treat me like a little girl.' She says this without any trace of resentment. 'They were strict but they loved us. My father would have done anything for us.'

George is nodding. 'The Greek family unit is very strong. It's a commitment not just between husband and wife, but between brothers, sisters and all the family. Our parents were strict, but they would sacrifice everything for the children. They didn't spend their time in the pub drinking or running around. And we respected that.'

As I listen to Mattie describe her restrictive upbringing, it occurs to me that to some extent all of us migrant children, girls especially, suffered from the attitudes and expectations that our parents brought with them. The limits of acceptable behaviour which were drawn up in a far-off land at another time were frozen rigid by distance and uncertainty. There was little they could control in this foreign environment except their children, in whom they tried to instil the respect, obedience and morality they had learned at home.

I remember how shocked my father was the day I told him not to be silly. What to me was a playful comment seemed to him the height of disrespect. The day he found some photographs of himself and my mother in the waste paper basket, he was white with anger. 'You threw away photos of your parents?' he said in a voice heavy with incredulity and shock. For him, family photos were precious because he had been able to salvage so few. The fact that I had discarded only the blurred ones was no excuse. Playing in the street was forbidden because only common children did that. Going steady was immoral because it compromised a girl's reputation. My friends couldn't understand the rules under which I had to live and, like Mattie, I perched uncomfortably on the edge of two worlds, forever trying to explain one to the other.

As we compare notes on our foreign upbringing, the doorbell rings and Mattie jumps up. 'I've got a surprise for you!' she cries, as two men in their sixties walk in. They are her cousins Stan Travasaros and John Comino who travelled with her on the *Derna*. John, a portly fellow with an extroverted personality, dominates the conversation with his loud voice and strong Greek accent. 'My father was already in Australia when I arrived but my mother never came out here. After a while, my father went back to Kythera, but my brother and I stayed,' he says.

Like the rest of the family, John worked in the café when he arrived. 'Earned two pounds a week and saved it all. When I started working in the shop, I had to sweep the floor. I didn't mind it because sometimes I found two bob under the table. Later I found out they put it there on purpose to make sure I did a proper job!' His hearty laugh fills the room. 'People were more friendly in 1948,' John says but Mattie is shaking her head.

'They called us dagoes, that was an awful word.'

'We served steaks, eggs, mixed grills. One fellow used to come in from the Hume Weir and every week he ordered steak and twelve eggs! I had to put the eggs on top of the steak to fit them all on the plate!' John booms.

Stan, who hasn't got a word in since they arrived, now ventures a comment.

'We came out here because there we had nothing and we heard that Australia was a rich country.'

That's all he gets to say because a moment later John shouts him down.

'If he hadn't come here, he would have had to go into the army! We didn't know nothing about Australia, didn't even know how far it was when we got on that ship. We were young, excited about going somewhere, we didn't know nothing. We thought that after two or three years we'd go back. Stan, he goes back to Kythera almost every year.'

Inevitably the conversation takes a sentimental detour to Kythera which has been described as Australia's seventh state because around 60,000 Kytherians and their descendants live in Australia today. For Mattie and her family, it's the place of their heart, the eternal spring of their soul. 'When we talk about Kythera, we think about the way it was, not the way it is now,' says George and there's a nostalgic gleam in his eyes. 'We long for the days when we were close to nature, when everything moved with the seasons and we lived close to the land. Like the Aborigines, that's how we felt about the land we grew up in. Every scrap of land was cultivated and divided into fields. We had no electricity, fetched water from the well, and ate the fruit and vegetables that the seasons brought. The people who live there now don't want the old times back when they couldn't buy anything in a shop and had no electricity or water. But our image hasn't moved with the times.'

As they reminisce, they see fields dotted with wild red poppies, smell the air perfumed with wild thyme, oregano and wild flowers, and taste the honeyed sweetness of sun-warmed figs and melons whose juice runs down their chins as they bite into them. In this vision of Kythera, it's their childhood they're longing for, not the harsh island life.

Like Mattie and Stan, John also married a Kytherian. He went back to the island to marry the girl his father had chosen and brought her back to Australia, but the marriage ended a few years ago. He tells me proudly that his daughter Mary became an acrobat who was part of Albury's Flying Fruit Fly Circus. Two of his children have visited Kythera, and all three of Stan's daughters have been there several times. So has Mattie's daughter Koula who has just joined us. She has organised a late lunch break today at the pathology laboratory where she works as a technician, so that she can meet me. A sensitive girl with thick dark hair framing her face, she has Mattie's gentle manner. 'I felt a bond as soon as I got there,' she says in a dreamy voice. 'I grew up hearing so much about Kythera that when I got there I recognised everything. I cried when it was time to leave.'

What is it about Kythera that exerts such a powerful pull on its people?

'I think it's not so much Kythera, it's us Kytherians that have a special feeling for the place,' Mattie says. 'It's like Homer's story about Ulysses. After he'd been away from home for many years, he said it would be enough just to see the smoke from the chimneys of Ithaca. And that's how we feel about Kythera.'

George says, 'You live in a small place, you know all the people. Your ancestors have lived there and worked the land all their lives, most of them are family. You hunt for quail and partridge, fish for barbouni and snapper, plant your own vines and vegetables, make your own olive oil and wine, grow your grain, take it to the mill to be ground, and bake your bread in a wood-fired oven. All that ties you to the land. You milk your goats, get wool from your sheep, eggs from your chickens. The animals get attached too. We had a dog that cried every day after we left, and died a few weeks later.'

It strikes me that the things he praises are the very things people today would complain about: how hard the life was, having to haul water from the well, no electric light or radio. 'When I go back to Kythera I'm not interested in the developments and modern things. I want to find the nooks and crannies that I remember,' George says. 'The little white church up on the hill, the myrtle bush, the old olive tree. I'd love to find it all the way I left it, but my little village has been completely abandoned. In those days every house was full of people and the happy noise of children. There was life in the land.

'I love the traditional food we used to eat. Goats' milk, game. In the summer during the hunting season when you woke up, it was like being in the front line. *Rat-tat-tat!* All the rifles going. We made ricotta cheese. The oil on Kythera is the best in the world. It's that heavy virgin oil, you can't get it anywhere else. And the honey! No chemical pesticides or fertilisers, everything was natural. We used to make delicious chicken soup — *avgolemono* — and fish soup too.' They embark on a heated discussion about the food they used to eat.

'There wasn't any refrigeration, so to keep the quail they put it in salt and it kept for weeks like that. My mother used to hang meat and cheese inside the well in baskets to keep them fresh,' Mattie recalls. Stan's wife Jenny brings out a spiced honey cake she has baked in my honour and that sets them off in an ecstasy of praise for Kytherian honey, which they claim has the best flavour in the world, because the bees gorge on myrtle and wild thyme.

'I'll tell you what amazed me here in Albury a few weeks ago,' says George. 'We went to a good restaurant and the first thing they put on the table was a dish of olive oil, coarse rock salt and thick chunks of bread. And everyone says you should eat lots of fish. Just like we did on Kythera years ago!'

Mattie continued working in her father's café until she and George married in 1957. By the time their three children were at school, George had opened his own Riverina Café and she worked with him until they closed it down in the seventies.

'The café era ended because life became more sophisticated and affluent. People started going to restaurants, clubs and bistros instead,' George says.

He spends most of his time these days gardening and trying to keep the Greek community together with dances and social functions. They have a low rate of intermarriage and they'd like to keep it that way.

'Do the young people come to the dances?' I ask, glancing at their daughter Koula.

'Sometimes they come, yes. Do our best,' says Mattie. 'Sometimes Koula she comes.'

'Ah the Koula!' John roars. 'She the best. And Mattie's two sons! I can't find the words.'

Mattie goes pink, hangs her head and beams and returns John's compliment. 'That's because Koula she has a good godfather!'

Mattie's mother has never learned English. She couldn't speak because she never left the house, and she never left the house because she couldn't communicate. She helped in the kitchen because she couldn't talk to the customers, and her husband never gave her the opportunity to step out of that role. When I recall that this was the feisty woman who took care of two small children on her own in her village for ten harsh and hungry years, I wonder how she coped with becoming a traditional wife again after being independent for so long.

'She coped because she was taught from a young age that the husband is the boss, so that's what she expected,' Mattie explains. 'Our way of life has been passed down from generation to generation. She accepted it then, but now she realises how much she has missed in all these years because she is completely cut off from everything. I have to take her shopping and to the doctor. She can't listen to the radio or watch TV and doesn't know what's going on in the world. For fifty-one years she has been living in Greece in Australia.'

As we discuss the issue of ethnic identity, Mattie looks pensive. 'I like it here but I don't belong here. When my children were born I knew that this is it, I'm here to stay, but I never stopped missing Kythera. I miss real friends, people who really understand. I miss not knowing everyone. Here I feel a stranger among strangers. I never stopped feeling I'm in a foreign country. I can't talk to Australians the way I can talk to Greeks. They don't understand me. I can talk about the weather and general things, but not about things that really matter to me. Maybe being a girl and being so strictly brought up had something to do with it, but it continued after I was married.

'I only mix with Greeks. I don't feel comfortable with Australians. They're good people but I just don't have any connection with them. It's partly because I don't think they accept me, and also I don't express myself so well in English. If you mix with Australians you have to go to their parties and clubs and I don't feel comfortable in those places. I'd go back to Kythera and live there for sure if not for the children,' she says. 'There the doors are left unlocked and the windows stay open all night.'

Looking fondly at her daughter, Mattie adds, 'But my Koula, she won't accept that. She's already told me. She is Greek but not fully, not like me or my mother. We didn't bring her up the same way, it was impossible. Maybe I was too soft, but I didn't want her to go through what I went through. As for boys, Koula knows what I think. While she was at school, she didn't go out, but we let her go to college in Canberra. She stayed with my sister Katina. My mother would never have let me go, but I trust my daughter. If I tried to restrict her like I was restricted, I'd lose her and make her life miserable. We have to go along with changes in the world, have to be a bit flexible.'

Before I leave, they show me a video taken on Kythera in 1987. They must have seen it a hundred times but their enthusiasm hasn't waned as they lean forward to explain the blurred scenes on the screen. 'That's Koula walking with her grandfather along the dirt path to the monastery,' Mattie says. The little whitewashed church where she was baptised comes into view and I can almost smell the incense and feel the heat from the candles burning in the multi-branched brass candlesticks. I can hear the men's deep voices resonating in the dim interior as they chant the Greek liturgy and feel the wind blowing through the tall dark pines beside the path that winds outside the church. Olive trees, older than time, cling to rocky soil. There's a well in the middle of the yard, and on the other side, patches of vegetables in rows: beans, zucchini, tomatoes and cucumbers. I can hear the buzz of conversation and the scraping of wooden chairs outside the *kafenion* where the men sit at small wooden tables and eat their olives and drink their *ouzo* under the fig trees. I've fallen under Kythera's spell.

37

When Mattie's shipboard friend Vassiliki Fatseas finally reached Mackay, she was on the point of exhaustion. For the past four months they had been constantly on the move, on boats, planes and trains that had carried her from Kythera to Athens, then Cairo and across the desert to Port Said. With each move, the familiar world had receded even further and been replaced by strange countries where people had skins of a different colour, wore long robes and babbled words she couldn't understand. Dazed from so many journeys and impressions, Vassiliki had covered her eyes with a handkerchief as soon as she reached Mackay. 'I was so exhausted, I didn't want to see another thing!' she tells me. 'I'd had enough.'

Vassiliki, who has anglicised her name to Vi, is recalling her arrival as we sit in her comfortable brick home in Sydney's upper north shore where large blocks of land stand in tree-lined streets and cafés are few and far between. I found her thanks to Mary Conomos, my best friend from Waverley Primary School. As I hadn't had much luck locating the Greek passengers, I turned to Mary for help. Recognising some of the surnames I read out from the passenger list as belonging to Kytherians, Mary had suggested placing a notice in the Kytherian newsletter to publicise my search. A few weeks later, a friendly woman called me.

'I've just read the newsletter, darling, and I think you're looking for me!' It was Mattie's friend Vi who had sailed on the *Derna* as a ten year old with her brother and two sisters.

It would be difficult to imagine a bigger contrast to the stony terrain of Kythera than the lush region in which Mackay is situated. Halfway between Brisbane and Cairns, it is surrounded by fields of sugar cane which provide a tropical backdrop for cars that whiz along the Pacific Highway on their way to the holiday playgrounds of far north Queensland. Cut in half by the Pioneer River, Mackay is a compact town with a neat grid of straight streets over which, during burn-off time, hangs the bitter-sweet smell of burning cane.

Vi was amazed by the size of her brother's restaurant. In 1948, the Tourist Restaurant in Victoria Street was the biggest and most popular in town. For the family, life revolved around the shop and George's word was law. The whole family lived upstairs and spent most of their waking hours working downstairs. On rainy days when there was no work done on the properties, the farm-hands would come into town, sprawl their sunburned legs under the tables and order huge meals while the staff ran in and out of the kitchen balancing plates of grilled steaks, eggs and chips.

From the moment they arrived, Vi and her brother worked in the restaurant before school, at lunchtime and after school. When the school day ended Australia ceased to exist, because their siblings always spoke Greek among themselves.

'We never went out to play,' Vi says without any rancour. 'I didn't question it. I didn't have any standard of comparison and did what I was told.' They wiped and set the tables, cleaned the cutlery and cut fruit for the fruit salad. After school, their classmates would head down Gordon Street to Town Beach, tear off their shoes and socks and splash in the shallow water and chase each other, whooping and shrieking, along the stretch of sand and mud flats. Australian children didn't have to sweep floors, wipe dishes and set tables in a restaurant.

Vi and Petro's only outing was to their weekly violin lesson with a strict nun. They didn't mind the lessons, but as they didn't do their homework they were invariably in trouble. One afternoon as they dawdled towards their lesson, Petro suddenly asked, 'Does she ever give you the cane?'

Vi giggled. 'I get it on the legs every week because I don't practise.'

They stopped and looked at each other, the same thought forming in their minds. Her dark eyes brimming with devilry, Vi tugged her brother's arm. 'Let's go and play. George won't know!' There were swings and roundabouts in the park, and for the next few weeks they felt like caged animals let loose in the savannah.

Unfortunately for them, the nun rang George a few weeks later to ask what had happened to her pupils. When they ran home from the park that afternoon, he was waiting for them and from his expression they knew the game was up. But although she was scared, Vi stood up to her older brother.

'She's horrible, she gives us the cane! We don't want to go back!'

To their relief, George didn't punish them or insist that they go back, but he soon found another teacher who gave lessons at the café, making it impossible for them to play truant again.

Vi and Petro were the only foreign children at school. As they couldn't speak English, they started in first class and gradually went up one class at a time until they reached their own age group. 'We had the most wonderful headmaster, Mr Cairns,' Vi recalls with affection. 'Every lunchtime he would teach me a few extra words in his office to help me catch up. One day when everyone had to recite a poem, Petro and I didn't know any English ones so he said we could recite a Greek one instead. While I was in the middle of it, one of the boys started giggling. Mr Cairns said, "It's rude to laugh at other languages!" and gave him the cane! When he left the school a year later, he came and said goodbye to Petro and me. He shook our hands and said, "I hope when we meet again you'll speak perfect English!" I've never forgotten him.'

Vi looks wistful. 'I liked school and would have liked to stay on, but that wasn't to be,' she says. 'As soon as I turned fifteen, I had to leave because my brother needed me in the shop. I was upset about it, but there was nothing I could do. I was brought up that family was everything and you had to respect your elders. You didn't argue or answer back.'

Vi became the cashier and trained new girls. 'By then we had a staff of about forty, together with cooks and cleaners,' she says. 'I can't say I enjoyed the work but there was no choice. My brother was a hard boss, stern and tough, but he was fair. That's why he succeeded in life. It was a big responsibility for him to bring us out when we were so young. He was our father figure and whatever he said went. But Petro and I were very close and did everything together. We're still very close, even though I'm in Sydney and he lives on the Gold Coast.'

Unlike Vi, however, Petro felt rebellious about working in the café. Even now, while talking about those early years in Mackay, his voice has a resentful edge.

'George was very hard on us,' he says. 'Before school I had to fill up the salt shakers and sugar bowls and wipe down all the tables. At lunchtime, I had to stand on a Coca Cola crate to reach the sink and wash the dishes. After school, we had to cut up two boxes of apples and pawpaws and a box of pears and pineapples to fill up two five-gallon containers of fruit salad. Too bad if you had homework. Then there was the washing up. There was no time to play, no time for anything except school and work at the restaurant. I'd never been to the pictures or to a dance. All I did was wipe dishes and cut fruit. George was always going crook on us. We weren't allowed to make any noise in case the customers heard us. At school, the other kids sometimes bashed me up, called me "little dago bastard" and ripped my shirts, and when I got home, my brother went crook on me for ruining good clothes.'

Even his first taste of ice cream at the restaurant has left an unpleasant memory. 'Not long after we arrived, the cook gave me a chocolate-coated ice cream bar. I'd never had an ice cream before and had no idea what to expect. "You got to bite hard," he told me. I did and got a terrible shock when the cold hit my teeth. I'll never forget that sensation.'

At sixty-two, Petro's face still has traces of the puckish little boy he used to be on the *Derna*, but a depressed air hangs over him. His breathing is laboured and he limps as a result of a recent hip replacement. Pinned to the wall of his loungeroom is a large poster of Kapsali showing an inviting sugar-white beach and a turquoise sea. On the sideboard are old family photographs from Kythera, including one of his grandmother, a white lacy shawl on her head, surrounded by her family. More recent photos show Petro's daughters and his grandchildren. He is alone at home at the moment as his present partner, a Filipina, has gone home to visit her family.

Petro lives on the Gold Coast in a small house overlooking a canal where ducks glide along the water. Paradise Waters is an ironic name for a soulless area of huge high-rises looming above the asphalt highway where cars speed between Southport and Surfers Paradise. 'This is a terrible place,' Petro shakes his large head. 'So easy to get into mischief with nothing much to do. Drugs, gambling, prostitution.' Pointing at the towers of apartment blocks he adds, 'You never get to know your neighbours.'

Despite his grievances against George, he lives close by and often visits his older brother. 'He should have done something for us young ones at least: educated us or sent us to learn a trade. I left school in Mackay after one year. That was the only year of schooling I had. We should have learned more than washing dishes. But what did we know in those days? We couldn't speak English, didn't know anything about this country, so we did whatever he said. I've never told him how I felt. What's the use? It's too late now. All my brother knew was work. He never had time for anything else. It was sixteen hours a day, seven days a week, 365 days a year. Anyway, George is dying,' he says. 'He's got cancer, he's just about finished. My sister Mary isn't well either, and Betty has spent years in an institution for depression.'

After Vi and Petro had been in Mackay for seven years, their parents travelled to Australia for the first time. They came to help Betty, one of the sisters who had come out on the *Derna*.

'My poor Betty,' Vi laments. 'She was such a lovely person. I loved talking to her. She was always ready to listen, so sensitive and proud. That's a real big story, darling,' she says. From her sigh, I can tell that it is distressing to discuss it.

Not long after arriving in Mackay, Betty married a Kytherian whose family owned banana plantations. After their first son was born, Vi, who was still at school, stayed with her for a few months to help. 'They were living above the ripening room where huge machines hummed day and night and one day Betty said to me, "That noise is going to drive me crazy." I went home with those words ringing in my ears.'

As Petro remembers it, Betty had post-natal depression after the first baby, but although she had been warned not to have any more children, she had two others. According to Vi, she had a nervous breakdown between the second and third child. 'Maybe she hadn't been happy from the beginning but was too proud to speak out,' she says in a troubled voice.

'When she got ill she couldn't cope with the housework or the children. On one occasion, a fire started in the kitchen, another time the littlies climbed onto the roof and slid down. She couldn't look after her things so all her beautiful clothes were ruined and the tablecloths from her glory box rotted. Finally she couldn't stay at home any more and we had to put her into hospital.'

It was then that their parents arrived from Kythera to help take care of the children.

'Mum and Dad cried when they saw poor Betty like that. They couldn't believe it,' Vi recalls. 'She used to be so fastidious about herself, but she got terribly thin and neglected. Instead of getting better in hospital, she got worse. Ever since then she won't go near a doctor or a hospital or take any medication. I think it was the shock treatment, maybe they gave her too much. One day I went to see her and she kept saying, "They ruined me. They ruined me." I'll never forget it. I don't know what happened there, but it must have been terrible because she would never talk about it. Her illness has affected all of us. She doesn't cope that well even now, but at least she manages to live in her own house.'

While their mother helped to look after Betty's children, their father helped George in the café. 'He couldn't wait to get back to Kythera, that restaurant nearly killed the poor bastard.' Petro shakes his large head. 'He was wiping knives and forks all day and couldn't straighten his arm in the end.'

Vi shows me a photo of their parents: the father a fine-looking grey-haired patriarch with a white moustache; his wife plump and motherly in a floral dress.

'My mother wanted to stay here but my father said he was too old to start a new life,' she says. 'He missed his village, his farm and his neighbours. It was one of the saddest things I've ever seen in my life, because my mother wanted to stay with the family so much. It broke her heart to leave.'

At nineteen Vi accompanied her parents back to Kythera and stayed there for two years before returning to Mackay. She never saw them again. 'I suppose if I stop to think about it, I didn't really spend much time with my parents,' she says. 'But I've never analysed it or thought *what if this or that had happened?* If I did, maybe I'd start feeling sorry for myself, but I'm not that type of person. I loved them, they were wonderful people and did the best they could for us in every way. I can't say I've missed out on anything in life. My family always took good care of me. If we celebrated something, we all went out together. My brother made sure I had the best of everything. I always had lovely clothes that I charged to his account. We had accounts everywhere.' Suddenly she bursts out laughing. 'I didn't have a clue about ordinary shopping. When I got married and my husband gave me some money to do the shopping, I went out and bought two cases of soap! I didn't realise that the money was supposed to last a fortnight!'

While Vi was in Kythera with her parents in 1957, Petro became ill. He had been complaining of aches and pains for a long time and could hardly walk. George sent him to a podiatrist who said that he was flat-footed and needed special shoes. But after Petro deteriorated so much that he could hardly move, they called a doctor who arranged for him to be flown to the Royal Brisbane Hospital immediately. He had rheumatic fever which had damaged his mitral valve.

Petro hobbles out to the kitchen and plies me with homemade butter cake and crisp spinach and feta triangles he has just taken out of the oven. Returning to the painful past, he says, 'That eighteen months in hospital was the worst time in my whole life. They put me in a big ward with older men. Ward 1C it was. People were coming and going all the time. They gave me Aspros and shoved horrible penicillin injections into my backside every day with a thick needle. Those injections left a lump under the skin and hurt so much that I started crying as soon as I saw the nurse coming. I was so lonely. My family only came to see me once in all that time, and that was when the doctor told them they'd better come and say goodbye because I wouldn't make it. I was so happy when they finally sent me home, but two weeks later I was back because I had a relapse.'

By 1960, he couldn't stand the thought of going back to work in the restaurant.

'I asked my brother, "Why don't we take one day off a week?" But George said he couldn't afford it. At that stage he was paying me ten shillings a week. Don't forget that the Tourist Restaurant was a big business, it was full all the time. No wonder, because it was cheap and served good, hearty food. On Saturday nights the police had to hold back the crowds, because people queued up outside for a table. But it was no good to me. I was working for peanuts.'

Vi was still working as a cashier at the restaurant. A lively girl with masses of dark hair, a sparkle in her eyes that belied her demure demeanour, and high-spirited repartee for every occasion, she was a magnet for young men who would come to the restaurant to ask her out.

'Come on, George,' the aspiring beaux would plead. 'Let Vi go to the dance, she won't be out late.' Vi would hold her breath but she knew what the answer would be. Her only outings were to Greek parties and dances that George approved of, where either he or one of her other brothers came to chaperone. She was never allowed to go on a date alone, and certainly not with anyone who wasn't from Kythera.

Vi met George Comino while holidaying with her older sister Anna in Armidale.

'It was lovely having a bit of freedom to go out with boys at last,' she giggles. Although her husband was born in Australia, he was acceptable because his parents were Kytherians. After their marriage they lived in Armidale and that's where she enrolled in a fashion design course. 'I always regretted not staying on at school, but after I married I went to college, learned shorthand and finished up doing the design course I'd always wanted to do. But I didn't finish it until after we moved to Sydney and my kids had started school.'

Suddenly she jumps up. 'Come, I want to show you something.' She leads me into her husband's study where the walls are plastered with framed certificates, degrees and diplomas. Most are for his achievements in education. 'George is an education consultant,' she says. 'He was a teacher when we met but I could see even then that he was brilliant.' This is not just wifely pride, because I have heard George Comino mentioned admiringly in educational circles.

These days Vi spends her time pottering in the big level garden at the back of their home, playing tennis and meeting friends. 'When I look back, I can see that I've put all my energies into my husband and children,' she says. 'I'm not sorry I did it, but sometimes I wish I'd put more energy into my own life.'

At Paradise Waters, the afternoon sun is dropping behind the high-rises and the waterway outside Petro's house darkens. As we look once again at the poster of Kapsali, Petro sighs. 'Life in Kythera was wonderful. If I'd stayed there I would have had an easier life. People there live forever!'

38

Unlike Petro, Bob Grunschlag never wished to be back in his native land. Even now, decades later, local thugs still chase him in his dreams, pitchforks raised to strike, until he wakes up with a strangled scream on his lips, his body drenched in sweat. But although he never considered going back, he felt frustrated and alienated when he arrived in Sydney.

'The worst thing was not being able to communicate with anyone,' Bob tells me. 'I felt as if I'd suddenly become deaf, mute and invisible.' Not having a trade or being able to speak English, he was worried about finding a job. He was mulling this over during the welcome party his cousin gave for him and his father shortly after they arrived. As the evening progressed, one of the guests motioned towards him and said, 'I'll give him a job in the dyehouse and pay him seven pounds a week.' It was Frank Theemann, the textile manufacturer, who later launched the popular Osti label. 'I'll be away next week but I'll let the foreman know he's coming.' A heavy load slipped off Bob's shoulders.

On Monday Bob started working on the steam machines that stretched the fabric. His workmate was a young Australian called Wally. Clicking his heels and bowing from the waist as he'd learned to do in Germany after the war, Bob said in his careful English, 'How do you do?' The factory hand gave him a peculiar look and muttered, 'Get fucked'. In the days that followed, whenever Bob greeted him, Wally's response never varied. When the boss returned and asked, 'How are you, Bob?' without hesitating Bob replied with a big smile, 'Get fucked, Mr Theemann!' He wanted the ground to open up and swallow him when the boss explained what that meant.

When Bob collected his pay packet at the end of the week, he was disappointed to find only three pounds inside. Nobody had told him that to receive the full award wage you had to be twenty-one, and at nineteen he didn't qualify. Upset about the misunderstanding, he was complaining to his cousin when a man nearby overheard the conversation and offered him a job in his engineering firm, picking up off-cuts of steel and iron which the machine shop cut into washers. This time when asked his age, he said twenty-two.

The money stopped six months later, however, when along with tens of thousands of other labourers, Bob lost his job during the long coal strike in the winter of 1949. He was living with his father in a room in Kings Cross, a cosmopolitan area of cafés, bistros and jazz clubs popular with European émigrés. Bob and other unemployed migrants would meet every day in the Arabia Coffee Lounge, where the sympathetic waitress obligingly filled up their coffee cups for one shilling and didn't mind how long they stayed. With its coffee houses frequented by artists, gypsies, poets and garrulous intellectuals, Kings Cross had a bohemian ambience that appealed to the Europeans far more than the Anglo-Saxon tearooms which served raisin toast in a hushed atmosphere. Hungarians, Czechs, Russians and Poles, jackets draped around their shoulders and cigarettes hanging out of their mouths, would sit around the small tables for hours arguing about the excess of politics in Europe and the lack of culture in Australia.

When the strike ended, work resumed and so did Bob's distress at being unable to speak English. The only time he relaxed was on weekends, when he met friends from the *Derna* on the steps at Bondi Beach. Some evenings he went dancing at the Trocadero, a glittering ballroom in George Street where hundreds of young people whirled around the floor to the music of a live band. It was thrilling to see the pretty girls in their full skirts and well-brushed hair, but nerve-wracking to gather the courage to approach them because the response was often a rejection. Bob felt hurt when the girl of his choice would say that she didn't feel like dancing, but a moment later stepped onto the dance floor with someone else. Being a refugee meant losing not only your home, your country and your family, but also your self-esteem. Many Australian girls mistrusted 'the reffos' because their manner was too intense, their taste in clothes was too flamboyant and their English too hard to understand.

Bob's penthouse apartment gives sweeping views of the ocean across Bondi's red tile roofs. His walls are a gallery of Australian paintings. A solitary Aboriginal boy standing in an empty landscape, looking as lonely as Bob must have felt back in 1948, a nineteenth-century painting depicting soldiers and squatters, and a bush scene reminiscent of Heysen. His quick brown eyes follow my gaze. 'Well, after all, I am an Australian,' he says when I comment on his choice of art. 'I may not sound it, but that's what I am.'

On the bookshelf, the photograph of the bald man with a moustache and a bony face is of his father who also came out on the *Derna*. Moishe Grunschlag had never wanted to come to Australia. His first choice was America, where his sister had migrated, and on his first Monday in Sydney, he was already at the United States consulate applying for a visa which was never granted. 'My father was miserable in Australia,' Bob recalls. 'He'd had a heart attack in Germany and the doctors advised him not to do any manual work, so he stayed home all day with nothing to do, brooded and became depressed.'

In an effort to make his father feel useful, Bob would hand him his pay envelope each week and let him run the household, but that failed to dispel the gloom. Bob found it wearing to live with a demoralised man. It is difficult for children to cope with the role reversal when parents lose confidence and need parenting themselves, especially a man like Bob's father whose energy and strength had buoyed them up and helped them to survive during the time he continued to relive in his nightmares.

After his mother had been brutally murdered by the Nazis in their home town Bolechow, Bob with his father and older brother hid in a bunker in the forest where they lived like rats squeezed into a tiny lice-infested hole in the ground. Crazed from the itching and the claustrophobic conditions, Bob and his brother had been on the point of running away many times. Taking their chances with the Ukrainian Nazis who roamed the woods was preferable to this ceaseless torment, but each time their father had managed to persuade them to stay in the bunker. It was tragic to see him now, slumped in his chair, unable to make any decisions.

Eventually anger aroused Moishe Grunschlag to action. When the German government refused his application for a pension, he accused the solicitor in charge of the case of working against him, packed his bags and returned to Germany to fight for his rights. 'That's when he stopped being depressed,' Bob says. 'In Germany he could speak the language so he wasn't cut off from everything as he was here. And he had an aim in life again.'

Unlike his father, however, Bob had no desire to leave and as time went on, he came to appreciate the easy-going attitude of Australians. 'I can tell you the exact moment when I realised what a wonderful country this was!' he exclaims. 'I was working at Standard Telephones at the time and one of the guys said, "In company you never discuss religion or politics in case you offend people." That was the best news I'd ever heard. Coming from a country where I was discriminated against because of my religion, I thought it was marvellous that here the topic of religion was taboo.'

Bob came to appreciate other Australian traits as well. 'Before long I learned to be a real Aussie and drink beer, especially when I got a job as a store manager in Broken Hill,' he says. 'I liked the place and the pay was terrific, but after two years I thought I'd better get back to Sydney. I was becoming a real piss-pot!'

Back in Sydney he became the manager of a menswear shop in Park Street. At about that time he fell in love with Moyna Draper, a nurse who was third generation Australian. After becoming engaged in 1959, they were driving to Parkes to visit her family for Christmas when she turned to him and said, 'You know, if you were Catholic, I couldn't bring you home.' *What an incredible country,* Bob thought. You could bring a Jew home but not a Catholic!

When their car broke down outside Young, every driver along the road stopped to try and help, but the motor was dead and eventually Bob and Moyna fell asleep in the car. In the morning, a smiling face peered in through the window. 'I'm Tom,' the man said. 'Come in and have some breakfast. My son-in-law will be here soon and he'll know what the problem is.' When the son-in-law said the car needed a new starter, Tom went round to ask the garage owner to open up. Bob marvels about it to this day.

'Can you imagine? It was Christmas Day! He fixed the car and wouldn't take a penny from us. A few years later when I was driving through Young again, I bought a case of beer, dropped in to see Tom and we cracked a few bottles together.'

Bob looks thoughtful. 'That's what was so loveable about this country: the people. Unfortunately the Australian of today isn't like that. Maybe we brought about the change, the Europeans and the others, with our own ways and our prejudices. The Depression here bonded people together — they suffered and helped each other, but the young generation has no community spirit any more.'

Bob and Moyna's families were both opposed to them marrying on account of their different backgrounds. 'But Moyna and I weren't put off by what anyone thought, and went ahead. I only had one request,' he recalls. 'Although I wasn't religious, I asked if our children could be brought up Jewish, and she agreed.'

After trying a variety of jobs, Bob became a traveller for ladies dresses for Salezy Potok, whose daughter Alina he had befriended at the DP camp in Munich before they boarded the *Derna*. Recalling the miserable voyage with the arrogant chief purser, Bob mentions that his friend Alina had a romance with one of the officers.

When I ask Alina about this several weeks later, however, she shakes her head.

'There was no romance whatsoever,' she insists with a dismissive wave of her hand. 'Michael let me do my washing and ironing in his cabin, but that was all. I don't even know how we communicated because I couldn't speak English or Greek.' Then she shows me a photograph of Michael Sikoutris, the handsome young Greek officer, and turns it over. On the back he has written: '*For remembrance to Alina with love. Derna 2.11.48.*'

Alina Jarvin is a tall woman with an air of sophistication. Her short hair is well-cut and her linen slacks are not creased, even when she stands up. At the age of thirteen she fended for herself for three years during the Holocaust, and managed to survive alone and on the run. She crossed borders without documents, constantly searching for a safe hiding place, as one by one, nannies, chauffeurs, cousins, peasants and strangers offered a reluctant refuge and then betrayed or abandoned her.

Alina narrates this succession of terrifying incidents in a flat, unemotional voice as though all this happened to someone else. And in a sense that's true. Most of us who lived through traumatic times have distanced ourselves from them emotionally. Detachment was a survival strategy which became a way of life.

'I don't know where I found the strength to do all the things I did, or how I sensed what to do and what not to do,' she shrugs. 'I didn't talk about these things for years because it just seemed too unbelievable that a thirteen-year-old girl had done all that.'

The only time she shows any emotion is when recalling her return to Poland from Austria after the war. 'I was skinny and sick and thought that all the Jews had been killed. Suddenly on the tram, I heard two women speaking Yiddish and knew I wasn't alone after all.' Tears well in her eyes.

Having come to Australia with her father under duress, because like Helle Nittim she had fallen in love at the DP camp in Germany and didn't want to be parted from her sweetheart, Alina was miserable in Sydney. 'Our sponsors disapproved of me from the moment I arrived,' she shrugs. 'It seems I never did the right things, didn't keep the right company and didn't dress right. They were scandalised when a postcard arrived from Michael, my friend from the *Derna*, saying he could still see me sitting on his bed! They were appalled when I started going out with a Greek guy I'd met on the ship whose family had a milk bar. On top of that, I'm no good at languages and it took me two years to feel confident enough to speak English. All I wanted to do was run away and join my boyfriend in Israel.'

Alina's father, who had a degree in economics, started working in a shirt factory when he arrived, and later went into business with his ship-mates Emanuel and Raisa Darin, making shirts to measure in the Royal Arcade. By the time Alina married Marcel Jarvin in 1951, she was still working with her father who was manufacturing dresses under the 'Maxwell' label.

'Bob Grunschlag worked for my father as a salesman, and I often saw him and his wife Moyna who was a lovely, genuine person,' she recalls. When Alina's father became ill, he asked Bob to run the dress factory.

Ten years later when business slumped, Bob called another friend from the *Derna* to discuss what he should do. Abe Goldberg, whose opinion he often sought, had just acquired Sydney Woollen Mills at the time and suggested that Bob should take over the dyehouse.

The new enterprise took off like a rocket. Their partnership worked well for three years, until Abe's oldest daughter got married and he made his son-in-law manager of the dyehouse. 'That's when my problems started,' Bob says. 'We didn't see eye-to-eye about running the business and had a big row. Naturally Abe stood up for his son-in-law so we fell out, which was a shame because we'd been friends since the *Derna*. Much later Abe went bankrupt and moved to Poland to avoid being arrested by the Australian government for fraud. When I was in Poland a few years ago and tried to see him, I got a message from an intermediary to leave the name of my hotel and he'd get in touch. I said, if he doesn't trust me with his address, he needn't bother.'

Moyna was diagnosed with cancer in 1978 and died two years later. 'In spite of all the dire warnings and predictions about mixed marriages, we had twenty happy years together until she left me for good,' he sighs. Meanwhile in Germany, his father had become blind. As he couldn't look after himself any more, Bob brought him back to Australia so that he could look after him. 'He had become totally paranoid and accused everyone, including me, of trying to cheat him.

You can imagine how distressing that was, but by then he was so irrational that you couldn't convince him. He died two years later.'

Throughout the years, Bob never spoke about his war experiences. 'Whenever I started talking, I would get so choked up I couldn't go on and then the nightmares would start. But in 1985 when my eldest daughter Caron was visiting a friend of mine, she broke down and said that I never told her anything about myself, that she didn't know anything about my past. My friend warned me that if I didn't start talking, I would lose my daughter.

'So I started talking. Caron was a very sensitive girl. She was already upset with me because I hadn't told her that her mother was dying when she was eleven, and now she felt I was keeping the story of my survival from her as well. Perhaps she thought I didn't trust her or wanted to exclude her from my life.'

Ten years later, when Bob and his brother Jack returned to Bolechow with a group of survivors and television crews from SBS and Germany, Caron went with him. By that time, Petro Ilnitsky, the Ukrainian farmer who had saved their lives by supplying them with food, was dead, but they had kept in touch with his family and helped them financially over the years. 'It was very emotional to see Ilnitsky's daughter Kasia again. I remembered her as a little girl with blonde plaits, but now she was a grey-haired woman,' he says. He had made the journey to his birthplace to find the bunker where he had spent the worst year of his life. The locals led them to the site of the mass grave where their mother's body had been hurriedly covered by quicklime and soil, but no matter how hard they tried, they could not find the bunker.

'I should have known I wouldn't find it, because a forest doesn't stay the same for fifty years,' Bob says. 'It's strange, because the thought of finding that bunker haunted me for so many years. But in the end just being in that forest was enough. When I stood in the shade of those birch trees and smelled the undergrowth, the need to see the bunker just melted away. It was no longer necessary to see it to validate the whole experience. The most positive result of the trip was that it gave Caron a better understanding of me and cemented our relationship. I had a sense of closure.'

Several months later, when Bob came to my talk at the Museum of Sydney about the *Derna*, Caron was sitting beside him.

Shortly afterwards, it was Bob's turn to speak to a gathering at a museum. There wasn't a murmur in the hall at the Museum of Newcastle in the year 2000 while he told a group of high school students about the courage and compassion of the Ilnitsky family. 'When I was thirteen, about your age, I had to hide in a small cave in the Carpathian Mountains for a whole year in 1943,' he began. 'Sixteen of us were squashed together in a bunker barely big enough for six. We couldn't even stand up and slept in shifts. We had to cook at three in the morning so that the smell of food and smoke from the wood fire wouldn't give us away. The lice were so bad that there were times I thought I wouldn't be able to stand it. If a Ukrainian farmer hadn't risked his life and that of his family to feed us, I wouldn't have survived.'

It's taken Bob almost fifty years to be able to talk about the terror and humiliation he suffered during the Holocaust. 'I'm not used to speaking in public, and talking about those times brings it all back, but I decided to tell my story as part of the Courage to Care project because schoolchildren are our future. It's important to show them what hatred and discrimination can lead to, and that even an ordinary person can make a difference,' he says.

Like Bob, Alina also started talking about the past in recent years. By then she had divorced her husband and wound up the Astronaut travel agency she had opened in Double Bay twenty years earlier. 'The travel business has completely changed,' she says. 'The margin of profit is minimal, and people don't come for advice any more: all they want is the cheapest prices.'

Reflecting on her life in Australia, she says, 'I feel Australian but there's no emotion attached. It's the only place I could live in, the best place to be, but I don't feel any affinity with the country. Somehow life here doesn't seem to have any purpose. No matter how hard I try, I can't get passionate about Aborigines, Mr Howard's preamble to the constitution, or the republic. I'm interested but it doesn't touch me. My heart isn't here, but it isn't anywhere else either.'

It was only after she had been interviewed for Steven Spielberg's Shoah Foundation about her Holocaust experiences that Alina began to talk about the past.

'At first I found it very hard. A lot of anger came out,' she says. Like Bob, she has taken part in the Courage to Care project. 'When I spoke to schoolchildren in Armidale, their comments made me feel I'd done something worthwhile. I got involved in that project because it doesn't focus solely on the Holocaust. Other terrible things are happening in the world. It's time to move on and see the Holocaust in a wider context.'

39

When Silva Rae arrived in Australia with her parents and two small children, she felt optimistic about the future. The glamorous young Estonian had enjoyed the voyage and her unexpected role as assistant purser. She was young, strong and not afraid of hard work, and with her mother to help her take care of the children, she was confident of building a better life for them here.

Her father, who had owned a restaurant in Tallinn, was also an optimist. 'I don't mind what work I do,' he would say, 'I'll pick oranges and sell them if I have to.'

Most European migrants had been led to believe that Australians were so easy-going and devoid of ambition that anyone prepared to work hard would do very well. As for Silva, she couldn't wait to start work at the Mitchell Library. Her aunt who sponsored them had written to tell her that she had made enquiries and had been given to understand that a job would be available for Silva when she arrived. She had also found a little house for them to rent in Waitara, close to where she lived. It looked as though everything was falling into place.

But one week after they had moved into the house, the landlord gave them notice to quit because he didn't want small children. Silva sat on the doorstep, holding her head in her hands. What kind of a country was this, where people could be evicted simply because they had children? Where would they go? Suddenly she heard a cheery voice from next door. 'What's up, love? It can't be as bad as all that!'

It was the next door neighbour whose cottage often resounded with the shrieks and screams of her four children. Although Silva usually kept her problems to herself, her neighbour's concern broke through her customary reserve. 'I don't know what to do,' she said. 'We have to leave but don't have anywhere to go.' Looking thoughtful, the woman disappeared inside but emerged a few minutes later.

'I'll tell you what we'll do,' she said. 'I'll put my boys in the sleep-out and you and your family can have their bedroom until you find a place.' Silva gratefully accepted her offer but insisted on paying one pound a week.

But the worst blow was yet to come. All the colour drained from Silva's face when the personnel officer at the Mitchell Library told her that the library diploma she had gained in Germany was not recognised here. They could offer her a job if she had a Bachelor of Arts degree, but she could neither afford the sixty pounds for the course nor the time to study, as she had her children and parents to support. Coming to Australia had been a terrible mistake. If only she had the money to return to Europe.

That's what she says to me now in her unemphatic, reflective way, with a soft Baltic lilt. 'I did wish I had the money to go straight back to Europe. I didn't think I could survive here.' Silva speaks excellent English, elongating the vowel in a way that's typical of Baltic speakers, pronouncing the word 'survoive'. Slim and elegant now in her late seventies, I can imagine how alluring she must have been on the ship when her ash-blonde hair curled down to her shoulders. Beneath the understated manner and soft voice, however, I see an unflinching gaze. This is a woman who may stagger from life's unexpected punches but stays on her feet.

I found Silva through the *Derna*'s Estonian network, which led me from Helle Nittim to Uno Mardus. Uno, the laid-back young man whom Colonel Hershaw had co-opted as his assistant, tells me about his life in Australia in the friendly manner that made him so popular on the ship. When he first arrived he worked as a baker, but eager to better himself, he studied engineering at night. Several years after graduating, he started working at the Atomic Energy Commission at Lucas Heights and he stayed there until he retired thirty-two years later. 'As soon as I started working for the government, I began to feel I belonged here and stopped thinking about going back to Estonia,' he says. The legacy of the *Derna* lives on in Uno's life because several years ago he married Aino Liivat, who had sailed on the ship with her late husband, Karl.

It was Uno who gave me Silva's telephone number. Now widowed, she lives with her dog Sally, a honey-coloured Sydney silky terrier, in a handsome white house situated in a leafy crescent in south west Sydney, about an hour's drive from the city. 'My children would like me to live closer to them, but if I did, they would tell me what to do. I want to stay independent as long as possible,' she says with a wry smile.

When the job at the Mitchell Library fell through, her aunt's employers organised a clerical job for her at Angus & Robertson's mail order department. Although checking outgoing invoices was easy and the boss appreciated her diligence, the salary was very small. Poring over the bills at night, Silva racked her brains trying to figure out how to stretch two pounds seventeen shillings to cover all their expenses. Her solution was to work overtime. At six o'clock in the morning, just as the night mist was dissolving over Waitara station, her solitary footsteps echoed on the platform. At nine in the evening, she returned home, long after her children had gone to bed. By working long hours, she was entitled to an additional two shillings tea money each day. That paid for her lunch and the rest of her wages went on food and rent.

After they had been living with their neighbours for about six months, they heard of a vacant flat in Randwick. Delighted at the prospect of living in a more cosmopolitan area closer to the city, they were considering ways of raising fifty pounds key money when Silva's father came across Mr Tondi, a childhood friend from Estonia who owned a cigarette factory. He offered to lend them the money, but shortly after they moved in, the rightful tenant returned from his overseas trip. The agent had swindled them and they lost the money as well as the flat. Although Mr Tondi wanted to waive the debt, Silva and her father insisted on repaying every penny.

Mr Tondi became a caring friend who took them for drives and invited them to his mansion in Kensington. Inside his study, Silva was puzzled to see two flags hanging on the wall: the Estonian flag with an emblem of the president, and a Russian banner with Stalin's head embossed in gold. She didn't think any more about it until the day she was called to the telephone at work. Without identifying himself the Australian caller said, 'Did you know that your friend Mr Tondi belongs to the Communist Party? If you know what's good for you, stop seeing him. You're a newcomer and you'll have trouble.'

Silva's mouth went dry. 'Who is this?' she asked, but the caller had hung up.

So that was the significance of the two flags. She and her parents had fled from Estonia to escape from the Communists, who were already creating turmoil in Australia in the coal mines, on the wharves and on the railways, causing strikes that paralysed the country with blackouts, rationing, transport chaos and fuel shortages. Mr Menzies, the new Liberal prime minister, wanted the Communist Party banned, a move that many of the Baltic migrants would have approved.

One sunny autumn day not long after the anonymous phone call, Silva was walking past the colonnaded town hall at lunchtime. It was May Day and workers carrying red flags and banners were marching along George Street. 'A group of big shots were standing at the top of the town hall steps and I was amazed to see Mr Tondi among them,' she recalls. 'And when I saw what he was doing, I just couldn't believe my eyes. He was throwing five-pound notes to the marchers! We didn't accept any more of his invitations after that.'

By then Silva and her family were no longer living together. She was renting a small room with a kitchenette in Paddington with her father, who worked the night shift at Dairy Farmers factory, while her mother was living with the children in a farmhouse in Granville where she was the cook. As she couldn't speak English, six-year-old Tarno became her lifeline to the outside world and she wouldn't board a train or enter a shop without him. 'Whenever she had something important to do, we had to take him out of school so that he could be his grandmother's interpreter,' Silva says.

It was a miserable period in Silva's life. She worked long hours and saw the children only at weekends. In Germany she'd had a responsible, well-paid position, a reasonable income and time to enjoy the diversions of a sophisticated city, while Sydney seemed to be a cultural desert where she drudged for a pittance. Even with overtime, it was a struggle to support the family on the wages at Angus & Robertson's.

Scanning the jobs vacant columns in the *Sydney Morning Herald* one day, she applied for a job as assistant book-keeper at an electrical firm. Seeing her potential, the boss asked her to move to their head office in Melbourne for six months to learn book-keeping. Aghast at the thought of studying in Melbourne, Silva argued that her English wasn't good enough, but her employer didn't budge. 'Numbers are numbers in any language,' he said.

The six months she spent in Melbourne were the longest and loneliest in her life. 'There were times I was ready to start walking to Sydney,' she says. After morning lectures she worked in the office, but her workmates were not as friendly and open as Sydney people. She rented a room in St Kilda and looked forward to Sunday mornings when she walked to the GPO to buy the Sydney newspaper. Sydney had become home.

The book-keeping course in Melbourne became a stepping stone to better-paid jobs. She became a book-keeper at Beard Watson, one of Sydney's classiest furniture stores, and later for an Italian winemaker. By then she was earning ten pounds, fifteen shillings a week.

But living apart from the children was disruptive for family life, and renting was expensive and insecure. The answer was to build a house of their own. They heard from friends that the Terminating Building Society were erecting fibro homes on vacant land at Revesby and some Baltic families had already started building there. They would need a deposit of 250 pounds for the land and another 250 for the house. Before leaving Germany, Silva had taken her aunt's advice and bought some Leica cameras, photographic equipment and watches duty-free as an investment. By selling them, together with the jewellery she had brought from Tallinn, she raised 250 pounds and her father borrowed the rest from a friend. Pooling their resources, they had enough deposit for a twenty-five-year loan.

At the time, Revesby was a vast paddock with a railway station. An open drain ran beside the unsealed road and rats skittered around at night. When it rained, Silva's shoes sank into the mud. It took nine months for the fibro cottage to be built and when they finally moved in, they sat in the bare room on boxes because they couldn't afford any chairs. But they felt jubilant because the roof over their heads was finally their own and they would never have to move again.

During one of his visits to the Estonian Club in Campbell Street, Silva's father heard that an Estonian manager at the Port Kembla Steelworks was looking for labourers. He poured cement five days a week for Australian Iron & Steel and came home at weekends. 'My father couldn't speak English so he could only do manual work here,' Silva explains. 'I don't know if he was disappointed with his life in Australia. He had a stoic temperament and tried to make the best of things.'

His stoic nature was about to be tested to the limit. During construction at the plant, the chain on the crane lifting the steel bars broke and a bar crashed on his foot. In the weeks that followed, the toes did not heal. Although he tried not to complain, the pain became so excruciating that Silva had to travel to Port Kembla and bring him to Sydney to see a specialist.

The doctor at the Auburn Catholic Hospital took one look at the toes which by then had turned black. 'Gangrene has set in,' he told Silva. 'I'm afraid we'll have to amputate his foot.' Self-contained and outwardly composed as always, Silva thanked him for his advice and wondered how she was going to tell her father what the doctor had said. It wasn't until she returned home and looked up *gangrene* in her well-thumbed dictionary that she fully understood.

'Telling my father that they were going to amputate his foot was the hardest thing I've ever had to do. But by then he was suffering so much that if losing his foot meant being free of pain, then he thought it was worth it,' she recalls.

The following day the hospital called her at work. 'Did you know your father is diabetic?' the doctor asked. She had to look up that word too. 'Before we can amputate, we have to get his sugar level down,' he explained. By now her father was writhing and sobbing with pain and if he could have got hold of an axe, he would have hacked the foot off himself just to end the agony.

'It was terrible to see him like that and not be able to help him,' she says. Although Silva's boss gave her time off to be with her father, she made up for it by working at nights, because they had to keep up payments on the house. Emotionally and physically drained, several evenings a week she dragged herself to Macquarie Street where she worked as a doctor's receptionist.

By the time her father's sugar level was under control, they had to amputate the leg above the knee, but held out the hope of a prosthesis when the wound had healed. Unable to work, he stayed home, demoralised at being unproductive and living on unemployment benefits. Although he couldn't understand it, sometimes he still felt intense pain in the foot that was no longer there, as though the phantom limb was still attached. 'Australian Iron & Steel only paid for the cost of the operation and his stay in hospital,' Silva recalls. 'We didn't know we were entitled to any more.'

For the next twelve months, his wife took care of him and learned to inject him with insulin to control the diabetes. Every fortnight he returned to Royal Prince Alfred Hospital to regulate his blood sugar. But about a year later, the toes on his other foot became inflamed, exquisitely painful and discoloured. This time Silva didn't need the doctor to give her a diagnosis or predict the inevitable outcome. They amputated his other leg above the knee as well.

By then, Silva had a husband to share her grief and help her look after her father. In 1952 she married her second cousin Ilo, who lived next door to them in Revesby. Ilo's mother had been a paediatrician in Estonia, but worked here as a seamstress because her qualifications weren't recognised. His father, a former judge, had started making leathergoods.

'Ilo was not just my husband, he was my soulmate and my best friend,' Silva says and despite her restraint, her voice becomes unsteady. 'We could talk about everything. We understood each other.'

When New Year's Eve came round, Silva's father wanted to spend it with them at their place. She was not very enthusiastic, as she had invited some friends over for the evening and wondered how she'd manage to look after him in his wheelchair. It was very inconvenient, but he was so insistent that she didn't have the heart to refuse. Already the tingling and numbness had started in his fingers and she dreaded to think about the future. In the diabetic ward at Prince Alfred, she had seen young men with their arms and legs amputated, and she froze whenever her father mentioned this new numbness.

That night he was happier than he had been for years. He laughed, sang and joined in the conversation, just like old times. After the party, she and Ilo bundled him into the car and drove him home. Next morning, Silva was cleaning up after the party when the phone rang. It was her mother. 'Your father has passed away,' she sobbed.

'At least he was spared the agony of losing his hands,' Silva says. 'Thank God I hadn't stopped him from coming over that night. I wouldn't have been able to live with myself if I'd deprived him of that last little pleasure on earth.'

When Ilo developed arthritis some time later, the doctor recommended that he give up his work as a machinist and find an occupation that involved outdoor life. As it happened, they knew some Estonian poultry farmers who had settled around Thirlmere in the 1920s. With post-war migration, this was now a thriving farming community of around 200 people, whose members often told them what a fantastic business this was.

'Why are you working so hard in the office and the factory when you could be doing so much better? We sell our eggs to the Egg Board and get a regular cheque for 100 pounds!' they would say. Silva and Ilo bought a poultry farm at Austral.

'That's when we discovered that it wasn't as simple as that,' she says. 'When we committed ourselves to paying off the farm in two years at eighty pounds a week, we didn't realise that the government cheques were only paid per fortnight. Another problem was that the chicken feed had to come out of our earnings, and we had to feed the chickens for six months before they laid a single egg.' She gives a rueful smile. 'I think the biggest fibbers in the world are poultry farmers and fishermen!'

In the meantime, Ilo's father became ill and asked Silva and Ilo to take over the leathergoods business so that he wouldn't lose his income. After Silva came home from her book-keeping job, she fed the chickens and then she and Ilo would sit up late into the night making fancy watch straps and suede souvenirs. Without any trace of self-pity, she says, 'We worked eighteen hours a day. I was so slow at first that it took me all evening to decorate one watch strap. Luckily my mother did the cooking and took care of the children.'

In time Silva became more proficient, and eventually they diversified to wallets, purses, keyrings and bookmarks. 'Most of our customers were Jewish shopkeepers who were very kind and recommended me to each other, so our business built up. Some of them even thought I was Jewish,' she chuckles. 'Whenever they mentioned a holiday, I would nod and pretend I knew what they were talking about, but at the next shop I'd ask, "What holiday was that?"'

Their clientele increased so rapidly that Silva relinquished her office job to keep up with the orders. At the same time they were paying off the poultry farm. In seventeen years, they did not take a single holiday. By the time they had paid off the farm and increased it to 5000 laying hens, disaster struck. England started subsidising its own poultry farmers and Australia lost the European egg market. 'Battery-produced hens were being introduced and everything was changing, so we sold the chickens. I was very glad to see the end of them!' she says.

Silva's leather designs were so popular that they sold all over Australia, while their kangaroo-skin goods were exported to the US. With the hens gone, Ilo and Silva turned the brooder house into a workshop and employed four full-time workers and some out-workers as well. During the Vietnam War they supplied the army with soldiers wallets and unit badges. 'I was angry when Indonesia, the Philippines and other Asian countries started copying my Australian designs!' she says.

But nothing stands still and in time the leather business changed too. Tanneries became uneconomical or were closed down for environmental reasons, the leather had to be sent away, tariffs increased and the costs became prohibitive. When Ilo completed his computer studies and became a programmer, they liquidated the business and in 1971 they moved into the house where she lives to this day.

'When we liquidated the business, I felt useless. Ilo thought after all those years of hard work it was time I stopped, but that was the first time in my life I wasn't productive and I didn't know what to do with myself. So I took up painting.' She shows me her portfolio of watercolours, which she donates every year to raise money for the Cancer Council and the Guide Dog Association. 'Last year someone paid $3000 for my waratahs and flannel flowers, which went to charity,' she says with quiet pride. 'I didn't know anything about art shows. The first time I saw a red dot on my painting, I asked someone what it meant!' Among her watercolours I notice a bunch of full-blown roses. 'They were the last flowers Ilo gave me,' she says.

Silva and Ilo had been married for forty-two years when he had a stroke, fell off a ladder onto the concrete part of the yard and cracked his skull in 1994. 'We were so happy, always together. When he died I lost my closest friend,' she says. I feel her loss so keenly that tears roll down my cheeks faster than I can wipe them away.

Silva has visited Estonia three times. 'I don't belong in Estonia any more, but to be honest, I don't belong to any country,' she reflects. 'When I travel overseas, I always say I'm Australian, but when I'm here I don't feel it. I brought up my children as Australian. They grew up here, this is their country. I thought it better to give them a strong sense of belonging here, than to encourage them to dream about something that doesn't exist. They know about their background but they never went to Estonian classes or folk dancing. When parents encourage dual allegiance, the children don't know where they belong and feel unsettled. A lot of Estonians insisted that their children marry Estonian partners — I never did. People have to choose according to their heart.'

Her son Tarno, the bright little boy who was instrumental in getting his mother appointed as assistant purser on the ship, became a stockbroker and a partner at one of Australia's leading stockbroking firms. Anneke, an English and History teacher, is doing her master's degree in English literature. When she came with her mother to my talk about the *Derna* at the Museum of Sydney in March 2000, they sat near Bob Grunschlag and his daughter.

Several months later, Anneke sends me some photographs of herself, Tarno and her grandparents that were taken on the *Derna*. 'I wish I had asked my grandmother more questions when she was alive,' she says. 'But I was never encouraged to ask questions. That's a matter of culture, and perhaps personality too. Whenever I asked Mother about things she didn't want to discuss, she would give me a cold stare and I got the message that questions weren't welcome. Like so many migrants, my family didn't want to talk about the past. They wanted to look to the future and build new lives.'

During my last conversation with Silva, she reflects on our migrant experience. 'Life was hard when we arrived, but we became strong because we had to struggle for what we achieved,' she says.

Her voice, usually quiet and measured, suddenly becomes more animated.

'You know, when we first arrived in Sydney, we had friends who lived in one room in Kings Cross. Everyone was so hard up that whenever we visited them we had to bring our own cups and plates and we sat on the bed, but we had the best time I can remember, sharing our problems and making plans for the future. Years later, when we all had our own homes and enough chairs, cups and saucers and cutlery for all our friends, we never enjoyed ourselves nearly as much. We had so little, but we didn't expect anything and enjoyed what we had. All those hardships made us strong. Today migrants demand so much. They should be happy to be here, like we were. Shouldn't a country expect something of its citizens, not just give them things? When a country gives you the opportunity to start a new life, you owe it your loyalty, don't you? You have to show your new country what you can do, and not expect it to do everything for you.'

40

Joe Neustatl ushers me into his flat, apologising for the chaos as we step over boxes, papers and stacks of books waiting to be unpacked, but the grey-haired woman near the window does not look up from her knitting. Curious, I step closer and burst out laughing. It's a mannequin.

'She was made for the Australian Bicentenary celebrations and I bought her at an auction,' Joe explains. 'When I used to supply mannequins for films, I sat her in my office. Everyone that came in spoke to her, thinking she was the secretary! After I sold up the business a few months ago I decided to keep her. I wonder what the neighbours thought when I brought her upstairs in a wheelchair when I moved a few days ago!'

Joe has white hair and deep-set eyes overhung by tangled, craggy eyebrows. There is something familiar about the low confidential whisper that makes me strain my ears even though I'm sitting across the table from him. For the past twenty years Joe has run a weekly classical music program on 2MBS-FM called *Thanks for the Memory* which has become a favourite with music-lovers all over the country. For years I have admired his depth of knowledge and been fascinated by the breathy voice that seems to be whispering into your ear, never dreaming that the speaker was a fellow passenger from the *Derna*.

When Joe arrived in Sydney from Czechoslovakia at the age of seventeen, his guardian employed him in his ladies underwear factory. Joe worked long hours at the knitting machine earning five pounds per week which only covered his board and lodging, so his guardian supplemented his income with a little pocket money. 'I had no idea how to organise myself or save money in those days, but my landlady and her husband treated me like their own son and organised me. They even found me a night job at a hamburger shop near Wynyard station,' he recalls. After finishing work in the factory, Joe would catch the bus into town and cook hamburgers until one o'clock in the morning. Next morning he was up at six to be at the factory at seven.

For the first few years he tried a variety of jobs, including making cigarettes for WD & HO Wills in Kensington. Although he had no goal for the future, he did have a vocation which seemed destined to remain unfulfilled. Joe dreamed of finding an outlet for the creative flair which had begun to flower in the unlikely environment of the Theriesienstadt Ghetto.

'I was eleven years old when they deported me to that place. The strange thing is that what I remember most clearly is not the terror or privation, but the culture. They had some of Europe's most prominent writers, musicians, philosophers, actors and artists interned there, and they passed on what they knew, though they had to teach us on the sly because lessons were strictly forbidden. Whenever the Germans would approach, we had to pretend we were playing. The art lessons and lectures about drama and art history sparked off my love for art. I often got so engrossed in drawing that I forgot where I was. Sometimes I even forgot about food.'

While he was employed in menial work in Sydney, Joe heard that a big store in George Street was looking for a window-dresser. Such openings were rare and he jumped at the opportunity of doing something creative. Although his wages as an apprentice were so low that he had to continue working on knitting machines at night to survive, financial hardship did not dampen his enthusiasm.

By the time he was thirty, he had become a successful freelance window-dresser, but over the years the business changed. 'In my day, window-dressing was a real art,' he reflects. 'We worked with pins and fishing lines, but gradually all that changed. To cut expenses shopkeepers started doing their own window-dressing, and these days they just drape clothes over stands.'

When the profession died off about twenty years ago, Joe looked around for some way of using his expertise and created a niche for himself in the industry he loved. 'I started collecting display mannequins and hired them out to exhibitions, functions, TV productions, film companies, schools, trade fairs and so on. You'd be surprised how many film companies use mannequins as extras in crowd scenes because it saves paying actors,' he explains. 'Shopfront Image became a good business, but I've just retired. Now I'm going to devote more time to art.'

To illustrate his point, he picks his way across piles of records and boxes bulging with papers and points proudly to his sculptures of lions and elephants which are already displayed on the shelves. Rifling through bulky portfolios stacked against the wall, he opens a folder and shows me charcoal portraits, nude studies and crayon drawings of animals which he is preparing for a forthcoming exhibition.

Joe's wife Cathy, who was born in Hungary, will not be living here with him. At a time when many couples resign themselves to remaining discontented, Joe and Cathy have found an unusual solution to their problems. 'We have a close relationship but we just can't live together,' he says. 'Now that our two children have left home — our daughter is an occupational therapist and our son is studying science — we've decided to live in separate units. Music, which is my passion, gets on her nerves. I like being surrounded by my pictures and sculptures, but she hates clutter and regards sculptures as dust catchers. We both have strong views and both want our own way. I'm seventy and I want to feel free to have relatives come and stay, spread my sculptures out and listen to loud music. Having two apartments is an expensive arrangement but you pay for everything in life. But even though we can't live together, we can't stay apart either, so we see each other a lot and are planning to travel together.'

One of the places Joe plans to visit is the site of the Theriesienstadt concentration camp. 'I want to convince myself that it's really there.

After so many years you start wondering whether it was real or some sort of hallucination. I feel very grateful to Australia and probably feel more bonded than many native-born Australians. I feel I owe it a lot for accepting me, giving me a second chance and the opportunity to devote my life to art and music.' Studying me with his intense gaze, he adds, 'I don't know about you, but when I arrived here, I didn't want to be important but I didn't want to be insignificant either.'

It's Thursday night and Joe's breathy voice fills the empty spaces in music-lovers' lives all over Australia as he introduces a melody by Franz Lehar. As I listen to this evocation of the world Joe left behind, his words continue to resonate in my mind. Like him, I have also had that unconscious drive to leave some mark on the world. Perhaps surviving the Holocaust made us feel that our lives had been saved for a reason, and that we had to make it count. My dreams were easier to achieve because I was not alone and my parents softened the way for me, but for orphans like Joe, the path was hard and stony.

It was because they knew that life would be difficult for the orphans when they arrived in Australia that the Jewish Board of Deputies appointed guardians for them. Their role was to provide guidance, emotional support, a family to visit on Friday nights and the security of knowing that in this foreign land there was one corner that offered a semblance of home. It was an idealistic plan with no defined parameters, giving each side the flexibility to spend as little or as much time together as they chose and to become as close or as distant as their personalities dictated.

But although they appreciated their guardians' benevolent intentions, some of the boys found it difficult to communicate with them other than in a superficial way. Part of the problem was that most of the guardians had left Europe before the Holocaust and although they sympathised with their wards, they were unable to grasp the depth of suffering and loss that these young people had experienced. As the survivors never spoke about their experiences, it became even more difficult to understand the grief and confusion that lay beneath a sometimes brash and over-confident façade.

'My guardian was a good man but I couldn't relate to him at all,' André Wayne tells me. 'He was so English, so proper. When I started explaining that I was actually a couple of years older than my papers said, because men over eighteen weren't allowed to leave Czechoslovakia, he was so shocked he didn't even want to hear about it. "But that's dreadful, it's dishonest!" he told me. So I didn't say any more about it. It was obvious we came from different worlds.'

Today the guardians would receive counselling to alert them to potential problems and help them understand their wards' contradictory mixture of bravado and vulnerability, their longing for warmth and guidance yet resentment of advice. No one who had clung to life as tenaciously as they had, suffered what they had suffered and lost what they had lost, could emerge from humanity's blackest night without becoming tough, determined and confident of their ability to survive anything. They missed their families, but having fended for themselves for years, the older ones were not disposed to take orders from anyone.

André's cabin-mate and lifelong friend David Weiss also found it difficult to connect with his guardian. 'He and his wife did their best to make me feel welcome, and I admire them for taking me on, but I didn't feel comfortable with them,' he says. 'Perhaps I was too sensitive, but whenever they introduced me to their friends as "my David" I felt I was being paraded as their show-piece. I couldn't discuss my problems with them because they were so affluent they couldn't understand how it felt to have nothing. I missed having someone who could give me advice without patronising me.'

David, a tall, balding man, still has the sunny smile and equable nature that made his friends on the *Derna* turn to him as a peacemaker. Speaking of the voyage, he recalls the shoes he bought from the hawkers in Port Said. 'They had thick white soles and brown suede uppers. I thought they looked terrific, but the first time I wore them a guy on the Bondi tram stared and hissed, "Bloody reffo!" As soon as I earned some money I went to Palmers and bought myself a pair of square-toed Aussie shoes, an Aussie suit and an Aussie briefcase!'

Dismissing the problems of the first few years, David prefers to put the past behind him. 'I try not to carry the burden on my back all the time,' he says. After working for a while as a house painter, he decided to go into business with his older brother who was a chemist, and together they started a pharmaceutical company called Orbit Chemicals. They started off producing sulphadiazene which was the current wonder drug, in the early sixties they made slimming tablets, and later on won a government contract to supply anti-malarial and salt tablets for the army. These days their small company produces vitamins.

At first David missed Prague so much that whenever he thought about it he would cry. 'For years I dreamed of going back to Prague,' he says. 'In my mind I would see the wide Moldau River, the lovely old square, the promenade, the bridge, the grand buildings and all the old haunts. But when I finally did return, what a shock! The river was narrow, the square was crowded, the statue was small and the buildings were shabby. And the people weren't the same either. They were scared of saying what they thought and looked over their shoulders all the time, whereas I was a free man and didn't belong there. That's when I knew that my dream really came true in Australia.'

Every Friday night, David and his Polish-born wife Nellie extend their dining table to seat fourteen members of their family, which includes their eldest son, who is an award-winning researcher in biochemistry, and seven grandchildren. 'When I look around the table at my family and I think how I came out here alone in 1948 with nothing, there's a beautiful glow in my heart,' he says.

When André Wayne realised that his cabin-mates Harry Braun and David Weiss had settled in Sydney, he moved here from Melbourne where he had initially been sent. With his thin moustache, smooth brown hair and slim build, André looks much younger than his seventy-three years. 'I looked terribly young when I arrived. That's why I grew a moustache, so when I applied for work as a jeweller, employers would take me seriously,' he says. His ploy must have worked because he was employed by a firm that supplied Sydney's leading jewellery stores, Dunklings and Percy Marks. 'I worked on the elaborate champagne diamond brooch with the Australian wildflowers design which Prime Minister Menzies sent as a coronation gift to Queen Elizabeth.'

André has never forgotten the debt he owes to the woman who made his life in Australia possible. 'If it hadn't been for Anita Freiberger, I would never have got out of Czechoslovakia in 1948. She's old and frail now and lives at the Montefiore Home in Sydney these days. I still go and see her, but not many of the others do.'

Although the orphans of the *Derna* are aware of the debt they owe Mrs Freiberger, some of them continue to feel uncomfortable about having changed their date and place of birth on their papers in order to leave Czechoslovakia. Conditioned to fear the heavy hand of power, a couple of them are still worried about the possible repercussions if the Australian government discovers that they entered the country with inaccuracies in their documents. The prospect of being exposed alarmed one of them to such an extent that he asked not to be named or even referred to in this book. Five decades of life in a tolerant country have not succeeded in dispelling the anxiety created by totalitarian regimes that controlled their lives and destroyed their trust.

Bill Marr, another of Mrs Freiberger's protégés, reflects on the unexpected turns his life has taken since he arrived in Sydney. The first few weeks were not promising. He was living at the Isabella Lazarus Home for Children in Hunters Hill and had to travel for two hours to get to the garage in Oxford Street where he worked as a motor mechanic. Seeing a room advertised in Rushcutters Bay, which was much closer to his workplace, he put on his best shirt and tie and set off, hoping to make a good impression on the landlady. 'The mother and daughter looked me over and went into the next room. A moment later I overheard the daughter saying, "I think he looks suspicious. Maybe he's a French gigolo?"' Bill shakes with laughter. 'I must have looked too good! I didn't get the room!'

But that experience did not diminish his admiration for Australians. 'It seemed to me that they were a completely different calibre to Europeans,' he says in his slow Hungarian accent. 'Helpful, courteous, down-to-earth, open. Maybe they didn't love us, but they didn't hate us either. I had Catholic workmates who knew I went to synagogue and respected me for it. If I had an abscess or a cold, next day Mary

McKenzie would bring me some remedy. I'm not saying that all Europeans were bad, but when the crunch came they didn't stand with us. We couldn't rely on them. But here I didn't feel like an outsider.'

One thing that puzzled him was hearing Australians talk about the hard times during the Depression. 'It didn't make sense to me,' he says. 'With such a huge country, so much sunshine, a garden for every house and so much land everywhere, how could people go hungry? In Czechoslovakia, every little yard was productive and even in the ghetto we managed to grow a few vegetables.'

Bill has never returned to Czechoslovakia. 'Too many painful memories, no family left,' he says. 'I don't want to go back and dig up the sad past. But I can tell you this much: I never spoke about the past at all until recently. That's when I woke up that if we don't talk about the Holocaust, soon there will be no one left who can.' When he does talk about his experiences at Auschwitz, however, he breaks down and his fiercely protective wife Emi bursts in to suggest we change the subject.

Bill's son, whom he describes as a 'dinky-di Aussie', works with him in his busy panelbeating business. 'I can tell you this much,' he says, 'if anyone had asked me what I hoped for in Australia, I wouldn't have written half of what I did achieve. I know I owe it all to Mrs Freiberger, and I feel bad that I don't go and see her as often as I used to.'

Several months later I meet the woman whose tireless efforts on behalf of the orphans enabled them to leave Communist Czechoslovakia and start a new life here. Anita Freiberger, whose surname now is Glass, is old and frail and moves slowly with the aid of a walking frame.

'Would you believe it?' She turns to her devoted friend Greta Silvers, who has picked her up from the Montefiore Home on the other side of Sydney and brought her to her apartment for the day, as she does every two weeks. 'I've lived in the Montefiore Home for ten years now,' she says. 'I hate it. I don't have anything in common with the others. My daughter is buried in Israel and that's where I want to be.'

Greta is one of the orphans whom Anita Glass helped bring out to Australia.

'I can't forget how fantastic she was to us all,' Greta says. 'She put some of us up in her own flat in Prague for weeks and looked after us like a mother.'

Mrs Glass demurs. 'I did it because I felt sorry for the poor children,' she says. 'They had no home, no parents, nothing to hold on to. I wanted them to have a new life and a new family that cared about them. I remember them all, especially André Wayne.' Her face lights up when she mentions him. 'He is like my own son and comes to visit me to this day, but not many of the others do. They are too busy with their own lives.'

41

As she takes visitors around the Sydney Jewish Museum, the elderly volunteer guide with crinkly reddish hair introduces herself as Yvonne. In between explaining the exhibits, she describes her own experiences: how she felt when at fifteen she was deported to Auschwitz, where the rest of her family were killed; what went through her mind when she was pushed into a gas chamber and waited for the lethal gas to be pumped in; and then how she felt when she was pushed outside again, because on this unique occasion the efficient machinery of the death factory had broken down.

Most of the visitors are awed at meeting an actual survivor, but it's Yvonne's spirit that makes the most profound impression, because she speaks without self-pity and has rebuilt her life without bitterness. 'While I'm talking to the schoolchildren who come to the museum, I sometimes catch myself wondering whether I dreamed it all,' she tells me as we talk in her Maroubra home. 'Only last week after I finished telling my story, one of the students asked me how I could still believe in God after everything that happened to me and my family. I told her that every life has its ups and downs and believing in God makes it easier to cope with the bad times, because you don't feel you're alone. "I wouldn't be here talking to you today if I didn't believe," I told her. The girl was in tears. "You know, Yvonne, when I'm older I'll believe, like you," she told me.'

Like most of the orphans from the *Derna*, Yvonne Engelman did not talk about her experiences for over forty years. 'I didn't want to burden my children; I wanted them to grow up normally without hangups, and I didn't want them to feel upset and be sorry for me,' she says. 'When I first volunteered to be a guide at the museum, it was very hard. I would cry, become very emotional and have nightmares afterwards. But now I can talk to groups without breaking down. Inwardly I'm still very upset, but at least I can talk about it instead of bottling it all up. In a way it's like therapy.'

Yvonne's gift for making friends was already apparent on the *Derna*. Soft and affectionate without being flirtatious, she was popular with boys and girls alike. 'I wasn't a threat to anyone because my fiancé was waiting for me in Sydney,' she laughs. 'Knowing that I wouldn't be alone in Australia made the voyage much easier for me than it was for some of the others.'

While we talk about the voyage, Yvonne mentions my parents. 'Your mother was a very pretty blonde, and your father was distinguished-looking with grey hair. He walked with a limp,' she recalls. 'They spent most of their time with the Frants.' I'm surprised that she even remembers me. 'You were a well-behaved little girl with plaits.'

When she arrived in Sydney, the Jewish Welfare Society found her a room in the home of an Englishwoman in Darling Point. 'I couldn't communicate with her at all. That was bad enough, but I dreaded when the phone rang because she would tell me to answer it, but I couldn't speak English.' After six weeks of English lessons organised by the Welfare Society, Yvonne's English improved sufficiently for her to start working in a photographic studio in Kings Cross. 'The Jewish community here were very hospitable. People took us out on Sundays and Rabbi Porush's home was always open so we could come and talk over any problems.'

Yvonne and Johnny married the following year. 'It was a lonely life in the suburbs, because Johnny had two jobs so I was on my own a lot,' she says. 'Some of our group from the boat, including Sam and Esther, kept in touch, but I didn't feel I belonged because the Australians were suspicious of newcomers and didn't open their doors to us, but I didn't trust strangers either. After our son Michael was born though, I started to feel more at home.'

Thinking back about her life in Australia, she says, 'I've been very lucky here. Michael has a PhD in applied maths, my other son is a gastroenterologist, my daughter is a teacher and we have eight grandchildren.' Her eyes mist over. 'For a Holocaust survivor to get married and have children and grandchildren is a miracle, something I never even dared to dream about.'

One of Yvonne's friends on the *Derna* was petite dark-haired Kitty Lebovics, whose feline prettiness appealed to many of the boys. She is still petite, although the hair that frames her small features has now turned to pepper and salt. When she greets me in her white mansion in Bellevue Hill, she is stylish in a grey dress with a long burgundy cardigan and fine stockings with black dots.

Speaking in her girlish voice, softening 'r's to 'w's, Kitty seems more eager to tell me about her husband than about herself. 'Erwin is an architect and developer. He has changed the skyline of Sydney,' she says proudly. She seems to be a very private person, ill at ease talking about her own life, especially the tragic war years. After we've been talking for over an hour, flitting from one subject to another, she asks whether I mind if she smokes. As soon as she inhales, she relaxes visibly.

'I cried all night before we docked in Melbourne,' she says. 'I was sixteen, didn't know where I was going, couldn't speak English and didn't know anyone here. But by the time I disembarked, I dried my eyes and calmed down. I told myself to take life as it comes, work hard, and do whatever I had to do to live honestly and support myself. One door closes but another one opens. After all, I'd lived through so much, what more could happen to me? You know, I've never had any counselling — I've always worked through problems on my own.'

Listening to her I am struck by the difference in attitudes since we arrived. When I witnessed a fatal road accident several years ago, two sympathetic policemen came to my home later that week to ask whether I needed counselling. In 1948, however, the refugees who landed here after witnessing countless atrocities, losing their loved ones and enduring years of persecution, received no psychological help. In fact they were encouraged to keep their memories and feelings to themselves because it was considered bad taste to air personal problems in public. Everyone was expected to put a smile on their lips, keep their troubles to themselves and get on with life. And, like Kitty, that's what most migrants did.

Although she was not aware of it until she arrived, she did have a relative in Sydney. Her great-uncle had fled from Czechoslovakia in 1938, anglicised his name to Selby and opened a handbag factory called Gold Seal. Having noticed his niece's name on the *Derna*'s passenger list, he was waiting for her when she arrived. For the first two years she worked in his factory, and occasionally baby-sat Yvonne and Johnny's little boy Michael at weekends.

In 1950, Kitty married Eugene Grunstein, another Czech orphan who had come out on the *Derna*. Shortly after their wedding they moved to the Snowy Mountains at the instigation of their ship-mate, Bill Singer. Bill's connection with the Snowy River Hydro-Electric Scheme had begun as a result of a business he had started with a Czech tailor. Construction of the dam using an army of migrant labour had begun the previous year, and the labourers often came to Sydney when they had a few days off to stock up on items that were not available in the camps. Without having any premises, Bill and his partner hit on the idea of outfitting them. Bill, stationed outside Sydney town hall, would measure them up for suits right there in the street and the following week, when the suits were ready, he delivered them to the migrant camps.

From his frequent visits to the Snowy Mountains, Bill found out that they were looking for someone to run the canteen. After winning the tender, he suggested that Kitty and Eugene should manage it for him. His offer came when they were trying to save up to buy a flat and as the money was good, they accepted. 'We sold soap, beer, soda water, toothpaste, all the necessities,' Kitty recalls. 'The work was all right and we got on well with the workers, but conditions were very primitive. Whenever I had a shower, Eugene had to stand guard outside because there were hardly any women there. We lived in huts and used communal bathrooms. It was like the *Derna* all over again!'

Their marriage didn't work out and they divorced a few years later. 'It turned out that we had different ideas about what we wanted out of life, but we parted friends,' she says. In 1962 she married Erwin Graf, an architect who migrated from Hungary and formed a company called Stocks & Holdings. Their daughter Nicky is a pathologist and their son Michael works for IBM. Talking about her children, Kitty says, 'When I think about how I coped during the Holocaust, and afterwards when I arrived here, I wonder if my children would manage in those circumstances. But come to think of it, I was a spoiled little girl at home and I survived.'

She waves her small hand to indicate her luxurious surroundings. 'All I really wanted when I arrived was a simple, secure life where I wouldn't have to live in terror or hide under the bed so I wouldn't be killed. Life is give and take, but I never expected it would give me so much after taking so much away.'

42

Bronia and Heniek Glassman arrived in Melbourne on a Friday and by the following Monday, Bronia was already working in a dress shop. During the long days she spent on her aching feet serving capricious customers, she sometimes wondered why she hadn't accepted the offer made by an American millionaire to sponsor her to the United States and pay her university fees. But she knew the reason. By the time the American permit arrived, she had fallen in love with Heniek who was set on migrating to Australia.

Having worked in textiles in the Polish city of Lodz before the war, Heniek had no trouble obtaining a job in a Melbourne textile factory. He hadn't been there very long when he looked up from his machine one morning and saw a strangely familiar face at the other end of the workroom.

'Who's that?' he asked the foreman. 'I think I know him.'

'You're crazy, you can't possibly know him,' the foreman argued. 'That's Mr Fink, the boss. He just got back from overseas.' Heniek slapped his forehead with his hand. Now he knew where he had seen the man before. It was the textile manufacturer he had met in Lodz back in 1936 who had offered him a job in Australia, and whose signature, by sheer coincidence, was scrawled on the bottom of his landing permit twelve years later.

'Tell Mr Fink that Glassman from Lodz is here,' he told the incredulous foreman, who went off shaking his head but ran back a few moments later, more amazed than before.

'The boss wants to see you!' he said.

Mottel Fink shook Heniek's hand and showed him around the factory. 'Remember I told you one day you'd be a partner in this factory?'

'One day I'll have my own factory,' Heniek retorted. Mottel Fink couldn't help smiling at the chutzpah of this refugee who had just arrived with his wife and mother-in-law without a penny to his name.

Not only did the Glassmans have no money, but they were already in debt because of the *Derna*'s late arrival. Bronia's cousin had found them a room in a weatherboard cottage in Acland Street, but the Czech landlord who had kept the room vacant for six weeks demanded rent for that period. As the rent was three pounds — half of Heniek's weekly wage — they owed eighteen pounds before they received their first pay packet.

By saving Bronia's wages each week, they managed to repay the landlord and as soon as they could afford it, they rented a separate room for Bronia's mother. After being forced to sleep in different cabins on the ship for almost three months, the young couple were desperate for a room of their own.

In the cosmopolitan atmosphere of St Kilda, with its babble of foreign tongues, bustling streets and busy cafés, Europe did not seem so far away, but it didn't take long for them to appreciate the advantages that Australia offered.

'From the moment I went out into Acland Street I knew this was the country for me,' Heniek says in a Yiddish-Polish accent. 'By me, a place where you can earn enough to eat and pay your rent is a beautiful country. I can tell you, in Lodz people used to work their guts out, but at the end of the month they had to borrow from everyone they knew just to pay the rent. After I worked here a few weeks it was Christmas and they gave me holiday pay. I couldn't believe it. Ten pounds in my pocket! I never changed my mind about Australia or Australians, and believe you me, we've had some hard times here.'

For Bronia, the hardest time began with her pregnancy the following year. The nausea which is usually confined to mornings persisted throughout the day. Unable to stop retching and vomiting, she had to give up her job at the dress salon.

'It was even worse than being on the *Derna*,' she shudders. 'The only thing that cheered me up was knowing that if I hung on for a few more months, until the baby was born, everything would be all right.'

But after Judy was born, the nausea was replaced by depression. Now that she had a baby of her own, the scenes she had witnessed at the hospital in the Krakow Ghetto began to haunt her. She was unable to erase those memories of German guards tearing warm babies out of their mothers' arms and tossing them out of the window as though they were bundles of rags. In her head she could still hear the mothers' demented screams.

Now, as we talk in their bright bungalow in Caulfield, she looks at me with a sad expression. 'The things I saw during the war changed me. In the camp I started hating myself because I became a different person. Before the war, whenever I saw a pauper, I always stopped to give him money. When a schoolfriend had no lunch, I would share mine with her. Kindness was second nature to me, a reflex. But in the camps I became numb; I didn't feel anything any more. When they took my best friend away after one of their selections, it made as much impact on me as if she'd gone on holidays to Krynica. On the Death March, we had to lie in the snow at nights and by morning many people lay dead. When I saw that the woman lying next to me didn't get up because she was frozen stiff, I just stepped over her and kept going.' There's an air of desperation in Bronia's voice. She is blaming herself for behaving in a way that people behave when starvation and exhaustion dulls their finer feelings and the instinct to survive takes over. 'Do you understand what I'm saying?' she continues, 'I was stepping over dead bodies. And I didn't feel anything. So what kind of person am I? That's the worst thing the Nazis did to us, they dehumanised us.'

With harrowing wartime newsreels screening in her head in Melbourne while she tried to look after the baby, Bronia became paralysed with anxiety. 'I longed to be a normal mother and to enjoy my baby, but ever since that episode at the Krakow Ghetto, everything connected with the baby terrified me. I was even petrified of bathing her because I was sure I'd drown her.' Her nervousness transmitted itself to little Judy who cried so much that the sound reverberated in Bronia's head day and night.

The paediatrician who assured her that there was nothing wrong with the baby suggested putting her on the bottle, while her friends urged her to continue breast-feeding. But no matter whose advice she took, Judy continued to scream. When she followed Dr Spock's advice and let her cry, the baby became so overwrought that she developed hiccups and soon fell asleep, too exhausted to suck, until Bronia became distraught.

These days her condition would be diagnosed as post-natal depression, but in 1949 she thought she was an unnatural mother. 'Luckily Heniek was a good father. He did everything for Judy: he wasn't afraid to hold her and treated her like a human being, not like a piece of fragile porcelain,' she says.

The man her family had thought so unsuitable that five minutes before the wedding ceremony her cousin whispered that she could still change her mind, has been by her side for fifty-four years. Bronia's mother had hoped that her quiet, intellectual daughter would make a better match than this opinionated, uneducated man who dominated every conversation and would no doubt dominate her as well. But Bronia wasn't swayed. With refreshing candour, she says, 'He appealed to me sexually. I wanted to sleep with him. But I also felt that he was strong and resourceful and that we'd be all right together.'

Her instinct proved correct, although the contrast in their personalities is still noticeable. Heniek exudes a restless energy and expresses his opinions with absolute certainty, while she considers her words carefully and seems introspective and depressed. Although Heniek is close to eighty, in his French navy sweater and smartly co-ordinated check shirt, I detect the snappy dresser who made Bronia's heart beat faster back in 1946.

Like most of the Polish-Jewish women of her generation, Bronia looks after her appearance and keeps her blonde hair well-groomed by regular visits to the hairdresser. When she has stopped bustling around preparing lunch and plying me with rye bread, cheese, cake and coffee, she hunches over in her chair and a preoccupied look appears on her face as she tells me about something that has made her feel guilty for over forty years.

'Not long after we arrived in Melbourne, I got a letter from the German consulate,' she begins. They had traced her because Captain Friedrich Fischer, who was the commandant of the Luftwaffe camp where she had been a forced labourer, had asked for references about his character and behaviour during the war.

Bronia heaves a deep sigh. 'I've always felt guilty about him because he was an angel. Really and truly. One day, when some SS men arrived at the camp and accused him of fraternising with the prisoners, he came out with a whip, but under his breath he kept warning us, "Girls, I have to look as if I'm hitting someone, because they're watching me, so get away from me!"

'So when that letter came, I wanted to write and tell them how good he was, that he saved our lives, but,' she gives Heniek a reproachful glance, 'my dear husband stopped me.'

Heniek is waving his arms impatiently in the air. 'All I said was, you can't say he was a good man. All you could say was that he did this and this while you were there. Because I saw how they changed depending on circumstances.' He leans forward, jabbing the air with his forefinger as he speaks. 'At the end of the Death March, we got to a camp at Mildorf, near Dachau. We got a pillow for our head and a blanket. There were showers. And soap. Let me tell you, soap we didn't see in years. Two plates of soup a day, bread, even a piece of cheese they gave us. No work. I couldn't understand what was going on. The other inmates said that the commandant had changed because the Germans knew they'd lost the war and they wanted us to tell the Allies how good they were.'

Wound up now, he launches into another story. 'In the next place they transported me to, I didn't have a spoon, so I started eating with my hands like an animal. Suddenly' — he pronounces it 'suddenly' — 'the commandant appeared, a tall good-looking guy in a light suit, so I sprang to my feet — we all feared commandants like the devil — but in a kind voice he told me to sit down. Then he asked, "Why hasn't this man got a spoon?" and ordered someone to bring me one. I thought I was dreaming. One of the inmates said that only a few months ago this same commandant would have beaten me to a pulp for no reason, but all of a sudden he was acting human to save his skin.'

Turning to his wife to make his point, Heniek adds, 'So all you could say was that from this date to this date he was good to you, but what happened before or after, how could you know?'

Bronia sounds weary. 'Heniek, Captain Fischer was good to me all the time I worked there. I wanted to write that in the letter to the consul but I was talked out of it. Later I heard that his wife divorced him, and I have that on my conscience.'

Heniek shrugs. 'Out of all those war criminals, only a small percentage ever got punished, so if your guy did nothing wrong, believe me, nothing happened to him.' But sins of omission weigh heavily on the heart, and no rationalisation that her husband offers can relieve Bronia's sense of guilt.

In 1956, with the compensation they received from Germany for their losses and years of suffering in concentration and forced labour camps, they bought a milk bar like so many migrants looking for a lucrative business. They worked together and returned home late at night. Heniek sits forward, eyes alight with eagerness to tell a story.

'One night we just came in when a neighbour came over with a tray of food — some soup, two big steaks, bread and a bottle of beer — and said, "You both work so hard and you've got two small children to look after, you have to eat properly!" '

Bronia is nodding her blonde head. 'I fell in love with Australian people,' she says. 'When we moved into our first flat, one room needed painting. We'd never done any painting before but Heniek said we can do it ourselves, it can't be such a big job. He bought pale green, my favourite colour, and worked on it all weekend, but he got paint on the window panes and it took us a whole day to scrape it off. Next day there was a knock on the door and a woman was standing there with a jar. "Sorry to come uninvited, but I can see you've been spending all your time on that window. Use this instead." She had brought us some paint remover!'

'Wherever we lived, our neighbours were always good people, salt of the earth, and treated us like family,' Bronia says.

Heniek is nodding. 'Our neighbour on the other side was a panelbeater. One day when we were going away for a holiday, the car wouldn't start. I asked our neighbour to have a look. "Henry, don't worry about a thing, I'll fix it," he said. A few minutes later he comes out with a car part, works on it for half an hour and says, "It's fixed, you can go." When we got back I found out he took the part out of his own car without telling us, and wouldn't even let me pay for it. "No worries, Henry! We'll drink a beer together," he said.

'Whenever we go on holidays, we always bring something back for our neighbours and they do the same for us. Our neighbour on one side is a scientist, but if he sees me climbing a ladder he shouts for me to get down and says he'll do the job for me!'

Bronia is looking pensive. 'I had another bout of depression when I put my mother in a nursing home when she was eighty-nine. She died three years later. Mother came out with us on the *Derna*. She helped me to look after Judy and helped us financially. I felt terrible, as if I was putting her away because she was useless. My conscience was eating me up.'

It's a heartache I understand only too well. My mother died in 1993 and even now I can hardly bear to think about her last months in a nursing home, her independent spirit destroyed by Parkinson's disease. I wonder whether one ever gets over the loss of a loving mother.

Bronia is continuing her story. 'When I went to a psychiatrist he said, "Don't think about these things any more. Try to forget them." Well, forget them I can't, but I try not to talk about them. I've always reproached myself that I did the wrong thing with my mother. Just as I did the wrong thing with Captain Fischer.'

43

As I'm driving in the soft Sydney rain to meet Morris Shell, I remember that my father mentioned him once many years ago. I can still hear his admiring tone as he told me that Morris Skorupa, our ship-mate on the *Derna*, had cleverly anglicised his Polish surname simply by translating it into Shell. As for Morris's wife Ruth, she had been friends with my Aunty Mania when they both worked at French Millinery in Bondi Junction, fashioning the veiled and flowered hats that were so popular in the late 1940s.

Morris is waiting for me in the foyer of the apartment block and his neatly trimmed white beard brushes softly against my face as he kisses my cheek. The young man who lost everything during the Holocaust has recently moved into a palatial apartment with marble floors the colour of whipped cream, a terrace the size of a theatre foyer and a harbour view that makes me catch my breath. When I say how happy he must be to have moved here, Morris shrugs. 'I didn't exactly live in a dump before. We moved here because Ruth has trouble with her knees and can't walk up stairs.'

His grey eyebrows bristle like a thick upswept brush above piercing blue eyes that are unusually bright and clear for a man close to eighty. With his white hair and beard, he looks as though he has spent his days behind a lectern, discussing philosophy, but this is a man whose knowledge comes from life, not books. The young man with the round face and brushed-back light brown hair who sailed on the *Derna* has become more distinguished-looking with age, but age and affluence have not brought serenity. Beneath his affable manner runs a vein of sadness. This is the man who built railway junctions without machinery, levelled potato fields with his bare hands, and survived labour camps, death camps and death marches only to discover when it was all over that there was no one left to go home to.

'We have everything but we have nothing,' Ruth tells me, resting her concerned gaze on her husband. 'Morris is obsessed with the past. We've just renovated our apartment but instead of enjoying it, he just looks around and says, "What's the good of it when my family aren't here to see it?" He still has nightmares and can't stop going over the past.'

The three of us are sitting around the table in their gleaming kitchen and while Ruth bustles around making herbal tea in floral porcelain cups, Morris opens his photo album. 'I was the youngest of nine children but not one of my brothers and sisters survived,' he says. In one photograph, two beautiful young girls with raven tresses and radiant faces look so vibrant that I can almost hear their laughter. 'They were taken from the Warsaw Ghetto to Treblinka,' he says flatly. A shiver flickers down my spine as my imagination supplies the details he omits.

Turning the page, he points to a young man with a serious expression. 'That's my brother Abram. He had a chance of surviving but didn't take it,' he says. 'At Auschwitz, Dr Mengele ordered him to go to the right because he looked strong enough to work, but told his fourteen-year-old son to go to the left. So instead of staying in the group that had a chance of surviving, Abram went with his son. He couldn't let him go to the gas chamber alone.'

This album is all that remains of his large family, but as he continues to turn the pages to show me other relatives, the photos suddenly seem blurred. I can't stop thinking about his lovely sisters, about his brother who chose to die with his son, and about the executioners who did these things and then went home to play with their own children. Perhaps we overestimate the power of the conscience and underestimate the callousness with which the morally fragile wield brutal power when given permission to do so.

Morris has been studying me across the table. 'I remember you from the ship,' he says. I look up expectantly but from his description it sounds as though he has confused me with someone else. It's not surprising. A solitary child who sat knitting in a corner like a Mademoiselle Defarge is not likely to stay in anyone's memory after fifty years.

Just the same, I feel disappointed. But Morris does remember the little French girl who was crowned Miss Derna when we crossed the equator, and shows me a photograph of her with a paper crown on her head.

He met Ruth in Germany after the war, through her brother who had been interned in some of the camps with him. 'If Morris hadn't shared his food with my brother, he wouldn't have survived,' Ruth says, but Morris waves an impatient hand in her direction.

'Don't turn me into a hero,' he barks and changes the subject. When the war ended and he settled in a small Bavarian town, the locals couldn't do enough for him and the Americans put him in charge of a store in the heart of town. But although he did well financially, he found the atmosphere poisonous. Dazed and angry after all he had gone through, he regarded every German he met as a murderer. When Ruth sent him a landing permit for Australia, he took the opportunity to join her and start afresh.

As soon as the train from Melbourne ground to a halt at Central station in November 1948, Ruth was already running towards him. But the joy of being together again didn't diminish his shock when he saw the room she had rented for thirty-five shillings a week in a boarding house with an outside toilet. He couldn't understand how such a young country could have such decrepit old houses. Corridors covered with torn lino led to small dark rooms where the smell of bacon and lamb fat soaked into mildewed wallpaper and lingered in the grimy corners where cockroaches scuttled.

Ruth tried to mollify him. The boarding house was only temporary, they would soon save up and move into a flat. There was a flat she liked in Bondi Junction, but the landlord had demanded too much key money. Morris listened intently and said with the fiercely determined look she came to know so well, 'One day I'll buy that whole block of flats for you.'

She laughed indulgently at the absurdity of it. It was typical of Morris to talk about buying property when he had just arrived and had no idea how he was even going to earn a living. As far as she was concerned, as long as they were together she could manage anywhere.

'But I did buy it, about four years later,' says Morris with a triumphant nod. 'The whole block. It was the first property I bought in Australia.'

Their miserable living conditions added to his difficulty in adjusting to life in Australia. Compared to the warmth of the Jewish community in Perth, he found Sydney cold and unfriendly. He felt insulted by the insinuations they made and the questions they asked. Perhaps they were just expressing interest in his wartime experiences, but he sensed unspoken accusations behind their words.

'When they asked me, "How did you survive?" what I heard was, "How come YOU survived when so many didn't?"' To the lone survivor of a large family, the question was loaded with innuendo and reproach.

When people questioned and assessed him, he felt belittled. In the bestial world he had been thrown into, there was no room for ambiguity. You belonged to the realm of the living or the dead, and clung to the slippery precipice of life by your fingernails. You lived only from moment to moment and considered it a miracle to be alive at the end of the day. More insulting than their lack of understanding was the pity he detected in their eyes. How dared they regard him as a victim when he had survived by pitting his will against a system aimed at destroying him? '*Lagermenschen*, camp people, some of them called us,' he says, and his eyes flash with anger at the put-down.

But behind his abrasive manner, Morris was not as self-assured as he appeared. As so many young survivors discovered, the instincts that had enabled them to survive were now useless. People here were valued according to their level of education, but Morris had had no schooling to speak of. The camps had been his universities but graduation had not secured a degree. In a community where professional status counted, he didn't even have a trade.

People appraised your background but his family were dead. He felt that he was being denigrated, and resented the fact that migrants who had arrived in Australia before the war regarded themselves as his superiors. One day he would show them that he was someone to be reckoned with. No matter how hard he had to work, he wouldn't remain a nonentity. No one was ever going to look down on him again.

His first job, working at a loom in a textile factory at Annandale, didn't offer much hope for the future. Travelling to work involved jumping onto one of those slow-moving trams that clanked from Bondi to Central railway and held up the traffic as they halted at every stop. From Central, he caught a train to the factory. The sun blazed down on the corrugated iron roof until the workroom felt like a sauna. While Morris worked with a wet towel around his neck to keep cool, he practised speaking English with his workmates. He had noticed that whenever he and Ruth spoke Polish while walking along the street or on the tram, Australians would glare or mutter, "Bloody reffos! Why don't you bloody well learn to speak English?" The girls at work liked talking to this interesting foreign chap who managed to look neat and clean, even in the factory. When he got home, he pored over grammar books late into the night until he learned to speak fluent, grammatical English.

One year later, he went into business for himself. Having noticed that tailors were always sending out jackets and trousers to be pressed, he hit on the idea of providing an ironing service for the trade. He took a partner, bought four machines and a panel van, and operated from premises in Glebe Point Road where they paid their landlord, the Church of England, seventeen shillings and sixpence in rent. To transform the shop into a factory, they bought a big boiler for the steam, cut out the floorboards and concreted the machines into the ground so the floor didn't vibrate when they were ironing.

'The business was a gold mine from the minute I started,' he recalls. 'At a time when men were lucky to earn ten pounds a week, I was earning 150 pounds. We were so inundated with work that we couldn't keep up and had to allocate pressing quotas.' He would pick up the suits and coats in the morning and deliver them that evening, running up and down hundreds of stairs each day because, due to the coal strikes and frequent blackouts, the lifts often didn't work.

'One of the workshops was in the same building as your father's dental surgery at 21 Oxford Street,' he recalls. That evokes memories of the fish tank in the waiting room, the smell of oil of cloves and my father's gentle touch as he filled my teeth in the big dental chair. Although my father died of cancer in 1978, I still miss him, and he remains as vivid in my mind as ever.

At the end of the day, after Morris's employees had gone home, he would race the overtimers pressing skirts and trousers. 'All through winter I only wore a singlet and if I shook my head, I could have filled a bucket with sweat! I worked twelve hours a day. I left home before our two children were awake and by the time I got back, they were already asleep. What drove me was not the urge to make money, but the need to succeed and be accepted.'

Unable to maintain the punishing pace of the pressing business, in 1952 he bought a delicatessen in Chaleyer Street in Rose Bay, where he and Ruth worked together. Although the war had ended seven years before, some goods were still rationed. But having a shop entitled him to rations of tobacco and cigarettes which he sold on the black market. That proved more lucrative than selling bread, cheese and sausage. After ten months, however, he realised that standing behind a counter selling groceries was too slow and boring. He needed something with a challenge.

At around this time, while watching their children play at Waverley Park, Ruth got talking to an American woman and noticed that she wore an unusual shawl-like wrap with cuffed sleeves. With her eye for fashion, Ruth saw the possibility of marketing this simple garment that consisted of a length of jersey with two seams. She and Morris copied it in jersey, the latest textile sensation, and made samples in various colours. David Jones and Grace Bros jumped at it and orders poured in.

Their success led to the next phase of Morris's career: knitwear. With a partner, he opened a factory they called Original Knitting Mills which produced high-quality cardigans and sweaters. 'People were hungry for merchandise in the 1950s and we sold as much as we produced,' he recalls. 'The problem was to obtain enough yarn.' In 1961, Morris travelled to a machinery exhibition in Manchester, bought the latest automatic machine and began producing Australian-made ski wear.

In 1965, the partnership split up because Morris had ideas for expanding that his partner didn't share. He was looking around for another business when he met a retailer who was looking for someone to run two dress shops, 'Jane Edwards' in Campsie and 'Jane Lester' in Burwood, which specialised in evening and cocktail wear. As he was about to move interstate, he made Morris an offer he could not refuse. All he had to pay was rent. At a time when retailers were charging 50,000 pounds goodwill, Morris could hardly believe his luck. He took a five-year lease with a five-year option and he and Ruth managed one boutique each.

The way Morris tells it, the shops were money spinners. They were well established and had a loyal clientele at a time when retail business was thriving and women splurged on outfits for special occasions. The mark-ups were good too. Morris would buy a full range of coats with fur collars from a Melbourne factory for thirty pounds each, and had no trouble selling them for 120. But the opening of Roselands, Sydney's first huge shopping mall, lured away much of their clientele. The death knell for small retailers had begun to sound.

Morris was looking around for a business once again when an advertisement in the *Sydney Morning Herald* caught his eye. A thirty-six-unit motel called Randwick House was for sale, across the road from the Randwick race course. Although the business was run down, Morris saw the possibilities straightaway, but Ruth was worried. 'Every time Morris went into a new business, I felt sick inside, because each time he was taking bigger and bigger risks, but there was no stopping him,' she says, shaking her grey head with the resigned exasperation of wives whose husbands never listen. One of the owners of the motel was Jim Killen, the federal minister from Queensland. While Ruth held her breath, Morris made an offer that Killen and his associates accepted.

'I didn't have a clue how to run a motel, but the couple who were managing the place agreed to stay on, so I wasn't worried,' Morris says. 'But the minute the contracts had been exchanged, the managers said they were leaving. This was just before Easter, one of the busiest times of the year. Can you imagine the state I was in?'

He made a frantic phone call to an acquaintance who knew the motel business and showed him how to run it efficiently. The work was constant and required seamless efficiency but it wasn't difficult. 'Slowly, slowly, we were running it the way I wanted,' Morris recalls. 'We renovated it to look Spanish with white stucco arcades, and put in a licensed restaurant.'

While Morris was running the motel, he became involved in yet another business, importing clothes and textiles from America, Italy and Taiwan. 'My partner was a delightful man, but the business was in trouble, so I had to restructure the whole enterprise,' he says. Within two years it was showing a healthy profit.

When his partner retired, Morris sold the motel for half a million dollars, twice as much as he'd paid for it, and bought him out. 'Business was good until the government opened up the market to foreign countries in 1990. These days there are too many people importing, they're killing each other. And the big shopping centres are killing small business.'

Mystified by the world of business, I ask what it takes to be successful. 'Hard work and a bit of luck!' cries Ruth.

But Morris adds, 'Common sense, judgment, but above all, you gotta believe in yourself. You need a goal. And don't stick to something just because you've always done it. If it's not working out or you don't like it, don't be afraid to try something new. I took risks in business, but I've always been ready to take a gamble. If I hadn't been adventurous, I would have been shot or hanged a hundred times during the war.'

Morris and Ruth have two children, Allan and Rita, and two grandchildren. 'I wanted Allan to study textiles in Leicester, and promised him the best knitting factory in this country, but all he wanted to do was medicine. I warned him that with medicine you only have your two hands, but with a factory, other people are bringing in money for you, even when you're not there. But he wasn't interested.' Allan Shell did become a doctor, but he has inherited his father's entrepreneurial spirit. In 1998 his company introduced the Heartline Monitoring Service.

As I'm about to leave, I take one more look at the harbour view outside the terrace. Following my gaze, Morris shrugs. 'I feel sad that there is no one from my family here to see that I've succeeded. They'd be so proud. You see, I always come back to the Holocaust. When the war ended, I swore I'd never be a Jew again, and it's only in the last few years, since I gave my testimony to Spielberg's Shoah project, that I've started talking about my war experiences, and now I can't get them out of my mind. I've been on the board of the Sydney Jewish Museum and still work there as a volunteer guide because I feel it's my duty. Today I'm well accepted in the Jewish community. I'm proud that whatever I've done, I've done it honestly. But I feel sad that I can't share it with my family.'

44

When I call her in Melbourne, Ginette tells me in a clear, resonant voice that she doesn't want to discuss personal matters on the telephone. In any case, she adds, her story is long and involved and will take too long to tell. When this fails to dissuade me, she agrees to answer some questions, but first she wants to ask a few of her own.

'You want to know about me, so tell me something about yourself first,' she says in the ingenuously assertive manner of a little girl who knows that she is everybody's favourite.

And that's exactly what she was during the voyage. I'm talking to Miss Derna 1948, whose coronation was recorded by Bruno Tohver, Fred Silberstein and Morris Shell. With the paper crown on her smooth fair hair, the Panamanian flag draped over her thin shoulders and a happy smile on her face, she looked like any normal nine year old. It's only when she begins telling me her life story that I am struck by the infinite variations on the themes of loss and pain that the passengers of the *Derna* have suffered.

Ginette was born in France in 1939, shortly before the war, and cannot remember her mother who placed her in a convent to keep her safe from the Germans. Although she managed to save her daughter's life this way, she wasn't able to save herself and shortly after the

Germans occupied Paris she was deported and killed. For the next three years the convent became Ginette's home, until a Catholic French couple became her foster-parents. After an idyllic existence at their château, she was brutally wrenched away from them by her cold aunt in Paris and sent across the seas to Australia. As Ginette tells me her story over the phone in her matter-of-fact manner, it sounds like a fable and I catch myself hoping that it has a happy ending.

Several months after our telephone conversation, I'm ringing the doorbell of her Melbourne home whose façade resembles an English manor house. Dressed in black slacks and T-shirt, Ginette is trim and pretty with streaked fair hair cropped fashionably short. Pointing to the photograph of the passengers craning over the rails of the *Derna*, she says, 'That's me in the front with the big bow in my hair.'

Peering down from the rails that morning, Ginette trembled at the prospect of parting from her friends on the ship, when she heard someone screaming her name: 'Ginette Wajs! Ginette Wajs!' Looking down, she saw that it was a tall, stately woman in a turban with a scarf draped over one shoulder. Even in her distraught state, Ginette was impressed by this woman's elegance. The stylish woman was her dead mother's sister, whom she had never met before. When her aunt looked up, she saw a little girl in a winter dress, howling, 'I don't want to go! I want to go back to Paris!'

Squeezed into the back of the small Austin with her new cousin, unable to understand anything that her aunt and uncle said, Ginette glared at the city unfurling in front of her. She was even more distressed when they reached the drab semi in Carlton where she had to share a room with her cousin and use an outside toilet. Using the bathroom made her nervous in case someone looked in and saw her through the glass panel door. To shut out the unpleasant reality of her new existence, she would often daydream that she was back in Paris. In her favourite fantasy, she was standing at a Metro station when the carriage door suddenly slid open and her beloved foster-father stepped out, swooped her up and took her to the home she loved so much that she ached just thinking about it. Then she would open her eyes and sob because she was still in the gloomy house in Carlton.

At the age of nine, Ginette was living with strangers for the fourth time in a life that had been marked by partings, loss and tragedy. 'I was wild, naughty and miserable and gave them a terrible time,' she recalls. 'I screamed, had tantrums and ran away. I didn't want to be here and I didn't want them to be my parents, but there was nothing I could do and I had no one to turn to.' Unable to cope with her niece's disturbed behaviour, her aunt was at a loss to understand why the child wasn't grateful and well-behaved. Searching for love, Ginette encountered coolness and disapproval.

'The only thing that saved me was my cousin who was always like a sister to me. If not for her, I'm sure I would have gone mad or died,' she says.

Misunderstood, miserable and mute because she couldn't speak English, Ginette found school such an ordeal that some days she became hysterical and had to be taken home. In her distressed state, everything upset her and whenever she had to walk to school in the cold and rain she became so anxious that she was often ill. Being adopted was another source of anguish. 'Whenever anyone referred to my adoptive mother as "your aunt" I got terribly upset,' she says. "She's not my aunt, she's my MOTHER" I would shout at them. I was desperate to fit in. Everyone had a mother and I didn't want to be different.'

When she had lived in France, she felt comforted by prayers and services in the chapel, and now she missed the solace of those rituals. Although she knew she was Jewish, alone in her room she continued to pray to Jesus. But whenever her aunt caught her, she would rebuke her sharply and say, 'Stop that! You're Jewish. We don't do that.'

'Actually it took me a long time to feel Jewish, even though they sent me to the Kadimah Centre in Carlton to learn Yiddish,' she says.

While she reminisces, Ginette bustles about in her modern kitchen, preparing spinach and mushroom pasta for dinner while her husband Ervin pours the wine. As I listen to her experiences of growing up in Australia, it strikes me that she and I were the same age on the *Derna*. As I had learned to speak French in the six months we waited in Paris for our passage, we would have been able to communicate, but we can't remember each other from the ship.

During the first few painful years in Melbourne, it was Ginette's cousin, whom she lovingly describes as her sister, who showed her more understanding than anyone else. 'She was five years older and put up with a lot from me,' Ginette says. 'She even let me sleep in her bed because I was too scared to sleep alone, and whenever she went out, she left chocolates under my pillow.

'Sometimes she even let me tag along on a date. If I got frightened when I was on my own at home, I'd ring her and she'd come back and take me to the party in my dressing gown. She was my very good luck.'

By the time her adoptive parents moved to Elwood, where she had her own room, Ginette could speak English, fitted in at school and had many friends.

'I was popular because I was happy-go-lucky and loved sport. I was always invited to tennis parties, ice skating, horse riding and dances. And gradually I started feeling Jewish.'

As she grew older, Ginette noticed that Holocaust survivors were not very well accepted in Melbourne, even by some of the Jews who had arrived before the war and now felt part of the establishment. They felt threatened by the obvious foreignness of the newcomers and looked at them with the critical eyes of Anglo-Saxon Australians. Although they assisted the refugees in material ways, they were embarrassed by their un-Australian behaviour. In keeping with the prevailing government policy of assimilation, some of the local Jewish organisations distributed leaflets advising the immigrants to dress unobtrusively, speak quietly and learn English as soon as possible.

'But I was never treated that way because, for some reason, Australians were impressed that I was French. For me it was no big deal, but to them it seemed special.'

On Sundays she would meet her friends on the lawn outside St Kilda beach which became known as Little Jerusalem. On Saturday nights most of the teenagers went to dances at the Toorak synagogue. It was there that Ginette met Ervin.

'She was such a sweet little seventeen year old,' he says looking at her fondly. 'For me it was love at first sight.' From their wedding photo on the wall, I can see why he was besotted. With her delicate features and tiny waist she resembled a Dresden figurine.

'The night we met, Ervin asked if I'd like to sit on his lap and I said absolutely not!' Ginette recalls. The three of us burst out laughing because she's sitting on his lap right now in a black leather armchair in the study.

'When he asked if he could drive me home in his father's car that night, I said yes, as long as he took my girlfriends home too! The following day he turned up to take me for a drive in a borrowed MG. My mother took one look at the sportscar and said, "No way are you going out in that, and anyway, he's too old for you." He was twenty-three, six years older than me. She sent me to my room. Can you imagine? I was so embarrassed!'

Ervin gives her a sympathetic smile. 'While you were in your room, she interrogated me!' He's a slim, fit-looking man who has recently retired. Like Ginette, he is also a Holocaust survivor whose parents were killed, but this is a topic he prefers to avoid. While Ginette talks about the past, he occasionally adds an observation, asks her opinion, or helps to elicit her thoughts and feelings in a sensitive, non-intrusive way.

'I was eighteen when we married,' she says. 'My mother invited the whole of Melbourne to our wedding. She looked fantastic. Come upstairs and I'll show you her picture.' Proudly she points to the handsome Junoesque woman with a square jaw. 'She's still good-looking at ninety-two, and she's still a very strong woman,' she says in a tone that implies that their clashes are not over.

It was not until 1988 that Ginette discovered the identity of the young man who had dried her tears on the train to Marseilles forty years earlier. 'When I came up to Sydney for the fortieth anniversary of the *Derna*'s arrival, Abie Goldberg told me about the incident on the train.'

The bond formed by the orphans during the voyage was so strong that Bill Marr, André Wayne, Harry Braun, David Weiss, Leon Wise and Peter Rossler had organised the gathering which was as much a celebration of our arrival as a tribute to Australia in the Bicentenary year. I came to that reunion with my mother. Zofia Frant, who together with her husband had chaperoned the orphans, was also there that night. So was her daughter Christine, who has become a doctor like her father. The Frants and my parents had remained close friends ever since the voyage, from the uncertain early years when the men had to repeat their studies and the women became the breadwinners, to the mellow later years of grandchildren and retirement.

There were shrieks of recognition and hugs of joy as friendships were renewed after forty years, but for the four of us the occasion was tinged with sadness because my father and Dr Frant were no longer alive. In the flood of bitter-sweet nostalgia that swept over us that night, Zofia Frant and the orphans exchanged stories. They recalled the way Dr Frant would prowl around the decks, torch in hand, looking for his amorous charges, and laughed over the mysterious disappearance of the hated torch. Everyone remembered about the baby who was born on the ship, and a group surrounded Halina Kalowski to hear her story.

A sweet-faced brunette with a soft voice and a friendly word for everyone, Halina described her traumatic arrival in Australia. The ambulance was waiting for her on the wharf, and as it sped through quiet city streets she prayed that her baby would survive. At the Royal Melbourne Women's Hospital, the wards were full and they placed her bed in the corridor, in full view of everyone who walked past.

After Mietek and her six-year-old son Stefan had left, Halina felt panic-stricken. The nurse had taken the baby away and left her alone, unable to answer the simplest question or express any request. The hours dragged, until late in the afternoon a nurse handed her something. Seeing the rug in which she had wrapped the baby, Halina broke down and sobbed. She thought they were returning the clothes because the baby was dead.

Mietek returned in the evening with their suitcase. Impatient to take out her clothes, as she had nothing with her in the hospital apart from the nightdress she had arrived in, Halina froze. Instead of the clothes and gifts they had brought for their relatives, she was looking at stones wrapped in newspaper. Someone had stolen their things and filled the case with rubbish, as they had done with my parents' luggage and that of many other passengers.

*   *   *

Four days later, Halina was discharged from hospital because they needed the bed, but the baby had to stay there until she weighed six pounds. Halina moved into a hostel close by so that she would be able to come every day with the milk she expressed for her. It turned out to be a home for unmarried mothers, run by nuns who displayed little charity or compassion for the girls, some of whom were only thirteen. They served out their time there to keep their pregnancies secret and avoid bringing shame on their families. In return for accommodation, they scrubbed tiles and polished floors under the disapproving eyes of the nuns who served spartan meals and frequent reminders of their fall from grace.

Halina was distressed by their plight. While she had a loving husband and a baby she would soon take home, these unfortunate girls were treated like outcasts and would have to give up their babies for adoption without ever having held them in their arms. She was upset for herself as well, because Mietek was not allowed to visit and she had to sneak outside to see him.

Six weeks later, when little Jennifer was discharged from hospital, they flew to Sydney to join their cousins. If Halina had felt isolated at the hostel, she felt even more lonely in the cottage they rented in Lindfield. Alone all day with a fretful baby who was slow to gain weight, she worried about the future. As she pushed the pram around the leafy streets, she found the emptiness of Sydney's outer suburbia oppressive. Where were all the people? Occasionally a curtain moved and she detected a figure standing at the window, but she rarely met anyone.

While Halina was existing in a solitary suburban vacuum, Mietek was racking his brains for some way of earning money. After discussing the matter with his cousins, he bought a second-hand machine for making socks, but when it broke down shortly afterwards, he gave up the idea of hosiery and took a job in a saucepan factory instead. In the meantime, Halina learned to sew. 'I was hopeless. I told my boss he was wasting time and money on me, but he insisted that I would learn and finally I did. Later I made aprons at home,' she said in her cheerful way. She stopped sewing after they opened a menswear shop in Pitt Street.

Halina was excited to see her shipboard friend Matylda Czalczynski Engelman who had looked after her like a sister on the ship. Matylda, who had travelled from Melbourne to attend the reunion, brought copies of the two-part memoir she had recently written: *The Endless Journey* and *The End of the Journey*. In her books, she gave a moving account of her struggle to survive with her little daughter Karmela in Poland during the war, and her heartbreak when she discovered that her husband had given up hope of her returning alive and had formed a relationship with another woman. Several years after arriving in Melbourne, Matylda found happiness again and was thrilled that Karmela loved her step-father, but her joy was short-lived. Three years after the wedding, her husband fell to his death out of an apartment window.

An excited crowd gathered around Topka Barasz that night at the Maccabean Hall. Her former charges surrounded her, all talking at once, recalling their adventures and misfortunes during the voyage and holding up family photographs, asking questions and telling their stories without pausing for breath. Speaking rapidly in her accented English, Topka teased them about their flirtations, fights and foibles. Together with her supportive husband John, Topka had run several successful cafés in Sydney. Her sisters Bella, Ruth and Miriam were all married and had children, but Topka remained childless. Having spent most of her life mothering her sisters, she had no room in her life for children of her own.

Sam Fiszman, whom many remembered as a young hot-head during the voyage, read out the congratulatory telegram sent to him by the then prime minister, Bob Hawke. '*I am delighted to extend my best wishes to all those gathered here who arrived in Australia on board the* SS Derna *exactly forty years ago. In choosing Australia as your home you have helped to create the multicultural nature of our society. As a result, Australia is a richer, more exciting, more diverse, more prosperous society with a more distinctive identity. It is fitting that you are marking the Australian Bicentenary of European settlement with your own important anniversary.*'

An outpouring of emotion greeted Syd Einfeld when he rose to speak. Syd, a big bear-like man with an infectious grin, had always championed society's underdogs and had fought to have more Jewish refugees admitted. 'You were all called reffos or New Australians, and the unions were worried you would take jobs from their members. So was the prime minister, Ben Chifley,' he said.

Beaming, Syd recalled the day he had taken Mr Chifley to a Jewish kindergarten in North Bondi where his son Marcus was playing in the yard. 'Pointing to the children, I said, "Now, Mr Chifley, some of those children were born Australians, some were born to pre-war immigrants and others were born overseas. Can you tell the difference?" His reply was, "How many papers do you need?"'

Sitting across the table from my mother and me was a corpulent middle-aged man with a bald head and a double chin who had also travelled from Melbourne to be there that night. He was rather reticent and I found it difficult to engage him in conversation as he gave brief answers and volunteered little. If someone hadn't told me that he was one of Australia's richest men, I would never have guessed.

It was Abe Goldberg, who had brought three knitting machines with him on the *Derna* and had started off as a factory worker in his uncle's knitting mill. Three years later, he struck out on his own and over the next twenty years built up Australia's biggest textile empire. With his takeover of Bradmill in 1985, he became the king of the biggest textile and clothing group whose labels included Pelaco shirts, Speedo swimsuits, Exacto knitwear, King Gee overalls and Formfit lingerie. Finance writers nicknamed him the Square Dancer on account of his nimble footwork in taking over businesses and changing partners.

Alice Zalcberg didn't recognise him that night. A livewire on the *Derna* when she was part of Dr Frant's group, she had fallen in love with Abie during the voyage, but had no idea that this bald paunchy man was her shipboard beau.

'I was looking for the tall, slim, good-looking boy with thick wavy hair I remembered, but found this little butterball of a man,' she told me. Alice, who still works part-time as a pharmacist, married another migrant, Sever Sternhell, who became Professor of Organic Chemistry at the University of Sydney. They have three sons. Alice still has a merry laugh and a dimple in the corner of her mouth. When she asked Abie what he did for a living, he made a vague comment about being in the *schmatta* business. 'I must have been the only person in Australia who didn't know that he was one of the wealthiest men in Australia and that there were articles written about him every week in the business journals,' she said.

Not long after the reunion, there were even more articles written about Abe Goldberg, but they were no longer full of admiration for his business acumen. Within eighteen months, Australia's richest man had become Australia's biggest bankrupt and had fled the country owing creditors $793 million. He returned to his native Poland and set up a business manufacturing jeans, protected by the absence of an extradition treaty. Anxious to avoid publicity, he guards his address and telephone number jealously, even from old friends, as Bob Grunschlag discovered. When I tried to contact him through an intermediary to discuss the voyage or borrow his photographs, I did not receive a reply.

On the night at the fortieth anniversary reunion, however, Abe Goldberg passed around the photographs he had taken on board the *Derna* with his Leica camera, including one of the lamb carcasses being flung into the sea. Another photo depicted the crowning of Miss Derna, who was sitting at the next table.

'That's when Abie told me that he had looked after me on the train from Paris to Marseilles when I cried the whole way,' Ginette says.

Reflecting on her life, she says, 'My destiny must have been to come to Australia and meet Ervin. I've always been lucky. I had wonderful nuns looking after me at the convent, wonderful foster-parents in France, a wonderful cousin who made life easier for me in Paris, and then a wonderful, patient sister here who took care of me. I've had a good life. Ervin and I have been married for forty-three years, we have two daughters and a gorgeous little granddaughter. My husband is my everything. He's made up for everything I've lost and what I never had.'

45

Towards the end of a long day in 1970, a social work student researching low birthweight babies was in the middle of a ward round with her professor in the Royal Hospital for Women in Sydney when he introduced her to a tall grey-haired obstetrician. Fixing her with a piercing gaze, the specialist asked, 'Do you have a brother called Stefan?'

Puzzled, she nodded, and was even more surprised when he gave her an enthusiastic hug. Turning to the professor with a beaming face, he said, 'This is the first low birthweight baby I ever delivered!'

Dr Frant had come face to face with Jennifer Fay Derna Kalowski, the premature baby he had delivered on board the *Derna* twenty-two years before.

That baby who was born two days before the ship reached Melbourne and fought for her life in hospital for several weeks, is now an outgoing, energetic middle-aged woman. Jennifer, who has a husband, three daughters, elderly parents and a busy psychotherapist's practice, manages to combine all the demanding roles in her life. 'Sometimes I'm stretched to the limit, but I was brought up to have a strong sense of responsibility,' she says.

As we talk in the loungeroom of the Woollahra apartment she shares with her husband Les, two of their three daughters and a shaggy white poodle called Paddington, we return to her dramatic entrance into the world. 'I've always enjoyed the fact that I was born at sea, and that my birth certificate states my place of birth in terms of latitude and longitude and not as a town,' she says with a laugh. Then in a more serious vein, she adds, 'My birth symbolised my parents' hope for the future, but from an early age I realised that I was also carrying some of the burden of their past.'

Although Halina and Mietek Kalowski never talked about the relatives who had been killed during the Holocaust, Jennifer grew up with an acute sense of their loss. Growing up in Sydney, where her parents struggled to earn a living, she was aware that her schoolfriends had grandparents, aunts, uncles and cousins, while her family consisted only of her parents and her brother Stefan.

'From an early age I felt an emptiness, the loss of a family who were never spoken about because the subject was too distressing. Except for two cousins, my mother's entire family perished, including her seventeen-year-old twin brothers. We didn't even have a photograph of any of them. That lack of extended family has given me a strong sense that family and friends have to be cherished and held onto at any cost.'

Looking back over her early life, Jennifer feels that she and her brother lived in the shadow of their parents' history. 'Their grief, although silent, was so obvious that we grew up overshadowed by it. Everything else paled by comparison and I developed very little sense of my own importance,' she reflects. 'I felt a pressure to make up for the loss of the relatives who had died, and to protect my parents from any more pain.'

It was a heavy burden for a child growing up in the sunny world of Australian children. Like all the children of migrants, Jennifer became aware of the difference between the expectations and attitudes of her parents and those of her friends. While her schoolfriends had easy-going parents and seemed to lead a light-hearted existence, the atmosphere in her home tended to be serious and intense. Dislocated and anxious about the future, her parents seemed to be swimming against the tide in an unpredictable current. Their energy was focused on creating security for the family, and that meant not wasting time or money.

'When I was a little girl I wanted to learn tap dancing like my friends, but my father couldn't see the point,' she says. 'His attitude was that since I wasn't going to become a dancer, why waste all that time and energy?'

In 1971, one year after her unexpected encounter with Dr Frant, Jennifer graduated in social work, but fourteen years later she embarked on a new profession. 'It's not a coincidence that I became a psychotherapist,' she says. As the sun streams through the russet autumn leaves outside the large windows, flooding the room with light, she leans forward and speaks slowly and earnestly, weighing every word to make sure she gives an accurate account of the process that has illuminated her life. 'I did psychotherapy to heal myself and recover what I had lost. As part of my training, I had individual therapy, which helped me to deal with the issues that resulted from being the child of Holocaust survivors and migrants.'

As she tells me about growing up with little sense of her own worth, unable to express her feelings and uncertain of who she really was, I realise that she is speaking for many of the children of the *Derna* whose spontaneity and self-confidence were subdued by the long shadow of an oppressive past. In her case, as in so many others, the struggle to cope with loss, change and insecurity led to a fierce determination to believe that happiness and success lay ahead, and that she had to take advantage of all the opportunities that she was given in their new country.

'My parents always stressed the positive. Negative emotions were swept aside and anger was taboo, so I didn't learn to express my feelings. I became a compliant, co-operative child who never rocked the boat or made any demands. Compared with what my parents had gone through, my own problems seemed trivial. It wasn't until I started working on myself that I came to understand that my life has just as much value as theirs.' Like most descendants of Holocaust survivors, she doubted whether she would have the courage and resources to survive if she found herself in similar circumstances. 'I still respect and admire their strength, but now I know that I am also a survivor with my own inner strength. I have learned that I could hold onto myself and still embrace others,' she says.

In the process of exploring her own life and relationships, Jennifer gained a deeper understanding of human nature. 'I struggled for a long time with the concept of man's inhumanity to man. It was devastating to realise that we are all capable of good and evil and that goes for every person, including myself.'

We are discussing man's inhumanity to man on a dazzling April afternoon. It happens to be Anzac Day, the day when we pay tribute to the courage and sacrifice of our soldiers and remember the tragic waste of lives in war. Just as the Holocaust became the defining event for an entire generation of Jews and their descendants, Gallipoli has become the focus of Australian national identity, a legacy of courage and heartbreak to be remembered and passed on to future generations. And like the survivors of the Shoah, the soldiers who returned from Gallipoli buried their stories in silence because there were no words to express what they had seen. Decades passed before they were able to talk about the memories that haunted their waking and sleeping hours.

And that's what happened to Jennifer's mother. Halina Kalowski was so traumatised by what she had gone through that she could not bring herself to talk about experiences she relived at night in terrifying dreams. 'It seemed to me that the vacuum which surrounded my mother stemmed from not dealing with the past,' Jennifer says. 'One of my reasons for becoming a psychotherapist was to find a way to communicate more openly with her. For years she didn't speak, and I didn't challenge her. But it wasn't until I was able to cope with my own emotions that I became strong enough to bear her tears and her pain. And that's when I found the strength to ask the questions which eventually produced the answers I was searching for.'

Training as a psychotherapist gave Jennifer the strength to ask those questions, but it took a pilgrimage to Poland in 1993 for her mother to start answering them. It was Jennifer who suggested that she and her brother Stefan should visit Poland with their mother, because she felt that it might help her to heal and come to terms with the past.

'It was a profoundly emotional experience for us all,' she says. 'Going to Poland helped me to understand my family's roots and reclaim my Polish identity in a way I hadn't been able to do before.'

But the most powerful effect of the trip was the transformation in her mother. 'From the moment we left Sydney and stepped onto the plane, she started to open up. For the first time she talked about her parents and her brothers, described their home life and told us what happened during the Holocaust. That's the first time I had a sense of what her life had been like before I was born. That journey broke the wall of silence which had always surrounded her. Being able to talk with my mother brought us closer. It was the turning point in my own emotional growth.' At the age of forty-five, Jennifer came out of the shadow of her mother's past and began to blossom.

Suddenly Paddington leaps off the couch and rushes to the door, barking excitedly as Jennifer's younger daughters Elise and Lauren come into the house, laughing and chattering. Showing me some of their paintings and sketches, she says, 'It's interesting that my brother and I both chose helping professions — Stefan is a specialist physician — but all my daughters are very creative. They don't feel the need to rescue the world; they feel free to explore their artistic talent. Although they respect their grandparents and know what happened to them, the Holocaust does not rule their lives. They feel secure. There's a lightness about them, an absence of guilt and anxiety.'

In her capacity as a psychotherapist, Jennifer counsels couples and individuals, helping them to improve their communication and self-esteem and to deal with anxiety and depression. As a result of her own experience, she is currently setting up workshops for Holocaust survivors and their children, to help them deal with the issues that she has resolved in her own life. 'Part of my reason for becoming a psychotherapist was to make a difference, to give something back and help to create a better world. But I have never stopped working on myself, so my own journey is still continuing.'

EPILOGUE

The pageant at the opening ceremony of the Sydney 2000 Olympic Games linked all Australians in a series of tableaux depicting the past. From tribal Aborigines enacting Dreaming legends passed down for thousands of years, to migrants and boat people seeking more recent refuge on our inviting shores, the ceremony paid tribute to all the ethnic strands woven into our multicultural quilt.

To evoke the migrant experience in the presentation program, the Olympic Committee selected an extract from my book *Mosaic: A Chronicle of Five Generations*. It seemed an extraordinary coincidence that they had chosen to quote my first impressions of Australia shortly after arriving on the *Derna*, just at the time when I was researching the voyage.

But as I reflected on this apparently fortuitous set of circumstances, it began to assume a significance that transcended mere synchronicity. It was as though, from the moment I stepped aboard the *Derna*, I was destined to tease out the strands of the past and become a voice of the post-war immigrants.

Some journeys lead us far beyond our destinations and I came to understand that the voyage that began with the postcard from Marseilles came full circle in the Olympic program. On 30 August 1948, my parents cast off from the world they knew with the hope in their hearts that, transplanted in a new land, I would push up through the darkness and brush off the crumbs of soil clinging to my head as I emerged into the sunlight.

PASSENGER LIST

This is a transcript of the passenger list. Some names were incorrectly entered or mis-spelled.

EMBARKED IN MARSEILLES

Abrahamsohn Irene
  "   Eva Maria
  "   Gretchen
Altman Lejbus
  "   Rozalia
Ament Leon
Ancsel Andor
Antmanis Janis
  "   Zinaida
Asz Justina
  " Anna
  " Chil
Aufrecht Margot
Augul Rosalie
Bacher Bodriska
Barasz Bela
  "   Gucia
  "   Miriam
  "   Toba
Bendik Salomon
Berger Blima
  "   Dany
  "   Madelene
Berkhut Zelig
Bernstein David
  "   Bertha
Bevc Franz
  " Johanna
Birnbaum Herta
  "   Barbara
Blok Marek
  " Helena
  " Josef
Blonski Marian
  "   Hella
Bode Richard
  "   Martha
  "   Harry-James
Boguslawski Henryk
  "   Bronislawa
  "   Danuta Julia

Borenstein Bella
Borensztajn Roman
  "   Miriam
  "   Jacob
Braun Herman
Brausendorf Gisela
Bogarska Chana
Bukszpan Chaim
  "   Berta
Bunzl Adolf
Busel Mordchaj
Czalczynska Matylda
  "   Karmela
Czarnes Izio
  "   Sara
Czuszak Alexandra
Darin Emanuel
  " Raisa
Duzenman Ala
  "   Zelik
Diament Leon
Dzonsons Laimdota
  "   Arilde
Eliadis Alexander
  "   Fela
Engel Jachat Chaja
Espere Rudolf
  " Ida
Falek Jankiel
  " Ida
  " Jojne
  " Maria
  " Jadwiga
Feigin Marek
  " Fela
  " Daniel
Fellner Fryderyk
  "   Wanda
Feingesight Chaim David
  "   Leah
  "   Perec
Feinmesser Halina
  "   Zdislaw

Felman Szmul
  "   Szaja Josef
  "   Ruchla
Ferszt Moses
  " Cyla
  " Slawa
Fiszman Esther
  "   Srul
  "   Maria
Fleischer Bertha
Fogel Adam
Frant Henryk
  " Zofia
  " Christine
Friedmann Moniek
Freiberg Sulek Pinkus
Frenkiel Israel
  "   Mina
Frid Mosze
  " Berik
  " Gitl
  " Zisia
Gewurz Anna
Ginzburg Naum
  "   Anna
  "   Sawa
Glassman Chaim
  "   Bronia
Glaubermann Pola
Gold Abraham
  " Louise
Goldberg Abraham
Goldschmid Karel
  "   Felix
Goldstein Menhart
Gottlieb Samson
  "   Gizela
Griszczajew Peter
Grossbard Josef
Grosz Alexander
  " Bela
  " Erna

Grunschlag Abraham
     "   Moses
Grunstein Eugen
     "   Irena
Grynberg Abram
     "   Pesa
Gurwicz Szala
Halm Otto
Heller Jindrich
Herzog Kurt
Hitter Martin
     "   Jeno
Hochrat Szyja
     "   Luba
Hof Ilse
     " Elfriede
Holan Jiri
Holandova Vera
Jarvisto Oskar
Jendler Sewerin
Juni Berta
Juurik Leonhard
     "   Lilli
     "   Georg
Kadak Villem
     "   Vilja
Kahan Antonia
Kalowski Mieczyslaw
     "   Halina
     "   Stefan
Kapp Harold
     "   Alide
Karp Zofija
Kaufmann Jozef
Kappel Antonina
Klausenstock Ruth
Knopf Klaus
     "   Maria
Kohan Jeno
Kohn Boruch
     "   Rifka
     "   Moses
Kopelovic Mendel
Korman Abraham
Kotek Isak-Berisz
     "   Jochwet
     "   Jozef
     "   Szajndl

Kosakiewicz Selina
     "   Josef
Kowadlo Josef
     "   Anna
     "   Etla
Krajsky Pavel
Kraus Imre
     " Klara
     " Peter
     " Paul
Krausova Marketa
Kucharski David
Kuczynski Szymon
     "   Guta
     "   Rywka
     "   Szymon
Kula Janis
     " Lilija
     " Arnie
     " Anna
Kuplis Elmars
     " Auguste
     " Ewalds
     " Rozalja
Lamensdorf Oskar
     "   Bronislawa
Lander Emil
     " Sysel
Lebovic Katerina
Lell Arnold
     " Alide
Lerner Salomon
Leppere Juban
     "   Magdalena
Lewkowicz Estera
Libek Ignacy
     " Stanislaw
     " Balbina
Liivat Karl
     " Aino
Lindemanis Sigride
     "   Alma
     "   Rita
     "   Eduards
     "   Ansis
Lipszitz Simon
     " Christina
Lopata Abram
     " Regina

Lubawski Natan
Lubawska Nysella
     " Irena
Lustig Laszlo
Luzerovici Josub
     " Zisla
     " Macs
     " Rosa
     " Relu
Mannik Arnold
     " Hilja
Makowski Zygmunt
Makowska Helena
Mardus Uno
Margolis Boruch
     " Miriam
     " Maurice
Marcovicz Wilem
Masalskis-Surins
Nikolajs
Matussewich Vassily
     "   Olga
     "   Alexander
     "   Nikolaj
     "   Anastasia
     "   Alexandra
     "   Veronica
     "   Vassily
     "   Nina
     "   Olga
Maulics Nikolajs
     " Lidija
     " Ligita
Meder Elisabeth
     " Lars
Metschersky Nadine
Metz Marthe
Michalowicz Szimon
Miller Chana
Minski Moses
Morgenlender Stanislaw
     "   Sara
     "   Anna
Moskwer Lolek
Neufeld Karel
Neustatl Josef
Niemann Maria

Nittim Helle Mall
" Andrus
" Selma Julie
" Rein
" Maret Liis
Ohtra Arnold
" Linda
" Tiia
" Lea
Orenstein Abraham
Osetek Tomasz-Michal
" Irena
" Marguerite
Ostroburski Szolem
Ostroburska Enia
Ozolins Juris
" Karlis
" Irina
" Andrejs
Pataky Ignatz
" Elsie
Panelz Hertha
Pawlyszyn Roman
(Lusia Pawlyszyn has
been omitted)
Peedo Leo
Perl Erwin
Pich Hermann
" Nelly
Pilichowski Henryk
Pilichowska Apolonia
" Rozalia
Poczebucki Sameul
" Tania
" Anna
" Alexander
Potok Salezy
" Alina
Ptak Solomon
" Rosa
Puurand Verner
" Friida
" Hans-Verner
" Mart-Jaan
Rae Silva
" Tarno
" Anneke
Rafalowski Chaim

Rafalski Theodor
Rakfreldt Willem
" Leida
Rakusan Jiri
Reich Kurt
" Magda
Reichman Jakob
" Sara
" Bluma
Ritter Dorothea
Rogozinski Salomon
Rogozinska Selda
" Edith
Rosenwasser Paul
" Frieda
Rossler Ludwik Peter
" Hanus
Rotschyld Salek
Rozenberg Maurice
Rosenberg Dina
Sachs Georg
" Hedwig
Salinger Ilse
Salcberg Chaim Schlomo
" Sara
Samonov Cyrill
" Jylia
Sapojnikofe Boris
Schmatlock Mariana
Schnur Sala
" Anna
Schroder Hilda
Schwartz Otto
Seitz Valentine
" Pauline
Sigal Max
Skorupa Moritz
Skowron Henryk
" Giza
" Michal
Silberstein Alfred
Singer Villiam
Slibar Josef
" Alexander
Spiethoff Alzbetta
Soostar Hans
" Juta
" Jutta

Stern Usher
" Lea
" David
" Jacob
Stockholm Uno
" Helene
" Friedrich-Vilhelm
" Friedrich
Szteinberg Henryk
" Wanda
Strom Leopold
" Blume
" Anna Aurelia
Sumin Helene
Surkis Juniu
" Fritzi
Szabason Joseph
Szafir Szymon
Szput Henryk
" Anna
" Ruth
Schwartzbard Burich-Maier
Sczwarcberg Josek
Szwidowski Waclaw
Tohver Bruno
Szwartzbard Mendel
Thieberg Henryk
" Mary Ada
" Ewa
Tonuma Juhan
" Linda
" Enn
Treufeldt Herman
" Elfriede
" Eha
Vaidas Helju
" Juhan
" Selme
" Mare
Vink Johannes
" Ida
" Helbe
" Villi
" Lidia
Virve Adeline
Vogl Franz
" Maria
" Helena
Wajs Ginette

Wajsbord Ginette
Waiselbaum Leon
    "   Henri
Weile Alfred
    "   Hedwig
    "   George
Weinberger Andrej
Weiner Pola
    "   Isak
    "   Mordchaj
Weiner Abraham
    "   Rosa
    "   Max-Mordchaj
Weiss David
Welner Jacob
    "   Salomon
Weyrich Harry-Ernst
    "   Selma
Wierzba Choma
Witting Carl
Zalcberg-Zwolska Alice
Zilberger Maurice
Hershaw Ogden
   Escorting Officer IRO

**EMBARKED IN
PORT SAID**
Bobilak Roman
    "   Helena
    "   Henry
    "   Rudolf
Bartolo Carmela
    "   Henry
    "   Mario
Bellia Christina
Cachia Mary
    "   Lillian
    "   Joseph
Calfas Alexander
    "   Calliroe
Casira Marie
Cassimatis Marie
    "   Stamatiki
    "   Annette
Catapodis Evangelos
Cilia Michael
    "   Lucy

Cominos Jean
Condoleon Panagiota
Cosma Calliope
Cumpi (or Platis)
   Dorothea
Coutalianos Evangelos
Coutsourkios Antoine
    "   Catherine
Diacomanoli Vassiliki
    "   Athina
Dianos Constantine
Durhan Guiseppina
Fatseas Pierro
    "   Marie
    "   Panagiotitsa
    "   Vassiliki
Fiorentino Erminia
    "   Mary
Georgiadis Photis
    "   Germaine
Giorgiou or Savas
George
Grima Rita
    "   Josephina
Hansel Pavao
    "   Yael
Hazak Edmee
Kaliou Ekaterini
Kamaratos George
Karanzia Despina
Leonardos Nicolas
Macri Valentine
Makrilos Emanuel
Michailidis Jean
Mouglalis Nicolas
    "   Catina
    "   Olga
Marcotis Athanase
Musto Rudolf (Ralph)
    "   Ina
Nasr Elias
Novello Romulo
    "   Emilia
    "   Dorotea
    "   Ivor
    "   Maria Teresa

Papakyritsi Marica
Pepi Sebastian
    "   Paola
Pizel Felice
    "   Sylvia
    "   Albert
    "   Robert
    "   Gilbert
    "   Eliane
Plowman Jeannette
Procida Maria
    "   Giuseppe
Provitis Leonidas
Sabath Ludwig Richard
Saccheti Marius
Saghredos Chrissi
Samson Mariane
Saul David
    "   Lorice
    "   Salomon
    "   Joseph
Scicluna Domenic
    "   Imelda
    "   Antoinette
Smith Mathilda
Spiteri John
Travassaros Stamatios
    "   Koula
    "   Catherine
    "   Stamata
Vakalaki Kyriacoula
Vassalo Joseph
    "   Josephine
Vassalo Fortune
    "   Silvia
Zarocostas Elias
    "   Despina
    "   Joan
    "   Melpomene
Zourlos Apostolos

EMBARKED IN ADEN
Marino Dafne
Sorotos Joannis (John)
Xynis Alexander

INDEX OF NAMES

* Indicates names changed by request. Names in brackets indicate a passenger's married name.

Abrahamsohn (Tamura), Eva 349–56
Abrahamsohn, Gretchen 349–54
Abrahamsohn (Valentine), Irene 106, 124, 187–8, 349–55
Ament, Leon 117, 141–2, 187, 229
* Anton 181–2, 189, 300
Barasz (Reading), Bella 10, 98, 114, 467
Barasz (Leski), Miriam 10, 467
Barasz (Goldman), Ruth 10, 467
Barasz (Greenfield), Topka 9–10, 34, 44, 45, 111–14, 119, 167, 202, 208, 216, 222, 467
Birnbaum, Herta 187–8, 352
Boguslawski, Bronia 3–4, 17, 20, 32, 59, 60, 87, 98, 114, 125, 127, 142, 164–7, 195, 203, 207, 231–2, 241–3, 266, 304, 320–3, 440, 450, 464, 468
Boguslawski (Armstrong), Danusia 3–4, 17, 20, 32, 39, 42, 59, 60, 87, 98, 114, 116–17, 119, 126–7, 164–7, 177, 203, 207, 231–2, 241–3, 266, 283, 285, 304, 320–1, 393, 433, 440, 450, 453, 456, 462, 464, 468
Boguslawski, Henek 3–4, 17, 32, 42, 59, 60, 87, 97–8, 102, 114, 116–17, 118, 141–2, 165–7, 177, 203, 207, 231–2, 241–3, 266, 285, 304, 320–3, 393, 440, 456, 465
Brouen (Jedick), Gilda, Gisa 18, 20, 23, 26, 27–8, 108, 122, 200–1, 229, 329, 337–9
Braun, Harry 53, 142, 172, 435, 464
Bunzl, Addy 62
Comino, John 72, 76, 169, 390, 394–5, 397
Czalczynski (Zandrou), Karmela 148, 467
Czalczynski (Engelman), Matylda 97, 147–9, 215, 218–20, 466–7
Darin, Emanuel 84, 86, 226–7, 330, 415
Darin, Raisa 415

Dick 154–5, 161–3, 206, 223, 288–9, 294, 297–9
* Ella 139, 181–6, 299–302
Engel (Engelman), Yvonne 138, 267, 439–41
Falek, Irka 95, 98, 99, 304
Fatseas, Betty 68, 71, 404–5
Fatseas, Mary 68, 71, 140, 216, 404
Fatseas, Petro 68–71, 102, 140–1, 152, 192, 215, 216, 401–8
Fatseas (Comino), Vassiliki, Vi 68–71, 140–1, 152, 215, 391, 400–8
Feigin, Danny 307–8
Feigin, Fela 177, 307–8
Fein, Leah 30, 304
Ferszt, Cyla 98, 122–3, 142–6, 167, 303–11
Ferszt, Max 98, 122–3, 142–6, 303–11
Ferszt (De Leeuw), Slawa 123, 146, 304–7, 309–10
Fiszman, Esther 8, 34, 89–90, 91–2, 137, 195, 266–7, 271
Fiszman (Price), Maria, Mia 8, 34, 90, 92, 195, 266, 267, 268
Fiszman, Sam 7, 8, 34, 45, 89–93, 126, 137, 195–7, 210–11, 224, 265–74, 467
Frant (Harris), Christine 98, 118–19, 171, 465
Frant, Henryk 9, 26, 34, 45, 49, 89, 98, 110, 118–19, 124, 171–2, 178, 181–2, 188, 194–5, 209, 212, 218–19, 222, 224, 226, 266, 337, 465
Frant, Zofia 9, 34, 98, 117–19, 171–2, 178, 195, 464–5, 470
Frid, Gitel 29
Frid, Jack 29
Frid, Morrie 29–30, 301
Georgiades, Germaine 212, 230
Georgiades, Philip 211, 230
Glassman, Bronia 27, 99–101, 146, 167, 444–50

Glassman, Heniek 27, 98–9, 444–50
Goldberg, Abie, Abe 10, 11, 104, 114, 172–3, 225, 228, 306, 415, 464, 468–9
Grunschlag, Bob 138, 172–3, 225, 409–13, 415–17, 469
Grunschlag, Moishe 411–12, 415–16
Grunstein, Eugene 442
Gruschajew, Peter 46
* Guta 154–63, 206–7, 223, 288–99, 302
Halm, Otto 98, 186
Hershaw, Lt-Colonel Ogden 21–3, 28, 45, 58, 61, 64–6, 67, 85, 88, 94, 96, 105–6, 108–10, 123–4, 152–3, 179, 181, 193–5, 197–8, 201, 204, 223–7, 233, 234, 235–7, 330, 331, 332–3, 337, 338, 420
Herzog, Kurt 121, 122, 209, 327, 330
Hof, Elfriede 19, 61, 122, 201, 213–14, 217, 329, 337
Hof (Kahn), Ilse 19, 61, 122, 201, 213, 329, 337
Kalowski, Halina 13–14, 45, 120, 148–9, 202, 212, 215, 217–20, 227, 465–6, 471–4
Kalowski (Rosen), Jennifer 219–20, 465–6, 470–4
Kalowski, Mietek 13–14, 149, 215, 218–19, 465–6, 471–2
Kalowski, Stefan 13, 14, 215, 218, 465, 470–1, 473–4
Kapp, Alide 370–4
Kapp, Harold 139, 369–74
Kopel, Emil 26, 49–51, 150, 210, 357, 363
Kraus, Clara 30–1, 141, 214, 312–19
Kraus, Jim 30, 31, 312–18
Kraus, Paul 30, 141, 214, 312–19
Kraus, Peter 30, 141, 214, 312–19
Kucharski, David 109, 323–4
Kuplis, Auguste 19, 45
Kuplis, Elmars 19, 45, 209, 231
Lebovics (Graf), Kitty 34, 221, 441–3
Liivat (Mardus), Aino 421
Liivat, Karl 421
Lindemanis, Jack 24, 25, 27, 63, 246, 250–2

Lindemanis (Ozlins), Rita 24–5, 27, 67, 150–1, 178, 193, 233, 234, 245–56
Lindemanis, Sigride 246, 255
Lindemanis, Ted 254
Lipschutz, Heniek 27, 34, 162, 306
Lipschutz, Krysia 27, 34
Mardus, Uno 58, 61–2, 94, 126, 172, 330, 420–1
Marr, Bill 53–7, 142, 190–1, 194, 202, 209, 436–7, 464
Matussevich, Alex 361–3, 368
Matussevich, Anastasia 368
Matussevich, Basil 361–3, 368
Matussevich, Nick 170, 214, 357–68
Matussevich, Nina 49, 150, 357, 363, 367
Matussevich, Olga (mother) 47–9, 214, 358–67
Matussevich, Olga (daughter) 150, 367
Matussevich, Vasily 47–9, 358–66
Matussevich, Veronica 176, 368
Maulics, Lidija 230, 235, 370
Meder, Elisabeth 64, 370, 375–8
Meder, Lars 43, 62, 170, 222, 370, 375–9
Metschersky, Nadezhda (Nadine) Alexandrovna 36–7, 41, 46, 229, 386
Nittim (Risti), Helle 23–4, 25, 26–7, 35, 62, 63, 67, 97, 102, 126, 149, 150–1, 152, 168–9, 173, 178, 180, 210, 224, 233, 245, 255, 256–64, 273, 414, 420
Nittim (Vesk), Maret 114, 233, 259, 264
Nittim, Rein 43, 233, 259, 263–4
Neustatl, Joe 171, 430–3
Ohtra, Arnold 43–4, 101, 102, 104, 174, 177, 211
Ohtra (Holm), Lea 32, 63, 212, 224, 257–9
Ohtra, Tiia 212, 258
Pataky, Elsie 61, 97, 120–2, 167–8, 209, 325–9, 357
Pataky, Ignac 120–2, 168, 326–9
Pawlyszyn, Roman 326
Pilichowski, Hanka 146–7, 304
Pilichowski, Henryk 147
Poczebucka (Irons), Haneczka (Anne) 62, 80, 148, 164, 179, 193, 301

Poczebucka, Tania 80, 98
Potok (Jarvin), Alina 78–9, 81–4, 152, 413–15, 417–18
Potok, Salezy 78–9, 81, 117, 152, 413
Puurand, Friida 275–6, 286
Puurand, Hans 191, 233, 275–7, 281, 282–4, 286–7
Puurand, Mart 275, 287
Puurand, Verner 8, 64, 94–6, 139, 140, 153, 169, 191, 205, 210, 223, 226, 233, 275–87
Rae (Twigg), Anneke 107, 209, 228, 428–9
Rae (Palgi), Silva 106–8, 151, 181, 209, 228, 419–29
Rae, Tarno 106–7, 228, 422, 428–9
Rafalsky, Archbishop Theodore 35–6, 46, 92–3, 177, 188, 192–3, 210–11, 224–5, 229, 265, 386–7
Rakusan, George 190–1
Reich, Kurt 150
Reich, Magda 109, 127, 136, 137, 150, 267
Ritter, Dorothea 11–12, 18–19, 20–3, 26, 27, 28, 33, 45, 62, 64–6, 67, 85, 88, 94, 103, 106, 108–10, 152, 193–5, 201, 225, 229, 329, 330–7, 339
Rogozinski, Edie 177
Rogozinski (Rogers), Zosia 177, 304
Rossler, Henry 323, 325
Rossler, Peter 171, 323, 324–5, 464
Sapojnikoff, Boris Arkadievich 150
Seitz, Pauline 35, 36–7, 39, 41, 46, 93, 122, 165, 192, 380–9

Seitz, Vala 35–9, 41, 46, 122, 165, 224, 381–8
Silberstein, Fred 20, 109, 127–37, 168, 180, 232, 337, 340–8, 371, 460
Singer, Bill 442
Skorupa (Shell), Morris 79–81, 451–9, 460
Stockholm, Pastor Friedrich 46, 226
Sznur (Lendvay), Anna, Aneczka 34, 164
Sznur (Raza), Sala 34
Szput (Stern), Anna 39–40, 143, 145, 210, 304
Szput, Ruth 39, 40
Tohver, Bruno 64, 89, 104, 169, 460
Travasaros, Katina 72, 74, 169, 228, 390, 392
Travasaros, Koula 72–7, 228, 390–3, 397–8
Travasaros (Veneris), Mattie 71–7, 169–70, 208, 228, 390–8
Travasaros, Stan 72, 76, 169, 390, 394–5
Wajs, Ginette 10–11, 111–14, 117, 167, 178–9, 193, 216, 228–9, 460–4, 469
Wayne, André 53, 114, 119, 132, 138–9, 142, 172, 200, 434, 435–6, 438, 464
Weile, Alfred 168
Weiss, David 52–3, 142, 172, 200, 434–5, 464
Wise, Leon 114–16, 175–6, 180, 464
Zalcberg (Sternhell), Alice 9, 25, 171–2, 468–9

SELECTED BIBLIOGRAPHY

Peter Coleman (ed), *Australian Civilization: A Symposium*, FW Cheshire, Melbourne, 1962.

Matylda Engelman, *Journey Without End and the End of the Journey*, Lantana, Melbourne, 1979.

Martin Gilbert, *The Holocaust, The Jewish Tragedy*, Fontana, London, 1987.

Martin Gilbert, *Second World War*, Weidenfeld & Nicolson, London, 1989.

Colin Golvan, *The Distant Exodus*, ABC Books, Crows Nest, NSW, 1990.

Donald Horne, *The Lucky Country* (second revised edition), Angus & Robertson, Sydney, 1965.

Ann-Mari Jordens, *Alien to Citizen, Settling Migrants in Australia 1945–1975*, Allen & Unwin, Sydney, 1997.

Jacqueline Kent, Bruce Elder and Keith Willey, *Memories: Life in Australia since 1900*, Child & Associates, Sydney, 1988.

Michael King, *After The War, New Zealand since 1945*, Hodder & Stoughton, Auckland, 1988.

Clara Kraus, *The Colours of War, Ten Uncertain Years 1935–1945*, Spectrum, Sydney, 1987.

Paul Kraus, *The Not So Fabulous Fifties, Images of a Migrant Childhood*, Kangaroo Press, Sydney, 1985.

Stella Lees and June Senyard, *The 1950s: How Australia Became a Modern Society and Everyone Got a House and Car*, Hyland House, Melbourne, 1987.

Ann Lehtmets and Douglas Hoile, *Sentence: Siberia, A Story of Survival*, Wakefield Press, Kent Town, South Australia, 1994.

Peeter Lindsaar, *Estonians in Australia and New Zealand*, Kirjastas Luuamees, Sydney, 1961.

Ann Mihkelson, *Three Suitcases and a Three Year Old*, Kangaroo Press, Sydney, 1999.

John Murphy, *Imagining the Fifties*, UNSW Press, Sydney, 2000.

Colin Rubinstein, *The Jews in Australia*, details not available.

Suzanne Rutland, *Edge of the Diaspora: Two Centuries of Jewish Settlement in Australia* (second revised edition), Brandl & Schlesinger, Sydney, 1997.

Anna Szput-Stern, *On the Other Side of the River*, Aussie Publications, Melbourne, 2000.

Helen Townsend, *Baby Boomers, Growing Up in Australia in the 1940s, 50s and 60s*, Simon & Schuster, Sydney, 1988.